Best Wishes

Mark O'Neill

Celtic ✿

VIEWS

stories from the Celtic Writing Competition

© 2002

Published by Celtic FC Limited

Designed by Celtic FC Limited & First Press Publishing
Printed by Grange Communications Ltd, Edinburgh

Edited by Paul Cuddihy and Joe Sullivan

ISBN: 1- 902704- 33- 9

Contents

Acknowledgements

THANKS to everyone who helped to make the Celtic Writing Competition a success and to those who contributed in putting this book together.

To Professor Willy Maley of the University of Glasgow, for helping to get the competition up and running.

To Roisin McClory of the Celtic marketing department.

To Sharon Gillespie from the Celtic Newsroom, who filmed every school visit made to promote the competition.

To Joe Sullivan, Beccy Nightingale, Eileen Monaghan and Alison McConnell from the Celtic Newsroom.

To all of the local authorities in Scotland who supported the competition by informing their schools, and in particular to Ken Corsar, Director of Education for Glasgow City Council and George Mackie, the Schools Industrial Liaison Officer for Glasgow City Council.

A special thanks to the staff and pupils of the following schools who invited members of the Celtic Newsroom to visit and speak about the competition: All Saints Secondary, Glasgow, Annette Street Primary, Glasgow, Arbroath Academy, Holy Family Primary, Kirkintilloch, St Joan of Arc School, Glasgow, St Aiden's School, Glasgow, St Benedict's Primary, Glasgow, St Bernadette's Primary, Tullibody, St Francis Primary, Glasgow, St Luke's Secondary, Barrhead, St Oswald's School, Glasgow.

Thanks also to Austin Barrett, Scott Munro and Ryan McGraw at First Press Publishing for their help with this book.

Foreword

THE Celtic Writing Competition has been a phenomenal success and from it has come this book, *Celtic Views*.

All of us have a Celtic story to tell, each with a unique slant but all displaying the same love for our club. Regardless of the subject matter of each entry, a common theme ran through them all – that of being part of the Celtic family.

That family to which we all belong stretches out from the East End of Glasgow all over the world.

From the rest of Scotland, to Ireland, England and Wales, Europe, Australia, New Zealand, the United States, Canada, Africa, Asia and South America, Celtic fans wrote of their love for the club and the players through the decades who have worn the green and white hoops.

No matter where you are in the world, you only have to wear the instantly recognisable Hoops to find a kindred Celtic spirit.

Supporters recalled their first game, a special victory, a poignant Celtic moment and many other events connected with the club.

The quality of writing has also been very high, with many entries of a standard to have graced any writing competition, but more importantly, their quality is in the way they will appeal to other Celtic fans, who may recognise the moment or the people described in the stories and poems, sparking fond recollections of their own.

It has been a labour of love for myself and the other judges, in particular my colleague Joe Sullivan, and Professor Willy Maley, to have read through all of the entries.

Over 3,000 people took the trouble to enter the competition and from that we have selected 245 to be included in this book.

My thanks to everyone who took part and I'm only sorry we could not have included more entries in *Celtic Views*.

This is a book written by Celtic fans for Celtic fans and I know people of all ages will enjoy reading the wide variety of stories and poems contained within.

Paul Cuddihy
News Editor
Celtic Football Club
August 2002

Chapter One

He Wishes for the Cloths of Heaven

SHE shouted Patrick back and handed him a packet of Rich Tea biscuits. Me and Francis were walking fast like real football fans and he had to run to catch up. Francis was nervous.

"What do we when we get there?" he asked Patrick.

"It's all arranged, it's okay," said Patrick. "We just ask for the guy, this Genghis McCann. He runs the bus. We just give him our names and I give him the money." Francis said, "Have you got the money." He wanted to see the money, just to make sure everything went right. Patrick showed him the money. That was better and now we could enjoy it.

The bus was in the car park at the shopping centre. It was already there and we could see it from a distance because we lived on the hill. I didn't want it to go away before we got there. It started moving and off and we all had to run fast this time shouting "Hey" and "Wait". Patrick waved the biscuits desperately, but it was okay. It was just getting into a different position. It had its back to us and we could see the flag at the back window. "Is that the Tricolour?" I asked Patrick.

"The very same," he said. "But it's not Tricolour, it's Try-colour. Don't say Tricolour if you talk to anybody there."

"I thought the yellow was at the front and then the green," I said.

"No, that's just stupid."

We got there and there were some big Celtic fans there. Men. They had the history. Some of them were drinking straight out of the bottle. Dad didn't do that no matter how drunk he was already. Maybe he did it when I was asleep.

Patrick gave a man the money. It was all arranged. I don't know whether that man was Genghis McCann, but he was definitely the boss of the money and had a little canvas bag to prove it. It jingled. It must have had a lot of money inside.

It was a fancy bus, a coach. It didn't have an upstairs, like the bus to the town did. You didn't get a ticket. The seats went up higher than my head. Francis let me sit at the window. He was next to me and Patrick was in front. It felt funny not having a ticket, as if you could get caught. I leaned forward to ask Patrick if they had an inspector, and he was already eating a biscuit!

"Hey you're already eating a biscuit," I said to him. "Hey Francis he's already eating a biscuit."

"Mum said I could get the broken ones," Patrick said. "That was a broken one."

The men were singing even before the bus moved. They were the songs. We left the car park. We were going to a Celtic game. We went along the road and I still recognised everything. At some point we left Drumchapel and I only recognised some things. The bus to the town didn't go this way. "We go a long way don't we?" I asked Francis. "It's faraway, to Parkhead."

"Patrick says it's nine miles."

"Nine miles!" The town was only seven miles. It said it on the sign.

I didn't recognise anything now. If the bus driver or somebody suddenly came up to me and said, "Get off", I'd be lost. Patrick gave us a biscuit each through the space between the seats. If he had been sitting next to somebody he would have given them a biscuit too I bet. It was taking ages but we had biscuits and it was a treat. Patrick was taking more than us and we complained. "They're just the broken ones," he kept saying.

On the bus they did something called a sweep. We had a dog called Sweep but it died. A man with a Celtic scarf on his wrist put a tin down to everyone and we took a bit of paper each. My piece of paper said '5. Billy McNeill'. I didn't know what it meant to have the piece of paper but it said Billy McNeill on it so it was important.

Near the stadium the bus went slower because of all the men on the road. They just walked on the road! Patrick showed me the floodlights from a distance. When we got nearer they were bigger than anything. There was a ladder for a man to go up. The lights at Kilbowie Park didn't go up that high, but Clydebank weren't in Celtic's league so maybe that was it.

"We're playing Clydebank today?" I asked Francis. "They're not in our league."

"It's a cup game."

"The Scottish Cup?"

"No the China Tea Cup, round robin we got a bye bye." He looked away and I couldn't see his face. We got off the bus. I jumped from the big step over a deep puddle. A man stepped in it and people laughed, even people not on our bus. We just followed Patrick who was following everybody. It was all arranged. Some boys were trying to get in but didn't have tickets or money. They just stood there and the rain was starting again.

I liked the turnstiles. You think you'll be scared but they were nice and lucky. The men put us near the front. The funny cars were there with three wheels. The ball came across and hit one of them. It left mud the shape of a ball. They were only warming up. The pitch looked big like a park and that's probably why they called it Celtic Park. It was curved going to the other side, like the world and that's how you have a horizon. I could see the faces of people near me, but not the faces of the people in the bits behind the goals. They were far away and looked like the pattern on a green carpet.

The Stand was all the way across the pitch. It was the stand but they sat there. High up above it there was another place, with windows. It looked like the bottom of the Hindenburg. The Hindenburg blew up on the telly and the commentator was crying.

The players went down the tunnel and then came back on again after the songs from the radio. They had their strips on clean and it was real, numbers on the bum and everything. I tried to see all the way to the back of the Jungle but it went too far. The men had jackets, coats and scarves. There was smoke and steam coming out of them like machines in the factory we went to with the school. Their heads all looked the same in the darkening. They were singing the songs even if it was only Clydebank. Patrick knew bits of the songs. Up high was the big camera for the telly. A man was behind it. A policeman was there too and he looked straight at me.

Paul Wilson was playing. He was Patrick's favourite, and Patrick watched him run near us for the first half. Billy McNeill wasn't playing and Roddie McDonald wore number five. He looked young compared to Billy McNeill but he was still a man.

He scored. Other Celtic players scored, and when Clydebank scored I cheered. Patrick told me to shush. "But Clydebank scored. We always cheer when they score." They played East Fife last week and we cheered when they scored. A big funny fat man shouted at the East Fife goalkeeper Ernie Cigar for the whole first half. He called him 'hen' at the end of everything he said.

"Well we don't cheer them here. This is different."

They didn't score again so it didn't matter. Celtic won 4-1. Everybody was happy. They walked along and said things I didn't understand but I would understand them when I was a man. Patrick remembered where the bus was. When we got on and were going home the man came up and gave me 75 pence. I didn't know what for and he said, "First scorer number 5. Big Roddie. That's your share, your winnings."

"They're your winnings," said Patrick. "Your winnings," said Francis. They seemed to understand. I held the money in my hand for a while and then I put it in my pocket. I could still feel it in my pocket. It didn't feel like anything else. Francis said to me, "What are you going to do with your winnings? How are you going to spend your winnings?" It was just money but they kept on calling it winnings so I started calling it winnings too.

"With my winnings," I announced in my best voice, "I'm going to buy a Celtic scarf."

"Where are you going to get a Celtic scarf?" asked Patrick.

"I've seen one. In Hunter Tomison. High up. I've seen it. I'm going to buy it with my winnings."

"I've never seen it," said Francis. "No way they sell Celtic scarves. Anyway we won't get back in time for the shop shutting"

"It's there, high up, round a neck. I'm going to buy it after school on Monday."

"You're lucky it's Sunday tomorrow because I bet you couldn't keep the money that long. You would spend it."

Sunday was the whole day and it was ages. I wanted it to be Monday even it meant school again. We played football until it was dark but there was the night to go. I washed my neck in the bath.

On Monday it was dark after school but the shop was bright. Patrick and Francis waited outside. I wasn't going to buy it while they were there because I wanted to bring it out like magic.

It was 69 pence. They didn't need to put it in a bag. I went outside with it. "There you go," I said, "one Celtic scarf."

Patrick looked at it. "That's not a Celtic scarf. In fact…look at it, those bits are actually blue."

"No, they're white," I said. "It's a Celtic scarf."

Patrick held it up to the shop window light. "They're blue, they're sky blue!"

"We'll see what Mum says," I said.

"Okay, it's your neck."

She said they were white. "Patrick, Francis, they're white and that's that. Stop teasing your brother." We were here and they were over there. She was behind me. She put her arms where I had the scarf on.

GERRY McLEAN, Glasgow

My first match

I WOKE up early on Saturday morning excited because my dad was taking me to my first Celtic match. Celtic were playing Dundee United. We stay in St Andrews and had to get the bus to Glasgow, which took three hours to get to the ground. It went in quickly as my dad told me stories about Celtic as he has watched them for a long time. When we got there, there were lots of people walking around with Celtic shirts and scarves on. Before we went into the ground my dad bought me a Celtic cap. I handed over my ticket and went to find our seats. When the match started all the fans around me stood up and started shouting and cheering – it was very noisy. Celtic scored early and everyone was cheering and before half-time they got a second. At half time I watched it again on the big TV screen. We got another three goals in the second-half and even let Dundee United get one. Celtic won 5-1 and made it well worth the three-hour bus trip home.

KIM McKAY (age 11), St Andrews

Celtic

I WAS just coming out of school where my mum was waiting to collect me. I was having a really boring day. All was to change when my mum told me that my grandda was taking me to my first Celtic match, which he always said he would. I was really excited and just couldn't wait.

The morning I was going I just couldn't eat because I was so happy. When I got to my grandda's house he made it even more exciting. I think he was more excited than me, even though it was my first football match. He gave me his Celtic scarf, which I still have. We left and my uncle James took us in his big van.

When we got there I kept thinking what the stadium was like. When I saw it, it was all really interesting to see thousands of people and a huge park. My grandda and I had seats behind the net. Celtic were playing Hapoel Tel-Aviv. It wasn't a big game, but it was amazing to see people that you had seen on television and then seeing them for real.

The best thing was being able to see Larsson score a goal about four metres away from you. The game was brilliant and hearing people cheer and sing was even better. The score ended up 2-0 to Celtic.

When we got home everyone was asking if the game was good. I said it was excellent because I really enjoyed it. A few people have said I was good luck because every game I've been to Celtic have won. I don't agree though because Celtic are such an amazing team that they usually win with or without me anyway.

Even though my first game wasn't such a big one it was still the best one I've been to because everything was so new to me and because my grandda took and he was Celtic mad. It was one of the best days of my life.

NICOLE BRYERS (age 12), St Luke's High, Barrhead

Paradise regained

SOMETIMES my life seems like such a complete failure. I can't seem to do the right things often enough. My wife says that I don't help her enough with the kids and the house. I try to tell her that she doesn't have to aim for perfection all the time, that she's trying too hard to make everything perfect when just okay would be all right sometimes. I try my best to be a good husband and father but sometimes it doesn't seem like enough. My work is okay but I sometimes wonder if I couldn't have done better.

When you reach a certain age you think to yourself, "Is this all there is?" It's all about dreams. When you're young, you're going to be a famous footballer or a pop star. I remember being young and going out with my mates and that feeling you would get in the pit of your stomach when you caught a nice girl looking at you before you looked at her. There was excitement in the air.

Now, don't get me wrong. I love my wife. She's beautiful and I know she really loves me but it's different. When you're older, those things don't happen all the time. You're caught up in your work or trying to get things done. You have responsibilities and they come first. When you're young, everything seems new and you can't wait to reach the next horizon. You can't get where you're going fast enough.

Now, time slips by so quickly, whole decades melt away before your eyes. You want to sit and admire the horizon a bit and hope that the journey is enjoyable. I sometimes wonder about dreams and what happens to them. I try to remember the kinds of things I dreamed about doing when I was a kid. I don't really remember wanting to do anything in particular but I definitely wanted to be successful so that people would respect me. I suppose I blended into the crowd when I was at school.

I tried to latch on to the right people and do all the right things so that people would think I was a great guy. Now people respect me mainly because I manage to hold down a job and provide for my family but I'm not so bothered about what other people think anymore. Sometimes it gets the better of me and I look at these guys with loads of cash and nice cars and I wonder, "How come these guys are so successful? How are they different from me?"

I think a lot of it has to do with the fact that I come from an area of Glasgow that people don't normally associate with success. I did alright at school but I wasn't brilliant. I make a decent wage but I'm not sure people respect me for my work. I just try to be a decent guy, keep my head down and hope for the best most of the time. So far, this plan has worked well enough. Nowadays, my dreams are more about my kids. What kind of people will they grow up to be? I want them to do better than me but not forget where they come from. I want them to respect their upbringing but reach for something more. I worry about the world my kids are growing up in. It seems so full of a hate and fear. I worry about the kids walking around, knowing full well that I was walking the same streets when I was their age. Somehow it seems different now. Maybe my parents worried about me in the same way. I've got two boys and two girls between three and 10 years old. My oldest daughter is 10 and my oldest son is eight. They have such strong opinions about everything. Life for them seems so black and white. You try to explain to them that there is hardly ever a completely right answer to any question and they just say, "No dad, we know the answer." How can you teach kids anything when they think they have all the answers?

They get so excited about doing new things. You can see it in their eyes. I suppose that's the one thing I've been able to do for my kids that my parents couldn't do for me. I have six brothers and sisters so there just wasn't money around for luxuries when I was growing up. I've been able to give my kids all kinds of things my parents just couldn't afford. I'm not ashamed of my parents for the way they brought me up but we all knew that money was scarce. Nowadays things are different. I try to give my kids whatever they want (within reason) and there's usually a little left over for me to splash out every now and again. I manage to get out to my local for a few pints with my mates once a week, usually on Saturday afternoon because they have all the football on the big screen.

I'm a big Celtic supporter and I can remember when I was a kid just begging for my dad to take me to a match. Finally after months of moaning at him, he took me to Celtic Park for the first time and I can remember the sheer pleasure of just walking into the stadium. I was so pleased to be there. It was a bonus that there was a football match on at the same time. My feet hardly touched the ground the entire match. There was singing and men around me shouting and cheering. It was an incredible experience. What's sad is that I haven't been to a match for a long while now.

All those responsibilities seem to pile up on you during the week and you just don't have the energy to think about sorting things out so you can go. I always seem to end up just watching or listening to the matches in the pub. The fact that I hadn't been to a match in so long started me thinking about everything and made me wonder if my idea of giving things up to be a good father and husband was right.

Maybe if I take time to make myself happier then the family will be happier too. So I said to my wife at dinner that I was thinking about getting tickets for an upcoming Celtic home match and this wee voice pipes up at the other end of the table and says, "Dad, can I come too?"

Then the floodgates opened. Everyone said they wanted to go and within minutes we were planning a family day out to Celtic Park. So the big day finally arrived and we dropped off the youngest at my mum's and the rest of us got on the bus to Parkhead Cross. The kids had their scarves on trying to look like the supporters on the TV holding them up in the air. You'd have thought that we'd fed them pure sugar for breakfast they were that hyper. All the people streaming in along the road added to their excitement. They'd never been to anything where this many people turned up before. We eventually got them through the gate and up the stairs.

In an attempt to settle them down a little, we bought them pies and a drink. I'll never forget what happened next. We came out onto the stands and the kids saw the pitch for the first time in person. My daughter turned and looked at me with the sweetest face and said, "Dad, this is the most awesome place ever. Thanks for bringing us with you." and gave me her hand to walk up the stairs to our seats.

My head was in the clouds the rest of the day. I tried to watch the match and the Bhoys did their usual magnificent job but I really only had eyes for my kids. They had such a great time watching the match and talking to all the people around us. The look of utter joy and excitement on their faces when Celtic won gave me an incredible feeling. At that moment, time just stood still. I hadn't grown old and I didn't have responsibilities. It was a perfect moment of pure heaven. That day Celtic Park was truly Paradise for me.

HEATHER LARNACH, Edinburgh

My wee Bhoy's first time

I'M sure all fans will remember the day when they first had their da to show them the way… Grabbing my hand, his mum's warned him "not to let go!" while I'm shouting "dinnae fuss wummin - it's Celtic Park you know!"

So there we are, among thousands of the world's best fans, My wee boy's looking about (we're still holding hands). It's just after Christmas and he's togged from top to bottomlike an advert for the whole Celtic shop. Then one of the lads shouts out to amuse the ladies. "Hey, wee man - brand new trainees!"

I laugh and tell him it's the boy's first game. He bends down, shakes his hand, and tells him his name. "It's Vinnie, wee man. I hope you'll never forget your first day at Paradise, and the people you met."

So in we go, (we're still holding hands), into the ground where I've grown from boy to man, and I think of the times, good and bad, and the times still to come with me and the lad. The match wasn't much - Motherwell spoilt the game. The wee guy still saw his favourite player score though - Larsson's the name!

All too soon it's over, but I'll never forget the look on the wee guy's face as Larsson burst the net. "He scored dad! He scored!" as he jumped up and down. I felt proud as punch - grinning like a big daft clown as we walked out, feeling grand. And (just for the missus' sake) - we were still holding hands! "Tell me son, is that the best day you've ever had?"

"Well, not really daddy - you huvnae bought me a flag!"

PAUL BRADLEY, Glasgow

A FEW years ago, my mummy and daddy took me and my little brother Thomas to Scotland for the New Year. We stayed at my gran and grandda's, in Cumbernauld. My daddy has two brothers who live in Scotland and have season tickets for Celtic, so they go to the football all the time.

Whenever my daddy goes to Scotland they try and get him a ticket to see Celtic. Anyway, when we went this time Celtic were playing Kilmarnock at Parkhead. I think it was around about the 3rd or 4th of January.

My uncles managed to get two tickets for the football match - one for my grandda, who is a Kilmarnock supporter and the other one for my daddy. My grandda's brother played for Kilmarnock. His name was Kenneth McDonald and he played against Celtic a long time ago when they were touring Canada. The tickets they got were for the Jungle – that's where my uncles have season tickets for.

So they were all ready to go to the match when my grandda, Jim decided that he did not want to go because every time that he has went to see Kilmarnock at Parkhead, Kilmarnock always get beat HA! HA!

So rather than give the ticket away to one of my uncle's friends, my daddy said that he would take me. At first my uncles and grandda were not to happy, they said that I was too young - I was four-years-old. My daddy said that he would look after me.

We were all sitting together at the game, so I could not go anywhere. So when I found out that I was going I was really excited and a little bit scared. It was my first time to see Celtic. When we got to the ground my daddy had to pick up his tickets at the ticket office. There were lots of people about so I had to hold on to my daddy's hand.

When we got to our seats I could not see that much because I was too small. My daddy said I was to look at the big TVs and I could see what he was seeing. I kept asking him questions because I didn't know who was kicking the ball, I knew Celtic were in green and white jerseys because my daddy has one. I asked him who were the numbers. When everybody started to jump up and down and shout, I was scared but my daddy was holding my hand, and he said it was okay because Celtic has scored a goal.

I was watching the big TV, everybody started to shout again, so I asked my daddy if Celtic has scored again.

He said, yes, so I started to jump up and down too; it was great fun. I jumped up and down six times and it was good fun. When it was finished I asked my daddy who scored all the goals. He said Larsson got four - he was No.7 - and Sutton got two. I think he was No.10, so Celtic scored six goals and Kilmarnock scored none HA! HA! HA!

My daddy said to me that he was so happy that he took me to see Celtic. I was to say to my grandda Jim Celtic 6 Kilmarnock 0, Larsson 4 Sutton 2.

My grandda thought I was kidding him on. I wasn't. So every time I see my grandda, I say that all the time, he thinks it is funny now and so do I.

When Celtic are on TV in my house, me and my brother, Thomas, watch it with my daddy. My brother Thomas can say Celtic and he is nearly three-years-old. His bed has got Celtic covers and he has a football strip just like my daddy's.

NIAMH McDONALD (age 8), Ardglass, County Down

My first Celtic match

I AM a true Celtic fan but I had never been to a game in my life, until one night my dad got home from work with the biggest surprise ever. He was offered two tickets by one of the men that he works with and he thought it was great. When he got home he shouted on my brother, Graeme, and announced that he had two tickets for the match. He blurted out: "Do you want to go?" and didn't even bother to ask me.

Now this was my lucky day. My brother wanted to go out. Dad didn't want to go himself so he asked my mum and I if we wanted to go together. We were delighted.

I ran upstairs to get ready while my mum got all uptight about going to the Celtic game. There were six of us going to the game, my mum and I, my brother, Jamie, his friend and his friend's dad. My dad, who was driving, wasn't going.

We found our way from Springfield Road to the ticket booths but when we got in it was a disaster. We thought that the door to the stairs was the men's toilet! Then when we finally got to our seats my mum started to think that a man fancied her - how stupid. Tony Hamilton, the MC, blasted over the tannoy the team line-ups for Celtic and Hearts. Then they all came running out on to the field to play. Henrik scored the first goal then Hearts tried but did not succeed then Larsson shot the ball into the back of the net and he scored. So the score at the end of the night was 2-0 to the Celts. That night had to be the best night of my life!

RACHEL MAXWELL (age 11), Sandyhills, Glasgow

I WAS eight-years-old at the time of the Hillsborough disaster in spring 1989. I distinctly remember dad coming out into the garden on that hot Saturday afternoon and saying, "There's been a big accident down south."

At the time I guess I didn't really realise the enormity of what had happened that day. Nearly 100 Liverpool fans had been crushed to death behind the pitch's perimeter

16

fence. As I watched this live horror movie unfolding before my eyes I could not understand why or how this was allowed to happen. There was no explanation for it, and no one could say or do anything to make it better.

The next week I recall my dad being on the phone to my uncle Pat, and while I paid no attention to what they were saying, my ears twitched when I heard my dad say the words "Celtic" and "Liverpool." I knew that Liverpool were an immensely successful club during that era and, of course, me and my dad and all my family have been Celtic supporters for as long as I could remember. I was desperate for my Dad to finish his conversation so that I could ask what it was he was talking about. He said that there had been an appeal match to be played between Liverpool and Celtic at Celtic Park next week.

"Your uncle Pat's managed to get a couple of tickets, do you want to go?"

Did I! I had never been at a Celtic match before, as my Dad said that I was too young. But perhaps the nature of this match made him change his mind. Match day couldn't come quick enough. I must have woken up at 6am that morning, like a child on Christmas Day. I could hardly contain my excitement. Uncle Pat picked dad and me up and the three of us made our way in from our home in Paisley.

As we drew nearer, the cars next to us were full of Celtic fans, and the kids in those cars looked just as excited as I did. After all, we were playing the English Champions. We struggled to find a parking space. I'm glad we did. The 15-minute walk from Alexandra parade let me savour the atmosphere. It felt strange. Everyone was walking in the same direction, everyone contemplating the game to come, and everyone wearing green. I felt a sense of belonging, a sense of being part of something. It felt good. When we finally arrived at Celtic Park, all sorts of things were going on. What an atmosphere! Burly men shouting at the top of their voices asking if "Emdy luckin' fur a ticket?" Caravans busily selling rolls with decidedly suspect fillings. Stallholders with a wide variety of memorabilia. I made my dad buy a scarf for me, and we made our way into the stadium. After we got through the turnstile we climbed up what must have been 50 flights of stairs! At the landing we only had to climb the few left to enter the stand. I will never forget the feeling as I reached that top stair. The view was amazing. A huge pitch laid in front of me, and terracing all round. I was taken aback; I had never expected it to look so huge. It certainly did not look as big whenever I had seen it on the TV.

Out came the players. "There's Paul McStay, son." "Look Kevin, there's Kenny Dalglish." These were the people who we, as schoolboys, held in awe. My favourite Liverpool player in those days, somewhat ironically, was John Barnes. He may not have made the best manager in the world but what a player he was. I was mesmerised just watching him warm up at the pitchside. As kick-off time drew near, the anticipation mounted. An announcement said that there was to be a minute's silence for the victims of the Hillsborough disaster.

The referee blew his whistle… Silence… an eerie silence… Not a soul stirred or dared to move. Traffic outside the stadium was clearly audible, but as the silence went on, I found myself being lost in my own thoughts.

Those poor fans. The people running on to the pitch. Young lads being lowered down from the upper tiers. Ambulances on the pitch. Police vainly trying to calm the situation…How they must all have suffered…

PEEEEEEEEP! A massive roar of cheering that was fuelled by the raw emotion of the event immediately drowned the whistle out. Then the start of the song which was to become so familiar to me, the song which Celtic fans and Liverpool fans loved to sing, and the defining bond between the two clubs: *"When you walk through a storm, Hold your head, up high And don't be afraid, of the dark…"*

All I could see around me was a sea of green and white scarves, held above fans' heads. All I could hear was thousands of people singing this song at the top of their voices, as the song reached its climax… *"…Though your dreams be tossed And blown, Walk on, walk on With hope, in your heart, And you'll never walk alone, You'll never walk alone…"* This was one of those moments when the hair stands up on the back of your neck. What a feeling. What an atmosphere. What a tragic occasion.

As for the actual game, I don't recollect that much. What I do remember is us getting beaten 4-0. But on occasions like these, scorelines don't matter. I like to think that Celtic and all its fans were representative of the way that everyone in the footballing world was feeling at that sad time. We wanted to do something, anything that could offer even the slightest bit of comfort that would attempt to ease the pain of the victims' families.

Of course, the money raised on that occasion was no replacement to losing a loved one, but like to think that that game did more than raise cash. We offered Liverpool the hand of friendship when they needed it most, and when it comes down to it, that is what matters. I was proud of everything Celtic Football Club stood for, and I was proud to be a Celtic fan that day.

KEVIN McARDLE, Howwood, Johnstone

"IT'S a kind of magic." Those are the words my dad said to me to describe Celtic Park. He was right! After nearly 24 years of waiting, January 24, 2002, was the day I'd discover it for myself. Our journey took almost 24 hours before kick-off, where we started our journey from Waterford, Ireland. The excitement, however, began on Christmas Day. One elder sister bought the airline tickets; another booked the hotel. Big brother got the match tickets and I couldn't wait!

It was a dream come true. All my life I've been surrounded by sport – especially football and even more so by Celtic. Birthdays would come and go and each year I'd ask my dad when he was taking me to Paradise. Finally, my dream was realised.

From Waterford to Dublin, I was kinda quiet (strange for me!). All I could think about was the next day and what it would be like. Fun in Dublin – pints and laughter – was followed by an early morning flight with loads of our Bhoys at the airport – it was perfect.

Arriving in Glasgow, I immediately wanted to go to Parkhead. Although, at 9.15am I thought I might have been on my own. We checked into the hotel and had a wander around the streets and shopped 'til we dropped in the Celtic stores. I was really on my way!

After a quick change – I needed my new Celtic gear on – and we were finally into the taxi and off to the ground. The driver asked where we were going and at the same time my dad and I looked at one another before I said proudly 'Parkhead'.

As we pulled up on London Road I was totally in awe. The pictures didn't do it justice, but the name certainly does – Paradise – how apt!

We stood with all the other fans and waited for the team bus to arrive. I was so overawed, I had to turn away. There I was, after years of waiting, and it was all too much. My back was turned, a lump in my throat but a huge smile on my face.

After the team arrived I joined my father in a toast to Celtic in the local hostelry. "'Twas a long time coming, but here we are." It was like music to my ears. As the countdown to kick-off drew nearer, the butterflies in my stomach got bigger and then we were going back to the stadium.

However I had felt before wasn't a patch on how I felt when I walked inside, up the steps and inside the stadium. I stood, with tears in my eyes, and felt like I'd finally come home. We got our seats, even though I couldn't sit down. The crowd, the team, the Huddle – it was magic!

We played St Johnstone that day and it might not have been the best game of the season, but it didn't matter to me. All I cared about was that I was there!

The whistle blew and so it began. Larsson got the first, the legend, and Thompson got a second- woo-hoo! The jumping, hugging, singing, cheering and sheer elation was brilliant.

The match flew by but I didn't want to leave. To see Celtic Park with over 58,000 people in it is one thing but to see it almost completely empty is just as special. We waited until almost everyone had gone because I had to savour every moment.

So, with the game over we went into the rainy Glasgow night and found a pub full of plenty of Celtic fans and I felt completely at home. The weekend lasted longer than I'll write – I don't think I could cram it into a couple of thousand words. The city, the people, the Bhoys, Paradise – it all went beyond anything I could have imagined.

On the Monday at the airport, I didn't want to leave. "I'm getting a job at Parkhead – Martin needs someone like me," Dad agreed and we had a laugh. Grudgingly I got on the plane. I hated to leave; it was as if I was leaving home for the first time. My heart was broken but the thing that made me go was I knew I'd be back.

And so, the season closes and we're Champions once again. My heart, I left in Glasgow – but I'll join it soon again. Hail! Hail!

YVETTE FLYNN, Waterford, Ireland

My first visit to Parkhead

AS the date approached I was very excited after hardly sleeping the night before, but I made it. Bag packed, phone charged and food and drink to hand, we set off on our four-hour journey down the A9 to Glasgow. We arrived at Parkhead with time to spare and parked the car. We made our way to enter Paradise. While in the queue, with the wind blowing strongly, a whisper reached us that the game was called off.

Half an hour later it was confirmed that the game was cancelled due to damage on the roof, so we made our way back to the car and another four-hour journey up the A9, but I wasn't bothered – just another day off school!

A week later, on a Tuesday, the re-match was on, so another four-hour journey down the road and another day off school. YES!

We made our way down the road, hoping to see the Bhoys play in style, so this time we phoned from Inverness to see if the game was still on and, yes, it was … but trouble had struck.

The car started to play up. Just what we needed! We arrived, eventually, at Parkhead after running from the car park, took our seats and sat down hoping to watch a good game against Inverness Caley Thistle, but I was wrong.

19

Unfortunately, they scored first and from then on Celtic seemed to go downhill. The match finished 3-1 to Inverness – my worst nightmare.

Sadly we made our way back to the car for the long journey up the A9. Surely things couldn't get any worse? ... But they did. The car broke down at Perth in a car park so we were stuck for a few hours. My auntie went into Tesco's to get help but they wanted us to go in for a free cup of tea until the AA arrived. We didn't go in because we really just wanted to get home after the tragedy at Parkhead. After a while, thanks to a local bus driver, we got the car going. We made our way home, which usually takes two-and-a-half hours from Perth but took us about four hours because we could only go 40mph the whole way home.

We arrived in the small village of Lairg in the far north at 7am and went straight to our beds after driving through rain, hail, sleet and snow. It was very scary, not knowing if we were going to make it home or not but, great, another day off school!!

JORDAN RENWICK (age 13) Lairg, Sutherland

MY first game was Celtic v Rangers with my cousin, James. I was nervous. I did not have a ticket. We were walking around and waiting to get in and my luck came and someone opened a door. Me and my cousin ran in. I was happy. I went through the doors and seen everyone. We went down to the very front. The first goal was Darren Jackson. I went mental.

About 10 minutes later a steward asked for my ticket and me and my cousin ran away. We ended up at the Jock Stein Stand. The last goal was Paul Lambert. It was a peach. A bar, post and in. After the game I went to the Hoops Bar and went back home.

MARK, St Aiden's School, Glasgow

MY earliest memory of watching Celtic was way back in October 1970, the year in which they reached their second European Cup final. The game was a second round first leg game against Waterford, the Republic of Ireland League champions. My father and I, a 13-year-old boy then, travelled down to Dublin for this game in one of the many supporters' buses that left Belfast at 10am that morning.

With anticipation and excitement I could hardly wait for this game to start. I was going to watch my heroes, Johnstone, Wallace, McNeill, Murdoch and Lennox in action. As we approached Lansdowne Road, there was green and white everywhere; everyone seemed to be supporting the great Glasgow Celtic.

At last the time had arrived and at approximately 3.45 the players walked from their dressing rooms and as the supporters saw the players entering the pitch, the stadium erupted in cheers and singing as the band lead the teams out onto the pitch. At 4.00 the Danish referee, Kaj Rasmussan, got the game underway. The game was only 12 seconds old when Willie Wallace slipped the ball past Waterford's Peter Thomas.

From then on in, Waterford were under attack. The attack started straight from the kick-off. A weak pass by John O'Neill was intercepted by Bobby Lennox, the ball was then passed over to Harry Hood and he in turn passed it on to Willie Wallace for the finishing touches. The ball was in the back of the net and the Waterford players and their supporters were stunned into silence. No doubt, that goal must be ranked as one of the quickest goals ever to be scored. Celtic knew that victory was in sight. With further goals from Bobby Murdoch (2), Lou Macari (2) and two more from Willie Wallace to complete his hat-trick, was enough to complete the goal rush for Celtic.

I will always remember that game and that particular goal. To this day I still have the match programmes, the match tickets and, most of all, the treasured autographs. What a day it was when Glasgow Celtic played Waterford on Wednesday, October 21, 1970.

LAWRENCE POWER, Belfast

First game is the deepest

LIKE many events in life, your first experience of something new is usually exciting, sometimes frightening and nearly always memorable. These can all be applied to my first Celtic game. The odd thing is that my first game arrived in a roundabout way, my younger brother in his pre-Celtic days had opted to support Hearts in season 1974/75, I think the maroon nylon strip swung it although previous favourites had included Leeds United, Arsenal and Manchester United. Whereas, I always liked the bright hoops of the Glasgow Celtic.

My father however, followed Glasgow's junior giants Pollok and on many a Saturday we had been taken along to Newlandsfield to follow the Lok. Little was I to know what bigger and better things were just around the corner.

And so it was in that season I was introduced to the huge family that is the Glasgow Celtic. My dad had decided as a birthday treat he would take my brother to see the Jam Tarts play Celtic and I would tag along to keep me out of mischief.

I recall looking at the inside back page of the *Daily Record* for the match details, as it was always a little advert which highlighted the opposition, the competition, kick-off time and the match prices, Adult, Child, OAP, Main Stand, Enclosure and the Parent/Child Gate.

Funny how it never mentioned the Priests got in for nothing, touched by the hand of God indeed! There was also the other little advert for the football specials on British Rail.

We were off, two buses required, one into the city centre and the other through the Barras up to the Holy Ground. Once off the bus there was a sea of green and white starting to snake its way up to the ground, loads of little boys at marching pace trying to keep up with their older family members.

You could start to feel the excitement and anticipation build up all around as the crowds came together through the housing scheme and up to Janefield Street. Up to the turnstiles, dad got a programme but gave it to my brother, he then lifted my brother over the turnstile and I was shuffled in front of him and pushed through the gate at the same time.

In under the stairs and the noise starts to get louder, it was becoming an explosion on my seven-year-old senses as we came up on to the terracing. Waves of green and white everywhere with flags, scarves, bobble hats and the Hoops everywhere.

Men and boys were chatting, laughing, singing, swearing, smoking and drinking. You could smell food, alcohol and cigar smoke all around.

Looking out on to the park and it, along with the stadium, was huge, the players were out on the pitch, bobbing and weaving, back and forward with the ball and seemed to be doing all the things my friends and I did on the school pitches (although they were red ash and it was never a good idea to do slide tackles).

We stated making our way round to what looked like a big school shed, the crowd was getting larger, the noise louder and the anticipation stronger. We were suddenly being jostled from side to side and for the first time an element of fear crept into the day, as my brother and I kept a tighter grip on dad.

This was the Jungle and we were situated right on the halfway line down at the front and the pitch was exactly at eye-level. The players then left the pitch and disappeared up a tunnel on the other side.

The atmosphere was more intense as the singing got louder and the chant of 'It's A Grand Old Team' rang out. Suddenly there was a massive roar as the team ran back out the tunnel kicking footballs all around, the fans took their scarves off and swayed from side to side singing You'll Never Walk Alone, it sent a shiver through my spine (and still does to this day).

Soon the game started and the chant of 'Celtic, Celtic' rang out, the crowd moved and swayed along with the action on the park, a few times we were lifted off our feet and tumbled forward though we always seemed to land back at our original spot.

Then all of a sudden there was a huge rush and cheers went up as men were shouting, hugging and backslapping, Celtic had scored much to my brother's dismay. Hail, Hail The Celts Are Here rang out as the crowd urged the team forward for another. I asked dad, who sat over at the orange seats facing us and he said it was for the posh people, I asked why do they want to sit, is it so they can see the game?

The game and the crowd seemed to settle down, fans were chatting and I started to hear some familiar names, Lennox, McNeill and Kenny Dalglish. He was great, he seemed to be everywhere on the pitch, when I could see it, and it sounded as though he was very much the favourite of those all around me.

It was turning out to be a great day for me but not so good for my brother, after all it was supposed to be his birthday treat. Half time arrived and there was a lot of activity around us, dad grabbed us and we bustled down under the Jungle and got a hot pie along with Bovril.

Aye, the first sip is always the hottest and to this day I still burn my tongue in the rush to get that little refreshment.

Back upstairs and we managed to get back to our same spot, the crowd was now very quiet and dad said the half time scores were being read out, cheers and jeers went up with each score announced.

Soon the teams ran out and the crowd was back on the move again as the Bovril proceeded to scald a thumb and forefinger. It wasn't long before Celtic added a few more and even Hearts got in on the act, which cheered my brother up at last.

King Kenny had scored two goals only to be substituted which the crowd did not like at all as the boos went out around the stadium.

Celtic were well in front now and it was unlikely they would lose the game, the crowd quietened down and every now and then would burst into a new song which would work its way round to the other parts of the stadium, the Rangers End, the Celtic End and the quieter Main Stand.

The songs would echo rather than be sung in unison and it seemed as though there was a little competition going round the stadium to see who could sing the loudest.

Dad would sometimes have to pull us back up the terracing to stand behind the emerald green wooden barriers when the crowd moved too far down.

The game petered out and spaces began to appear all around us, the fans started making for the exits keeping one eye ahead and the other on the game. The referee blew for full time and a satisfied cheer went up from all the fans. We headed out of the Jungle and went back into marching mode, the fans staying behind had an attempt at *You'll Never Walk Alone* but it wasn't as good as when they sang it at the start of the game.

We made our way out of the stadium and thoughts turned to two things, getting home and food! Dad promised fish suppers if we behaved, though my brother did have a little spell of tears because of the result. Once home we tucked into the fish suppers and the *Pink Sports Times* was read from front to back page as I read up on the magical experience that was my first game watching the Tic.

PETER BOLE, Monifieth, Angus

The first ever time I went to Paradise
It was like a dream come true,
It was a million times bigger than my school,
I was five rows behind the net,
Douglas was down my side of the pitch,
With Sutton scoring in the first half,
I didn't want to move from my seat,
I don't think I could have left my seat,
After the second half Larsson got a hat-trick plus one,
And Sutton scored another one,
Coming home, the boat wouldn't stop swaying.
But I didn't care all I could think of was the match,
I'll never forget that day - January 2, 2001.

SEAMUS CLARKE (age 13), Belfast

PERHAPS the most telling part of Nick Hornby's book *Fever Pitch* is when his father first takes him to an Arsenal game in the early '70s. Nick's parents are divorced and his father sees Nick every Saturday for an obligatory visit usually ending up in McDonalds. Neither particularly looks forward to these visits until, for a change, the father suggests that one Saturday they go to see Arsenal. Nick isn't enthusiastic but once he gets to the game he is mesmerised by what he sees and becomes a life-long Arsenal supporter. Supporting Arsenal develops into the central part of his life, he forges a new relationship with his hitherto estranged father and goes on to write the most successful book ever written about football; a truly life changing experience.

The book brought home memories of a similar experience with Celtic. My parents were separated and for me my father was simply this man I didn't know very well who existed on the periphery of my life. He was a lifelong Celtic supporter and suggested one day that we go to see Celtic. This turned out to be the Scottish Cup semi-final between Celtic and Dundee at Hampden in 1970 when I was 12. Celtic won 2-1 with Bobby Lennox and Lou Macari scoring Celtic's goals. It's amazing how the details are still clear more than 30 years later. Like Nick Hornby I was immediately hooked, going to see Celtic's next home game against Ayr United a few days later (3-0). I have rarely missed a home game since.

For me, though, it was a period when I began to develop a completely new relationship with my father through Celtic. Over the next few years we never missed a home game, travelled regularly to away games and even went to reserves games fairly regularly. This was a time when Celtic had an absolutely outstanding reserve team; Vic Davidson, Paul Wilson, Danny McGrain, Kenny Dalglish et al.

My father proved to be a real authority on Celtic's history actually living through most of it. He was very much older than me, more like a grandfather than father, having married late. When I was in my early teens he was already nearly 60 and had been taken to his first Celtic game in 1918 at the age of five. He had a wealth of stories; was at the game where Johnny Thomson died, was in Hampden at the cup final of 1931 against Aberdeen which created the record attendance for a Scottish game, was at the Empire Exhibition and Coronation Cup finals. He vividly remembered all the great Celtic players; Patsy Gallagher, Jimmy McGrory, Jimmy Delaney, Charlie Tully. Talking to him brought Celtic's history to light. He was fiercely proud of Celtic's Irish roots being born in Donegal but deplored sectarianism from any quarter.

We began to share experiences. At the Celtic v Leeds game at Hampden where neither of us could see a thing; my father being of that generation not overimbued with height. At the Ibrox disaster which left him genuinely distraught. At the European Cup semi-final against Atletico Madrid, where the Spaniards quite literally kicked Celtic off the park. We travelled all over Scotland to such far flung venues as Central Park, Cowdenbeath or Gayfield Park, Arbroath standing on open terracing (sometimes not even terracing) in the wind and the rain and enjoying every minute of it. We had our routines, usually meeting at the railway station to catch the football special. We always had a flask and a 'trannie' at the game and always bought a fish supper at the nearest fish & chip shop after. Although I remember one incident immediately prior to decimalization when we stormed out of a chip shop in Ayr when they bumped the price of fish suppers up to 1/6 because Celtic were in town.

Perhaps the most memorable event was our one and only trip abroad to see Celtic. In 1970 Celtic were drawn against Waterford from the Irish Republic in the second round of the European Cup. It was the first time Celtic had ever been drawn against Irish opposition in Europe and the away game was switched to Lansdowne Road in Dublin. This was to be watched by a record attendance for a club football game in Ireland, a record that still stands today. It had been a number of years since my father was last in Ireland and I had never been. We decided to go. Although the game was in Dublin my father wanted to travel via Donegal where he originally came from. He hadn't been there for many years but still had friends and relations there. At 12 who was I to argue?

We left by coach from the south side of Glasgow in the morning and by teatime had disembarked from the ferry in Northern Ireland. As I had never been out of Scotland before this was a big adventure. The coach then travelled south to Dublin minus us - my father and I about to travel east to Donegal. You know how there is a point in your childhood when you realise that your parents are not infallible, that they have their faults and weaknesses and make mistakes like the best of them. This I was about to discover. The game was on the next night; "we'll be there in plenty of time". Spending the rest of the day travelling across Northern Ireland we arrived in Donegal late that night booking into a small hotel. Out up and early the next morning we started doing the rounds of friends and places. By this time I was starting to worry; we had to be in Dublin that evening. Not to worry, my father said, there was a bus at 1pm, which would get us to Dublin in plenty of time and allow us to see a bit of 'God's Country'.

At 12.3opm we arrived at the bus station only to find that my father was using an out of date timetable; the bus had actually left 3ominutes before; the next not leaving for another four hours. We then spent the rest of the day on Donegal. My father didn't seem to mind so much although I was thoroughly disappointed. We eventually watched the game on a grainy black and white television set in the house of an old friend of my father. The house was packed with neighbours all wanting to see the biggest game that there had ever been in Ireland.

I continued to go to Celtic games regularly with my father for the next 20 years; he only stopped going when he turned 80. Celtic had become as much a part of my life as it had his. Now nearly 90 he lives in a nursing home not far from Celtic Park and suffers from advanced Alzheimer's Disease. He doesn't remember me or for that matter what he had for breakfast that morning and spends most of his time sleeping in a chair. The interesting thing is that the nursing home has a wide screen television, which regularly shows football. My father shows no interest in this except on specific occasions. This is when Celtic are playing and wearing their green and white hooped shirts. Then a spark of recognition comes over his face and he follows as best he can, what's going on.

I visited him recently with my nine-year-old daughter. We called into the nursing home on our way to watch Celtic play Hamilton in the League Cup. It was her first game. It dawned on me as I watched my daughter become hooked very much as I had 31 years before that through three generations we had been watching Celtic regularly for more than 80 years. For me, Celtic have always been more than a football team rather a living, breathing institution that binds a community together and gives them a sense of history and identity. From my nine-year-old daughter wide eyed and excited at her first game to my 90-year-old father and that flicker of recognition when he sees the green and white hoops, Celtic have enriched and transformed our lives.

WILLIAM BONNAR, Glasgow

The first time forever

THERE have been many memorable Celtic occasions over the years. The great European Cup nights of the 1970s at Celtic Park, instilled a pride of time and place that can never be erased. The bizarre experience, of watching Celtic being taken apart and taught a football lesson, by a superb Real Madrid side in 1963, only to see 60,000 Celtic fans refusing to go home, until their heroes emerged from the dressing room, to a tumultuous lap of honour. And of course, there was the May 25, 1967. These are but a few of the memories, that confirm the conviction, that once Celtic – forever Celtic.

But for me, buried among all the glory and collective success of every famous victory, Saturday, September 21, 1957, still remains the date that stands supreme among the many distinguished events in Celtic's recent history. For a start, it was my birthday, but more significantly, it was the day of my inauguration and confirmation into the Celtic Family. It was my first Celtic game and it was not even at Celtic Park and I remember very little of the football action.

At this time, I was a precocious and demanding 10-year-old, who spent many a Saturday afternoon crouched on my grandmother's living room floor, feasting on Irn Bru and Jammy Dodgers, listening intently to the BBC's radio commentary of that week's Celtic game. Every broadcast was enlivened by the knowledge that the man describing the action was actually there and that every cheer and every groan of the crowd contained the voice of my uncle Mick, who never missed a match, never stopped talking about it and would later confirm or deny the veracity of the BBC "interpretation" of Celtic's performance.

What started it all, was the 1957 Glasgow Cup semi-final against Rangers. Celtic, according to uncle Mick, dominated every inch of Ibrox. Bobby Evans was majestic, Willie Fernie was silky smooth and Charlie Tully ran Shearer ragged. He may not have expressed his recollections in quite those terms, he was more graphic and robust, as I recall, but, even at an early age, I could relate and empathise with his passion for Celtic. Especially on that occasion, when, it seems Rangers were 'jammy' and Celtic were terribly unlucky to lose 2-0. Before his match report ended and just after he had extolled the qualities of Bobby Collins, his agitation and disappointment at the result, provoked an invitation that was beyond my abilities to refuse.

"Yi want-tae come' tae Parkhead wi me, wee man?" he growled.

"Aye! – a' dae," I yelped. "But a'll hiv' tae ask ma granny furst".

"Never mind that". He said. "A'll sort it oot wi yir granny. Just you get yir scarf wash'd an' ironed fur next week".

Unfortunately, the next Saturday fixture was against Dundee at Dens Park and the following game was against Clyde at Shawfield. I missed my chance to attend the game against Falkirk at Celtic Park, because my cousin was being married, and I was a pageboy. But, to ease my obvious frustration and impatience and, to brighten up the surly expression I had adopted for the wedding, uncle Mick, promised me a special treat for my birthday.

"A've seen yir granny. It's aw right – Yir goin' tae see Celtic next Saturday. He whispered. But we're no' goin' tae Parkheid", he added surreptitiously.

"Where ur' we goin' then?" I demanded to know.

"Just wait an' see. A'll tell yi later" he replied.

I had been aware that uncle Mick had downed a number of toasts during the wedding reception, and I was not sure if he was fully in control of what he said. So, I went to see my granny, to ask her. As I recall, she was finishing a rousing rendition of one of her favourite Irish ballads and this usually brought on a bought of nostalgia for 'The Old Country' and a red faced expressions of Nationalist pride.

"Can I go tae Parkheid wi' uncle Mick?" I asked excitely.

"Aye son – gi yir granny a kiss – an' yi' can go and see the Celtic" she gushed, before bursting into song again.

It was Sunday morning, before I figured out who and where the following week's opposition and venue would bee. After catching up with the adventures of *Oor Wullie* and the latest instalment of *The Broons*, I consulted the Jack Harkness report on the back page of *The Sunday Post* and noted a reference to the Old Firm encounter at Ibrox the following Saturday. That was it, I exclaimed.

The realisation that my birthday treat was to be a trip to Ibrox, to see the Old Firm game, exploded like a starburst. I could hardly believe my granny had consented to it. And, as it turned out, my granny could not believe she had consented to it either. Uncle Mick, it seemed, had managed to catch her midway through the wedding reception, when she was at her most agreeable. And, it was said, she even confirmed her approval by raising a toast to the occasion. There was more to uncle Mick, than I had realised. Poor granny. For the rest of the week, she used every trick in the book to try and talk me out of it. She suggested I may be too young to go to a big match and offered alternative birthday treats, she even resorted to emotional blackmail at one point. But I would not budge. I had been raised on the back of heroic tales of famous Celtic victories. Memories of the Coronation Cup triumph, in 1953, were still being celebrated in song with a catch tune about 'Lizzie and Philip'. Arguments raged in our household, about the relative merits of past Celtic greats, such as Jimmy Quinn, Patsy Gallagher and Jimmy McGrory, who were ruthlessly compared against the contemporary skills of Willie Fernie, Bobby Collins and Charlie Tully.

Give up the chance of seeing Celtic? Sorry granny, no chance, and I refused to feel any shame for reminding her, that a promise was a promise.

However, waiting for Saturday did have its tensions. I had to be on my best behaviour, so as to deny granny any excuse for denying me my great day. But I did sympathise with uncle Mick, who was on the receiving end of his mother's wrath. He was in his early 20s at the time, lived at home and spent the rest that week hiding like a chastised child, trying to avoid being anywhere near her. At every confrontation between them, uncle Mick was reminded that he had taken advantage of her 'good nature'. She was relentless.

After school on Friday, I was careful not to step an inch out of line. The coal scuttle was filled, my bedroom was tidy and I even washed up the dishes after tea and went to bed without as much as a whimper. I had been a model grandson all week and granny had nowhere to go with her objections. So much so, that by Saturday morning at breakfast, she finally relented with a tirade of advice to me about not getting lost and to uncle Mick about not getting drunk.

It is strange. I can clearly recall every moment of the day leading up to the time when we left home, to travel to Ibrox. But everything else that followed, is just a mass of conflicting first experiences. It was the first time I had crossed the Clyde on a ferry: It was the first time I was lifted over a turnstile, but ultimately, it was the first time, I stood on a football terrace, watching Celtic. It was my first defining moment and one that influenced and confirmed my loyalties, for the years ahead.

Of the game, I remember very little of the action, and the drama of what was happening on the distant playing field, totally eclipsed me. The real impact on me came from my immediate surroundings. I may have only been 10-years-old, but perched on my uncle Mick's shoulders, seeing the passion and the joy on the faces of the supporters, each time Celtic attacked the Rangers goal and scored, had an immediate and lasting effect upon me. It is still the reference point, that defines the moment, that I became Celtic forever.

Forty-five years on, I still remember and treasure my first Celtic game. Not even the experience of attending the more historic Old Firm event a few weeks later, when Celtic retained the League Cup with an emphatic 7-1 victory, or the pleasure of being at Lisbon's National Stadium 10 years later, has been able to eclipse those first golden moments. As with many of life's initiations, maturity is enhanced by the quality of your first experience. I may not be able to recount the superiority of Celtic on that day, but Cyril Horne of the *Glasgow Herald* did. Concluding his report, he wrote:

"Celtic had the best full back afield in Fallon, a clearly superior half-back line, and as obvious an advantage in skill and shrewdness in the forward line. Perhaps their disadvantage in physique was to their advantage; in any event, they gained the reward of devoting more attention to the arts and crafts of the game".

JACK HIGHAM, Warwickshire

My first real football game

A YEAR ago in February 2001 I had the chance to be in Newhouse on a business trip. I live in the Midwest of the United States. Through my several days of meetings I overheard some 'discussions' on Scottish Football. These 'discussions' were mostly very short exchanges that were more like tests of one's physique than a chat over a pint. Anyway, I asked about the chance to see a game. The secretary of the group, Jane, went to work and found tickets available to that night's game at the National Stadium, Hampden Park, between Celtic and Rangers. She informed me I must choose whom I support. I knew the story lines for both clubs and easily selected the Green.

First my Mother is full Irish. Second wife is nearly full Irish; in fact she loves misery so much I am convinced she is more Irish than the ones living there. And third, I am a Catholic.

I ordered a taxi from the factory to first find the nightclub holding my ticket, 'wait there, and then drop me at my hotel in Glasgow'. The taxi driver was from the country and more lost that I trying to find the nightclub. At one point he actually stopped the car on a sidewalk went exploring on foot. I waited, wondering what kind of place we were looking for. Eventually he returned and we took off. He got me within a block of the nightclub and pointed me towards it. He would wait where he was parked, partially blocking traffic. He informed me that it was all right, since getting a football ticket was important business in Scotland. I worked my way somehow past the locked door and up three flights of stairs in complete darkness to find a small office. Sure enough, they had my name and a green ticket. The taxi driver was pretty excited to see me as well as the several delivery truck drivers, who were having trouble getting past his car. Anyway, he was surprised to see the ticket I was waving to all, and soon we were at the hotel.

By this time he had enough of the big city and was ready to head to his home. I threw my bags into the room and was soon back on the street waving for a taxi. I caught one's interest and he came the wrong way up the street, with a clever U-turn, and opened the door just for me. I told him I was heading to Hampden Park. He pounded the dash and exclaimed 'which side?' When I pushed the green coloured and silver-laced ticket in front of his face he really reacted. By this time we were already through the first red light and moving quite well. When he saw my ticket he nearly jumped in the back seat with me. He grabbed me with both hands and shook me with excitement. This made his day and now he had a mission to get me to the game safely and on time. I did not understand the 'safely' part but liked the 'on time' and really hoped he would turn back soon to avoid the cars coming at us. He told me of his loyalty to the Celtic and his history. It was quite an omen to him as just having come off a four-day continuous exercise with the pubs and a few hours sleep, to pick me up as his first customer. I got the sense he was fulfilling some unwritten duty as a Celtic fan to assist my virgin experience.

Anyway, I entered the stadium and was thrilled to find such a crowd on a cold night. I understood and even expected some of the happenings as the game opened but I was totally floored by the crowd and its team loyalty. I was really impressed with the gent sitting directly in front of me who jumped up about every minute and started a song. What was even more amazing was that within a few words nearly 20,000 people had joined him. I worked to learn the words and by the end of the game had a few of the songs memorised (I sometimes sing these songs at my local pub and the colourful words sometimes attracts extra attention). At half time I enjoyed a warm pie and a few words with the fans. The game was very exciting and of course we all celebrated with a win. By the end of the game I was nearly able to keep up with the emotion and the understanding of the game tactics. I could almost now blend in as a Celtic fan. On the way out of the stadium I bought a Celtic flag, that flies in my house today.

I walked back to the hotel, enjoying a few pints in the pubs and a few songs on the street with my fellow Celtic fans. My next trip to Scotland will definitely be planned around the Celtic football schedule.

JAMES LENZ, Minneapolis

A dream come true

FOR weeks my sister had been telling me she was planning a surprise for my 18th birthday. My birthday came and went. Catherine kept telling me that she hadn't all the details finalised. I was told to keep the weekend of December 1 free. Being the curious person I am, I began to look everywhere for clues but to no avail. Eventually I gave up looking. One day by chance when I checked the history file on the internet, I discovered Catherine had been on the Celtic website. My brain began to work overtime. As an avid Celts supporter I knew that they were playing Hibs on December 1. I was hoping beyond all hope that my biggest dream was about to come true. Maybe Catherine was taking me to see the Bhoys play.

When I asked Catherine if my suspicions were right, she told me I was way off track. My heart sank. Later as I thought about it, I wondered why else Catherine would go on the website as she didn't particularly like football. I tried to get Catherine to let the cat out of the bag but this proved impossible.

As December 1 approached, I must have driven my friends mad talking about the match. I was so convinced I was going to Parkhead. I was on a high, drifting around the house singing all the Celtic songs.

Friday, November 20 came. I still hadn't been told where we were going. All I knew was to take enough warm clothes to last until Sunday. It had to be the match! Mam and dad dropped me off in Newry where Catherine met me. As I was getting into Catherine's car, mam threw me a bag. She said I might need it where I was going. When I opened the bag my eyes nearly popped out of my head. I couldn't believe it!

It was the Celtic strip I had nearly bought the day before. I knew now that my suspicions had been right. My dream would at last come true. I was going to Parkhead to see the Bhoys last. I jumped for joy and gave Catherine what was probably the biggest hug she will ever get. At Catherine's flat in Belfast we packed our clothes into one bag. We tried to get a couple of hours' sleep before going to the ferry terminal. This didn't happen however, as I was so excited I couldn't sleep and so I kept Catherine awake too.

In the end we gave up trying to get to sleep. At 1.30am we got a taxi to the ferry terminal. As we sat in the departure lounge we heard a group of Celtic fans chanting the various Celtic songs on their way up the stairs.

They were a group of men from Portarlington. As soon as they saw my Celtic jersey they came over to talk. They were very amused by the fact that two women were going to a Celtic match alone. Even when we showed them our tickets, they still had their doubts. We made our way on board the ferry through the swarms of Celtic supporters. The craic was good with Celtic songs coming from all angles. As soon as the ferry shop opened I purchased my green and white top hat, which went down a treat with the other fans. I was in my element and still couldn't believe where I was going. The ferry docked in a freezing cold, wet and windy Stranraer. As most of the Celtic supporters on the ferry were continuing their journey by bus, our connecting train was quiet.

On reaching Glasgow, with the help of an A-Z, we made our way to our hotel in the city centre. After nice hot baths we made our way to Celtic Park. At the bus station, all the buses for Parkhead were delayed because of the match. The staff at the station were highly amused by my outfit - a green and white top hat, a Celtic jersey and a Celtic tracksuit. At last we got a bus. Soon, I would get my first glimpse of Celtic Park.

Outside Celtic Park, we made our way through the hordes of people. With just enough time to add a Celtic scarf to my memorabilia collection, we made our way to our seats which were in row X at the top of the North Stand. Even my fear of heights didn't matter now. It was some climb to the stand but luckily I'm a fit person - I wish I could say the same for Catherine! When we got to our seats I got my first real glimpse of Celtic Park. It was unreal. I was speechless for probably the first time ever. A traditional Irish band was playing in the background. Hoopy the Celtic mascot was dancing around the pitch. Birthday greetings were appearing on the large screens at either end. It was a truly magical experience.

Heart bursting with joy, I cheered my heroes on to the pitch as the fans erupted. We could see the small amount of Hibs supporters compared to about 59,000 Celtic fans. As the game kicked off I was on top of the world. I couldn't think of a better way to spend my weekend. I was delighted to see Chris Sutton return to the team after his son's illness. Hartson and Larsson were a brilliant pair up front. Celtic held possession and didn't concede frees. Fifteen minutes into the game, Hartson had put Celtic one goal up! The atmosphere was electric as the fans cheered for their heroes. Celtic anthems were pounding out all over the place. Mid-song, as play got exciting, songs would abruptly end and advice would be shouted to players. As we were so high up it was hard to make out which player was which, apart from Neil Lennon whose blond hair stood out vividly.

Hartson then put Celtic two goals up with yet another Larsson cross! Half-time came and it was time for hot dogs and hot chocolate to warm us up. Hoopy returned to the pitch for some half-time entertainment. I was loving every wonderful minute of it. The second half commenced and the Bhoys' play was as breathtaking as ever. On the one occasion Hibs dangerously got the ball around the goal, it was stopped by yet another great save from Scotsman Rab Douglas.

Then, about halfway through the second half, Lennon got clear of the Hibs defenders and landed the ball in the back of the net. It was 3-0! At this stage the Celtic supporters adjoining the Hibs supporters were waving flags and teasing the Hibs supporters across the police barricade. It was very funny to watch.

As the final whistle blew, Celtic Park was full of delighted Celtic fans cheering and singing. Everyone was so happy at yet another Celtic win. I was ecstatic. I couldn't believe that the 90 minutes were over. Because of this win, Celtic remained 10 points clear of nearest rivals Rangers in the Scottish Premier League.

Catherine and I eventually made our way through thousands of supporters leaving the ground and found a bus to take us back to the city centre. On the way back to the hotel, I replayed parts of the match over in my mind. It was even better than I expected. I couldn't find the words to describe the wonderful feeling that had come over me. Part of me still wanted to be in Celtic Park watching my heroes play.

That night as we found an Irish pub, Molly Malone's, I had to pinch myself to make me realise that my dream had come true. There was no other memory that I had that felt as good as this. I knew that my first Celtic match was definitely not my last. To this day my memories of December 1, 2001 are as clear as if it were yesterday and I know I will never forget my first experience of seeing my heroes the Bhoys.

CAROLINE HIGGINS, Carrickmacross, Co. Monaghan

THIS is my tale of impromptu Celtic glory, also known as a day when ignorance met coincidence and it all equalled bliss. On a tour of Europe in 2001, my mother and I came to Glasgow for a couple of days; we wanted to see the Hunterian, and the Burrell Collection....oh, who am I fooling? Sure, I like culture (to the point that an American is capable, I suppose) but I have followed Celtic FC from afar for several years and, really, I mostly just wanted to see Paradise.

So early in the afternoon on a chilly day in May, just after arriving in town, I went to the stadium to try to get a tour. I saw dozens of people gathered there but didn't really think anything of it because it was the day after Lisbon Lions legend Bobby Murdoch died. I figured the people I saw were there solely to pay tribute to him, as some had done with wreaths, scarves and so on. I had printed out the club's schedule early in the season and knew there would be no matches while I was in town; thus I reckoned a tour would be the best I could do. So I approached a woman who worked for the club who told me there were no more tours that day. I was depressed for a split second, and even entertained thoughts of laying on the pathetic "But I came a really long way" routine.

Then she told me the reason: The facility was being cleared because of the game that night. Now I was thinking, what is she talking about? Maybe a reserve game or something?' Not too bright, I know, but in fairness I had been on the road (European Grand Tour, remember) for a couple of weeks so I hadn't had a chance to check the club website. She told me the game that night was a testimonial match for Tom Boyd against Manchester United. Really. And then I finally figured it out: Those people were there because they were lining up for tickets for that game!

After being led around a bit by some very helpful locals eager, if slightly bemused, to guide a tourist, I joined the queue (well, it is Britain, after all). And that was how, seven hours after not being able to get in for a tour, I got myself into Celtic Park (my mother was ill and unable to attend) for something slightly better - a game featuring the Champions of Scotland against the Champions of England. I don't exactly know how proud I should be of this but I am a veteran sports fan at the ripe old age of 34: I have attended NCAA basketball tournaments, NFL and NHL playoff games, college football bowl games, Formula One, CART, baseball, MLS and more. Been there, done that. Except I hadn't. It was only a friendly, only a testimonial, yet I have simply never been to a sporting event like it in my life. Non-stop singing on the bus two hours before the game, non-stop singing at the game, and even afterwards on the bus.

All of this is as familiar as breathing to Celtic fans and fans of many European football teams, but quite foreign, and exhilarating, to me. I hadn't even sat down on the bus on the way to the ground before the whole top deck exploded in a chant of,

31

"If ya hate the (expletive) Rangers clap yer hands" and it got filthier and funnier from there. The experience was a true eye-opener: the dodgy pre-game hot dog, the rows and rows of street vendors, the (again bemused) folks who took my picture, and the old man behind me during the game who, at about the rate of an egg timer, would yell CAM OHNN, CELLLLLLTIC! sounding very much like every grizzled Scottish football fan I had ever imagined. What astounded me most was that all the chants were truly "up from the people" and it's like spontaneous combustion. Just when a lull happened, seemingly out of NOWHERE 50,000 people chanted. I found myself singing and yelling along without even knowing a word of what anybody was saying! Again, familiar turf for Celtic Park veterans, but anyone who has been exposed to the canned music and PA-induced clapping of American sporting events - which had been the only spectating life I knew - can well imagine my amazement.

Yes, the Bhoys lost 2-0, and yes, it rained hard after the end, and it was way too cold for mid-May (did I mention I live in Florida?) but for a time that night, the thought of cancelling my flight back, quitting my job, settling in Glasgow and buying season tickets seemed mighty appealing! It was only later that I reflected on the odds of me being in town for only one full day, and that day being the one were the Champions of Scotland and England meet, without me knowing about it or planning for it. There are a few events I have yet to attend that I must do before I die (the Super Bowl and the Indianapolis 500, among others) but right at the top of the list now is an Old Firm game. I'd love another chance to sing along. And next time I might even know the words.

JAMES D. TOMLIN, St Petersburg, Florida

IT was 7am when I woke up I knew I had to get up because I had a very, very special day ahead of me. The kick-off was at 12pm so I got up got washed and brushed my teeth. I got my new tracksuit on then I got my shoes on and brushed my hair. While I was waiting on my uncle to get ready, I got my money off my gran and when my uncle was ready we went to get my dad. We got my dad and then we were on our way to Parkhead.

When we got close enough to it, the traffic was murder but we got through it in a flash. As soon as we got there my dad took some pictures of us and the stadium. We kind of looked about to see if we could find our stand we found it quite quickly. Before the game started we got some chips, coke and some sweets. We got to our stand and we all sat down and waited for the players to come out. They came out very fast. Then the game began and Larsson scored the first goal then he got the other two goals then Hartson scored the other two goals as well then Livingston got just one then the game was finished. On the way home I got a big flag and I was waving it about everywhere. On the way to catch the bus the scarf my uncle was wearing had blew off his neck but I got it back and we were on the way home and I went to get sweets and some coke and I told my mum the whole story and then I showed her my big flag she said to me did you have a good day? I said it was the best day I've ever had and my mum said would you like to go and see them play again I said I would love to see them every time they were playing. She said we will see if we can get more tickets for Celtic and Rangers playing. I would love to see them play again.

TONI KEOGH (age 11), St Gregory's Primary, Glasgow

Chapter Two

Winter of discontent, Summer of joy

THE summer of 1978 is perhaps best remembered for the World Cup in Argentina. For anyone interested in Scotland's fortunes it was a time of anguish, yet most Celtic fans viewed this event from a distance, not caught up in the hype and hysteria of Ally's Tartan Army. The reason being that Celtic had no representation in Argentina. The previous summer Kenny Dalglish had swapped the green Jungle for the red Kop and in truth Celtic had still not recovered from such a blow. If that wasn't bad enough worse was to follow when Danny McGrain, Celtic's only remaining class player, injured a knee in October 1977. It took an eternity to diagnose the problem and it seemed, even longer to find a cure.

On top of all this Jock Stein's reign had come to an end with no trophies, fifth place in the league, and no qualification for European football. All was not well in Paradise. Billy McNeill, then manager of Aberdeen, answered the call from Parkhead and set about trying to put the Celts back on track. He initially succeeded with Celtic winning six of their seven league games to go top including a vital 3-1 Old Firm win on September 9. However, a heavy 4-1 defeat at Pittodrie on October 7 set Celtic back and by December 23 Celtic had won only one of their previous 11 league games. Fate then took its course as Britain suffered its worst winter for years when sub zero arctic temperatures struck the country with heavy snowfalls to add.

The winter of 1978-79 is referred to in political parlance as 'the winter of discontent'. The last days of James Callaghan's wounded Labour government were coming to an end with trade unions seemingly constantly on strike and a fateful General Election looming in May. The winter of discontent perfectly summed up Celtic's plight at this time. No one could see an end to this misery.

Because of the atrocious weather, Celtic did not play a league game between December 23 and March 3, a long time, especially in football terms, but the best thing for Celtic was the return of Danny McGrain against Aberdeen at Parkhead on March 3rd. Sporting what was now to become his trademark beard and a few pounds heavier, it was a tonic for this young Celtic team to have McGrain back. Celtic beat Aberdeen 1-0 with Alfie Conn scoring his last goal in green and white.

McGrain's inspirational presence helped Celtic pick up form and the team began to play consistently. Happily for Celtic, no one in the league had shown any great form and every team had a backlog of fixtures. Aberdeen, Dundee United and Rangers all had spells on top of the league but it was clear that if any side went on a run of wins they could take the title.

By mid April Celtic had dragged themselves into contention with some hard fought victories. On April 28th Celtic beat Dundee United 2-1 in front of a 37,000 crowd, a noticeably good attendance at this time. They had come from behind with Andy Lynch showing commendable coolness to score the winner from a late penalty. At this point the feeling was that maybe, just maybe, Celtic could come from nowhere to steal the title.

However, a body blow was suffered on May 5 when an inept Celtic crashed 1-0 to

Rangers at Hampden, Ibrox being under reconstruction at that time. Incredibly, despite this defeat, it was calculated that if Celtic won their four remaining fixtures they would be Champions. Accordingly, Partick Thistle 2-1, St Mirren 2-0 (played at Ibrox on a Friday night), and Hearts 1-0 were all disposed of. The last fixture of 1978-79 for Celtic was to be Rangers at Parkhead on Monday May 21, a fixture that was initially postponed from January 6. The winner of this crunch game would take the championship.

In May 1979, I was in first year at St Gerard's secondary school in Govan where some teachers would proudly relay to us that two Lisbon Lions, Jim Craig and Joe McBride, had attended the school and recall their epic achievements. However, on May 21 all the talk was of the present and not the past. Rarely had an Old Firm game been so keenly anticipated, this being the closest league race for years. It was a similar situation in Govan shipyards with bets and banter to-ing and fro-ing between rival fans.

My father worked in the yards and had the pleasure of working with three Newcastle men who were based in Govan for a short period. Upon hearing the excitement around the workplace the Geordie lads were informed of the big match and after some discussion tickets were produced and my father arranged to take them to the match.

On the night of the game it was glorious summer evening, short sleeves weather. I stood outside Donnelly's bar on the Govan Road with nervous anticipation. Inside the pub my father and his friends drank happily with the three Geordies who I suspect did not know what to expect. Then at 6.30 the pub emptied, the bus filled and we travelled to Celtic Park. This supporters' club was the Govan South West formed in 1947 and running until its sad demise in 1980. Rules were strict on this bus. No bad language, no offensive banners, no Irish Rebel songs and especially no alcohol. All this at a time when drink was not banned by law from buses and stadia. These men supported Celtic to the level expected by Robert Kelly and Jock Stein. There were high standards expected. This was political correctness before it became fashionable.

As with all big games at Celtic Park when you reach the Gallowgate its best to get out and walk because of the volume of people on the road. Up to the turnstiles at the Celtic End of the ground and the customary 'lift-over' the turnstile for me and the game could begin. We managed to get a decent viewpoint near the front of the terracing, mostly for my benefit.

After the kick off the pre-match nerves settled and it happened. Cooper of Rangers skipped down the right and crossed and Alex McDonald slid in to score. It was painful. We were so close to the front we could hear the swish of the net as the ball struck it. A second later the Rangers' End erupted in delirium. Celtic fought back, Roy Aitken hitting the bar, but half time came with no further scoring. In the Celtic End despondency reigned supreme. The three Geordie lads insisting that Celtic could go on to win but I figured they were only trying to please me.

Around the hour mark matters took a turn for the worse. Alex McDonald had gone down after a tackle and was lying prostrate. An angry John Doyle had remonstrated with McDonald and nudged him with his foot in an effort to get him up. McDonald then proceeded to roll around as if he had been assaulted, result being that the linesman informed the referee who in turn sent Doyle off for violent conduct.

One can only imagine Doyle's emotions as he ran from the field. Predictably, this decision riled the Celtic fans and they found new enthusiasm. So did the team and with nothing to lose Celtic drove forward at Rangers with renewed vigour. Roy Aitken equalised and suddenly Celtic had hope. Even with 10 men Celtic seemed stronger, sensing that Rangers were vulnerable. With 15 minutes left George McCluskey scored with a shot from just inside the area. That was it. We were going to beat Rangers and win the league – and with only 10 men. Funny things go through a young boy's mind at times like that.

Please God, let us win. I'll put my pocket money in the collection on Sunday if you will just let us hold out. I was still praying when Rangers won a corner. From it, Bobby Russell sent a shot through a thicket of Celtic players and it ended up going in off the post. More celebrating in the Rangers End while we stood stunned. A huge roar then emanated from the Celtic fans building up a deafening crescendo with every one in full voice in defiance. Surely if Celtic had scored twice they could get another. It was a case of win or bust. With five minutes left George McCluskey sent in a cross, which the Rangers goalkeeper punched away.

The ball struck his centre half Colin Jackson and rolled goalwards. In horror Jackson realised and chased in pursuit while the ball was still rolling towards the line. Rolling… rolling…rolling… and eventually… in! Bedlam broke out around us. In that split second the realisation that this was the third goal. I was being pulled and hauled all over the place and Dad eventually located me among the madness. Rangers, the reigning champions, were now alike to a heavyweight boxing champion who was on the ropes and in danger of losing his title. They were desperate to claw themselves back into contention. Just on time Murdo MacLeod strode forward to deliver the knockout punch the young contender required by sending a glorious shot high into the net from 25 yards. 4-2, and to this day I can remember nothing of it. I was standing praying with such an intensity that would have put a Benedictine Monk to shame, I missed the goal.

A fourth joyous celebration broke out around us. The final whistle came with few people realising as they were still on a high after the fourth goal. Men who had probably not shed a tear since VE Day or Lisbon were babbling incoherently. I have always had a good relationship with my parents but I don't think I ever felt closer to my dad than I did that night. At time up, embracing each other madly, there was no need for words. Many a cold winter's night has been warmed up when both of us recall that brilliant summer night. Eventually, much, much later, the fans left the ground. The journey back to Govan was euphoric with singing all the way home.

Not satisfied with that, the driver was persuaded to do a 'tour' of Govan with everyone still in good voice as the driver negotiated the dark streets, much to the puzzlement of passers by. The three Geordie lads made their way, dazed, into the night. There is a postscript to this story. Everyone rushed home with indecent haste to watch the highlights on television. Much to our horror it was announced that due to a strike earlier in the day, the game had not been recorded.

This was the only disappointment on the night and because of this the legend of the 4-2 game has continued to grow. In later years Pat Nevin recalled that game, stating that it was 'the closest I came to a religious experience'. I know what he means. Because I was there.

STEPHEN MURRAY, Renfrew

Tell me why…I do like Mondays

The year is nineteen seventy nine, and the date, May twenty first
A day that I'll remember coz ma heart it nearly burst
The close of another title race comes doon tae wan big game
The winners are the Champions, the losers jist go hame
Tae Parkheed come the Rangers for the last game of the season
Could smell the magic in the air, there had to be a reason
Another crucial Old Firm game yet unlike any others
Coz on this night the Celtic fans would "ALL" unite like brothers
Before ya know, its game time and the stadium is full
Its time to play some fitba' and tae take this mob to school
The match it started cagey and oor goal we did protect
As per bloody usual, we gie them way too much respect
Efter jist nine minutes, we gave a goal away
Jammy wee McDonald and against the run of play
They'd hardly kicked a bloody baw, it wis jist insane
But we see this crap from Rangers, time and time again

Now we're mad and wish we had a goal to show for it
We've hud a thoozin shots oan goal, and they've hud wan, that's it!
The ref he blows for half time, to re-group we must retreat
We're playin' the buggers aff the park and still we're gettin' beat
Half time so quickly came and went, Ah' could murder a pie and a pee
But if ah give up such a vantage point. The second half ah'll no see
Wee Johnny Doyle has been sent aff, Ten men, wan nuthin' doon
The pressure's on, "COME ON THE BHOYS", lets turn this gemme aroon'
Rangers sadly seem to be in control and they're 33 minutes away
But that over confident Ibrox mob tried to dictate the play
There's plenty of fight in Celtic and the game's no over yet
Provan flicks to "Feed the Bear"… and the ball is in the net
As is typical in an Old Firm game, it can change within a minute
The Celts have swung the flow of play and noo we're right back in it
Minute 75, and "Paradise" it came alive
as the ball falls once again to "Feed the Bear"
Quite hard he'll shoot but it comes back oot, McCluskey geez a whallop, It's There!

As jubilant fans, we sing and dance, "It's a miracle", we reckoned
But before we got oor breath back, Bobby Russell scored Rangers' second
Such a roller coaster of emotion and of passion and of pride
We threw at them all but the kitchen sink and would not be denied
Again wee Provan skins his man as he does time after time
He bobs and weaves 'wee Jinky' style and finds McCluskey doon the line
He crosses very dangerously and McCloy jist palms it oot
It runs Colin Jackson, the big grey-haired galloot
It hits the auld yin oan the chest, hearts stood still and so did time
In the biggest orgasm ever shared, the baw rolls oor the line

It's little less than frenzy as the place "ERUPTS"... 3 – 2
The richter scale reported shock waves felt as far as Timbuktu
The time is ticking fast away and the Championships in sight
There was only minute left but it seemed to take all bloody night
The anxiety reached a boiling point and as high as it could get
When a "Rhino" 30 yard thunderbolt, almost burst the net

The league is now a certainty; in fact it is a cinch
We huvny beat them for medals since '77 and Andy Lynch
Fever pitch has now been reached and we're all in Celtic heaven
Scenes reminiscent of another night in nineteen sixty seven
Absolute Pandemonium, what an amazing sight and sound
The screams of joy as big McCloy lies prostrate on the ground
Not too long after Murdo's Missile the moment of the truth, the final whistle
So overwhelmed with pure elation, our bursts Caesar for celebration
Too bad for all you Rangers fans, you tried but were outplayed
There's no a happier sight than seeing you all glum and dismayed
Watch them pouring out the exits, underdressed in Union Jacks
Every Celtic fan's favourite view of them, all you can see is their backs!
The Jungle, it is bouncin' oh my God whit an affair
The Cannonball Kid, Champagne Charlie...he was even there
However, on this glorious night, he was but one of us
But very soon after, we would sure know who HE wiz

Such a run towards the title, sometimes playin' three games a week
We truly chose the big one, to hit top form and peak
We beat the "Gers"; we won the league, and a European Cup berth
This underlines, and typifies "The greatest game on earth"
On the ground, exhausted the players are lyin'
All around the terraces, grown men are cryin'
From this event it can be derived, that all the world has been deprived
Of seeing such a magnificent sight, because of some stupid cameramans' strike
This magical night to which no others compare
I'm proud and lucky to say that..."Ah wiz there"
SCOTT RUSSELL, Phoenix, Arizona (Originally from Sandyhills, Glasgow)

Centenary Year

LIFE as a Celtic supporter was a bit of a whirlwind in 1988, life as a 7-year-old Celtic supporter was sometimes too much too handle. I was in Primary 3 at the time, a lovely wee Bhoy (so my mum maintains), all excited about making his First Communion, but there was a problem! In my day, the date of the Scottish Cup final often had a habit of coinciding with the First Communions and this was causing me a lot of concern. You might be wondering why someone barely out of nappies (I would just like to clarify that I was actually 3 or 4 when I graduated from the University of Diapers) would be so worried about these two important dates colliding?

Let me explain. You see, season '87/88 was my first season as a REAL Celtic supporter. Granted, I was born a Celtic supporter (with a mum and dad from Croy, I didn't have much option) and I had attended the odd game here and there, but that season I classed myself as a regular, a fully paid-up member of the Jungle! My eldest brother was about 18 at the time and in between perfecting his Tony Hadley quiff and sewing Def Leppard badges onto his denim jacket, he found time to go and cheer on the Bhoys. He went everywhere to watch them, Dundee, Edinburgh…. even Ibrox, and sometimes he or my dad would take me. I can't really recall how many games I attended (three years spent in student bars hasn't been great for the memory) but it must have been into double figures and I was having the time of my life.

You have to remember that 87/88 wasn't any normal season - it was the Centenary Season. Celtic Football Club was 100 years old and in the words of the Maestro, "there was a buzz about the place". A new badge was designed for the season, complete with Celtic Cross, while the kit manufacturers played a blinder and gifted us what I still regard to be the best ever Celtic strip. Even now, I still pull it out for a wee reminder of that glorious season, it's a bit tight but this is the 21st Century!

Caesar was back at the helm and he assembled a squad of superstars. Okay, maybe I'm getting a tad carried away but you have to remember that when you're seven, there's not much to choose between Anton Rogan and Paolo Maldini. It was a magnificent squad, with quality throughout. You had Packie Bonner and Alan McKnight between the sticks, two Irishmen who, despite sometimes appearing to be nailed to their line, pulled us out of the mire more than once. In front of them was a rock-solid defence. We had Chris Morris, Derek Whyte, Mick McCarthy and the afore-mentioned Rogan.

Even 'Captain Marvel', Roy Aitken was more than willing to step back from his midfield berth if needed. Three great Celtic men in Grant, McStay and Burns orchestrated things from the middle of the park, ably supported by the likes of Billy Stark and Joe Miller. In attack we had the experience of Mark McGhee, the goalscoring instinct of Andy Walker and the sheer class of Frank McAvennie.

Frankie Bhoy. What can we say about him? I must admit that, to this day, Frank McAvennie is still my all-time favourite Celtic No.9. Back then he was my hero. I'm not ashamed to admit that I owned a Frank McAvennie scrapbook, which was filled with anything to do with Frank – even pictures of Page 3 girlfriend. This of course didn't go down to well with the mother but I assured her it was all in the name of sport and she still maintained that I was a lovely wee Bhoy. My worshipping of McAvennie reached an all time high when my cousin pointed out that his name was actually Francis – my middle name.

That was it, from now on I was to be called Frank. I would answer to nothing else. I soon overcame this fascination with Frank but I still have to say that he is one of the biggest influences on my life – even today it is still my ambition to become a treasure hunter. Well, if it's good enough for Frankie, it's good enough for me! With the side gelling together perfectly, Celtic were storming to the title while the Scottish Cup was looking a distinct possibility. It was around April when the worry set in for myself. I knew that the Cup Final was pencilled in for May 14, but the date of my Communion was still unknown. I pestered my teachers for weeks until they broke news to me…it was on May 21.

They had to scrape me from the ceiling, five cartwheels later and I was finally back in my seat. I recall one teacher saying that she had never seen a young Bhoy so excited about wearing black patent shoes and having a sideshed etched into his skull, while another commented, "I think we've got a future Cardinal there." Of course, the real reason for my joy was that I would not miss the Cup Final. I had it all planned. It was unlikely that I would be able to go to such a big game, especially after I had managed to get into Championship-winning game against Dundee when it seemed half of Glasgow was locked out. Instead, I would get up early, play football with my brothers and then cheer on the Hoops to glory in front of the box. It didn't quite work out that way!

May 14 arrived. Most of my formative years are a bit of a blur but the memories of that day are very clear. Celtic had reached the Final and the dream was becoming reality. They were going to the Double in the Centenary season. It seemed to be destiny. Billy McNeill, Captain of the Lisbon Lions was back to lead the team to glory to celebrate 100 years, even Roy Race would have been struggling to emulate that. There was also a feeling that someone was looking after us from above that season. Martin O'Neill's side have a happy knack of scoring late goals, but in '87/88 Celtic seemed to perform miracles time after time when it looked like defeat was on the cards. It was one such miraculous recovery that paved the way for my Cup Final ticket.

I had been pestering my brother and dad to take me to the game, should Celtic get there, but I didn't make any headway until five minutes before the end of the semi-final. Celtic were trailing 1-0 to Hearts and it looked like we would have to make do with just the League. My whole family was pacing up and down the living room, cursing Archie MacPherson and willing the Celts to score. It was then that my brother, in his perfect Bono twang, made a pact with me. If Celtic won he would take me to the Cup Final! Well, we all know what happened next. Up stepped McGhee to pull Celtic level and then, with the game seemingly heading for extra time, Walker pounced to send the Celtic End of Hampden wild. Me? I was convinced I had extraordinary powers akin to Uri Geller but, whatever the case, I was on my way to Hampden. The briefs were bought the next day.

We all knew there was indeed going to be a show, and the Glasgow Celtic were going to be there. As I said, the day had arrived and I knew things were going to be okay from the moment I looked outside. The sun was shining, and Celtic always win the Scottish Cup when the sun shines. To say I was hyper would be an understatement. I had the full kit on by 8am and by 8.30 I was in the garden, with McAvennie having scored at least four hat-tricks. It was lining up to be great day and the family joined me in the garden for a post-Hampden kick-a-about. It was then that my eldest brother said something that will live for me the rest of my days. I can remember it clearly, him standing there in his T'Pau t-shirt and ripped jeans, looking over to me and saying, "I've got a feeling it's gonnae be McAvennie's day".

With 15 minutes of the Cup Final left, I wasn't caring whose day it was going to be as long as someone scored. We had left the house at 12.30, my two brothers and me, the wee overawed 7-year-old. Hampden was basking in glorious sunshine, even Maggie Thatcher was there and as 60,000 people brandished red cards in her direction I felt compelled to join in, even though I didn't know what it was for. Three years of studying Politics has left me with a very clear conscience over my political stance that day. The game itself was a disappointment. Dundee United were worthy opponents and for 74 minutes they had the measure of the Celts. It seemed as if the Cup Final was just one game too many for this tired Celtic team. It was stalemate at half-time, but United were soon in the ascendancy as Kevin Gallagher hared away from Aitken to crash his shot high past McKnight. Celtic pushed and pushed for the equaliser but it seemed as though they were running out of ideas until one moment of genius from a certain Northern Irishman. As 'Paolo' Rogan sprinted to the bye-line, the Celtic faithful pleaded with him to deliver a good ball, and in one inspired flick of his left foot, the ball was planted onto McAvennie's head and into the net. Cue Pandemonium. The Celtic faithful went mad; there could only be one winner.

To United's credit, they didn't capitulate amid wave after wave of Celtic attack and a further 30 minutes seemed odds-on. As I've said though, this was a Celtic team that built its success on late victories but surely they couldn't do it again? Well they could and did. It was deep into injury time when Celtic forced a corner and what followed will go down as one of the greatest moments of my life. It has been replayed thousands of times since on TV, but I can still vividly remember witnessing it in person. Joe Miller swung a low corner to Billy Stark who, with socks down, forced a great save from Billy Thomson. He only succeeded, though, in diverting it to the waiting McAvennie who gleefully pounced to win the Cup for Celtic.

Cue absolute pandemonium. It was too much to take in. Here was me, a seven-year-old Bhoy at his first Cup Final, witnessing his team clinch the double in their Centenary season and, to top it all off, just like my brother predicted, my hero had scored the goals that won the Cup. Everywhere I looked people were embracing, total strangers were coming up to me in a state of absolute ecstasy talking about, "the best day of their lives" and how they were going to join the Tories because Maggie was a good luck charm. (Sadly there were no Page 3 girls, well that would have topped the day off), I'll never forget the sight of Roy Aitken walking up the Hampden steps to collect the trophy.

I felt as if I had witnessed something very special that day and, in retrospect, I still do. Sure, in the years that passed after 1988, there wasn't much to cheer about but, if I ever got a bit down, all I had to do was think back to that sunny May day when Celtic Football Club were on top of the world.

DAVID FRIEL, Kilsyth, Glasgow

Hail! Hail! 1988

Hail Hail 1988 What a year that was,
It sounds so great.
The Celts got glory again and again.
The supporters all knew that Celtic would win.

Games came and went, and points multiplied,
a cup game a Double, the Treble they cried.
On Saturday, they play for the Double again
My fingers are crossed, will they win again?

Fans and players both old and new
Are proud and decent and their hearts are with you.
So to do your best is all you can do.
Hail, Hail We are so proud of you.
KIRSTY VEITCH (age 12), Holyrood Secondary School, Glasgow

Chapter Three

Euan and John

"DON'T go hame yet, I need someone to dae shooty in" pleaded Euan.

"I've kicked a million shots, ma leg is hanging aff," replied Cameron, rubbing his knee and to further emphasise his agony limped back towards the house.

Euan loved football but not for him the glory of the striker, no Euan wanted to be goalkeeper, the last line of defence, he thought of nothing else. Indeed he had already saved a last-minute penalty for Scotland and was carried shoulder high around Hampden until the cheers of the fans turned into light snores of his wee brother Cameron in the bunk above him.

Cameron was nine-years-old three years younger than Euan and was equally enthusiastic about football but only if the overhead kick was done with the daring twist of a joystick. "I'll just play maself," Euan thought to himself and started kicking the ball against the gable end of the tenement with Stephan Klos saving the re-bound.

Suddenly there was a shout from the terracing, "Hey stupid, stop kicking that ba' against the wa" Euan looked round the front of the tenement, a window was opened a tanned plump face of an irate woman was sticking out of it. Euan noticed she had an amazing amount of gold jewellery round her neck; the woman continued with her rant. "Dot Cotton is about tae get buried and you're rattling that ba aff the wall, have you nae respect, go and play at yer ain bit or I'll set the dug on ye." Defiantly Euan kicked the ball against the gable one more time and slightly less defiantly lifted it and ran when he heard a door opening.

He was in the ASDA car park before he stopped running. "This is rubbish", he thought, "I need tae practice if I'm going to get in that team". In his frustration he gave the ball a hefty kick. Euan followed the path of the ball as it headed straight in the face of a small child sitting in a shopping trolley. Euan went cold; he screwed his face up in anticipation of the impact. Suddenly a hand appeared and effortlessly caught the ball. Euan looked at the owner of the hand that had saved him from death by a thousand jabs of an irate mother's finger to the chest.

The hand belonged to a tall man in his early 20s. He smiled gave the child in the shopping trolley a playful rub on the head and walked over to Euan who blurted out his gratitude, "Thanks a lot mister". The man handed Euan the ball along with some advice, "Better be careful in the future, that wean's mammy might take exception to you using her child's face for target practice." Euan gave a sheepish reply "It was an accident".

The man then noticed the gloves Euan was wearing and enquired "What do we have here a goalie?" Euan's face brightened and he explained "Aye, I want to be a world-class goalkeeper and play fur wan of the top teams", Euan had now forgotten the near death experience of moments earlier as he was now talking about his favourite subject. "Like who?" the man asked. "Well I'm no bothered but if I had to choose it would be Rangers," replied Euan. "Well they say you have to be half daft to be a goalkeeper so you've passed that test", the man said smiling. "How's that?" asked Euan.

"Well, you support Rangers", the man replied, laughing at his own joke. He continued, "Only kidding, I'm a Celtic man myself but lets shake on the difference," and he offered his big hand to Euan who was a bit embarrassed at such an adult method of introduction, but he grasped the outstretched hand. The man's was cold but powerful. "I'm John", said the man, "and you must be Euan?" Euan looked surprised. "How did you know that?" he asked. "Well I'm psychic and I can read minds," whispered John. Euan was astounded, "Really?" he asked, "Eh, No, your name's on the back of your top," again John laughed at his own joke. John grabbed the ball threw it in the air, caught it, looked down at Euan and said, "Right let's see what sort of goalie you are."

The two of them walked to a large patch of grass at the edge of the car park and set up a goal using an empty Irn Bru can and Euan's tracksuit top. As Euan took the top off he thought to himself, how could John see ma name on ma shirt when I had my tracksuit top over it? He was about to ask when John fired in a low shot, Euan missed it and ran off to free the ball from under a parked car, a task he had to do time and time again. John soon realised that Euan's ambition was far higher than his ability however no one could doubt his determination.

After half an hour Euan finally asked, "I'm not very good, am I?" John replied rather diplomatically "You're a trier," but Euan was more realistic and moaned, "I'm rubbish, I'll never be ready for the tournament,"

"Tournament, what tournament?" enquired John. Euan went on to explain, "There's a school tournament a week on Tuesday at Celtic Park, our school team's usual goalie broke his leg, I was there you should have seen it was disgusting his toes were pointing…"

"Anyway," interrupted John.

"Oh aye, anyway," Euan went on, "there are trials for a new goalie on Saturday and I was hoping tae get picked but I've nae chance have I?" Euan looked up at John who smiled and said, "Well, you proved me one thing today."

"What's that? Euan asked.

"You'll make a great ball boy," John said, laughing, but then seeing that Euan was almost in tears became serious. "Look, we have a few days to go to the trial. I can help you with some training but you'll have to knock your pan in if we're going to get anywhere."

"Excellent! That would be brilliant," exclaimed Euan.

The two of them made arrangements to meet the following night and Euan walked home trying to decide who he would sign for, Barcelona or Real Madrid.

The two new friends spent the next few nights training. John's goalkeeping ability and knowledge were amazing and Euan quickly realised that this man really knew his stuff. However, he also sensed that John was holding something back. Euan tried to find out more about John but any probing questions was met with a smile or a frustrating "Oh that's a long story".

Saturday morning came and Euan was up at seven o'clock. He did not want to be late for the trial that started at 10, but then again he did have about 400 yards to walk.

The game finished with three different potential goalkeepers given a chance to impress. John walked home with Euan after the game and he listened as Euan talked through every save he made during the game. He talked and talked like a boy selected to play in goals for his school team.

Euan and John continued to work together in preparation for the big tournament at Celtic Park. On the day Euan was so nervous he could hardly get his socks on but he could still hear John's words from the night before, "Relax, go out there enjoy yourself but concentrate for every minute."

When Euan ran on to the park he was absolutely terrified. The stadium was enormous the magnificent stands seemed to touch the sky "What would it be like if this place was full?" he thought, his heart beating faster. Euan looked around and in the South Stand there was around 300 people cheering the teams out. Right in the middle of the fans Euan picked out the smiling face of John who was waving with both hands. Euan casually waved back trying to act cool and hide the quivering wreck he really was.

The first round began and Euan's team was involved and within a few minutes Euan had to make a great one-hand save, when the ball was cleared he looked up at John who gave him a reassuring wink. In what seemed a very short time Euan's school was through to the final. Euan felt so good he knew he had played well.

The whistle blew to start the final game it was a quiet first 10 minutes for Euan then the ball came towards him. It was not particularly hard effort and Euan was already planning in his head which player he would throw the ball back out to. He reached down tried to lift the ball but he fumbled it, he made a desperate attempt to get it back but the loud cheer from the opposition told him he had failed.

Euan was nearly in tears; he kicked the ball back towards the centre spot. "What an idiot" he thought, "if only I had…" but his self analysis was interrupted by the voice of John "Forget the goal, concentrate on the game." The advice was timely as their striker had passed the last defender and was bearing down on goal, without hesitation Euan dived at the ball and covered it. "Well done" shouted his defender, "you saved us there."

At the start of the second half Euan's team got an equaliser, then with five minutes to go a well-deserved second. Euan tried to concentrate but it was difficult "Nearly there" he thought "Only a few seconds to go" The opposition however were not giving up without a fight and were pushing forward. The referee blew his whistle. Euan looked at him hoping it was time up. No it was a foul against them at the edge of the area.

The ball was put in place and this tall stocky boy ran up and shot the ball over the wall of players. Euan knew instantly that it was heading for the postage stamp corner of the goals. Euan stretched his hand out and dived he knew in his heart he could not reach it. Then an invisible force had lifted him those extra few inches, and Euan touched the ball round the post. The corner was quickly taken and as Euan confidently plucked the ball from the air the final whistle blew. "Well done, great game," he heard it a dozen times as he ran off the park and loved it every time. Euan looked up to the stand but this time he could not find John. "I'll see him outside," he thought. "I bet he's really proud of me."

Euan got changed very quickly and was still going over that final save in his mind as he made his way out of Celtic Park. Suddenly he stopped at one of the many portraits on the walls. "What's wrong wae you?" one of his team-mates asked. Euan pointed at the picture and mumbled "That's John." A man with a green jacket was passing and joined the conversation. "Aye son, John Thomson, a great Celtic keeper, died at the age of 22 in September 1931 when he was accidentally kicked in the head during a game at Ibrox. Never regained consciousness, a tragedy a real tragedy." The man walked away, shaking his head.

Euan never saw his friend John again but he knows he's not far away and not a game goes by but he does not think about John Thomson, great goalie and Euan's pal.

FIONA WYLIE, Glasgow

My Ma! The Glaswegian

MY Ma! 'The Glaswegian'. I laugh at my ma she is so funny she's got red hair and big brown eyes, my da calls her his honey. She dances at the Top 20, helps us when we're down.

"Hey ma help me put the chain on ma bike!"

"I'll be in in a minute just wait," she shouts.

We've got cockney accents she is so Glaswegian. But she teaches us the lingo just in case we need it. Today Man U are playing Celtic out the front. Celtic are winning 10-1. My little brother's ball has gone into the tree.

"Ma get the brush out for me," he calls. There's ma again out with the brush getting the ball for him she's the only one in our street you see.

I know she's different from the other mas around here.

Our ma the Glaswegian.

Our ma the Glaswegian is so funny

"Git doon here fir yer dinner," she shouts and wash yer hons before ye's come doon, di ye hear mi, ye pair of dirty weans.

Our ma the Glaswegian.

"Git in here noo I'm telling ye," shouts our ma the Glaswegian or "I'll go aff ma heed if ye's don't stop yer carryin on."

Our ma the Glaswegian doesn't like to here greetin weans "They git on ma nerves", she tells us. "Yer are oh the same." Or it's "Hey ir ye up for school yit." Our ma the Glaswegian.

When it comes down to it our ma is the best, we cannot fault her, she's better than the rest..

ALANA MARIE McCALLUM (age 11), St Michael and St Martins, London

Chapter Four

Larsson

Henrik Larsson
Henrik Henrik show us your tongue.
Every time we see it we know what you have done.
Naturally gifted, you play the game so well.
Recovered real quick from your injury hell.
Idolised by thousands all over the sphere.
King Henrik your magic, glad you came here.

Legend status you'll have when you leave.
Adored by thousands, these people will grieve.
Rounding keepers we've seen you do so much.
Simply sensational, you have the golden touch.
Six Hundred and fifty grand you cost wee Wim.
OH what a bargain, we owe a lot to him.
Native of Sweden, You'll Never Walk Alone

STEVEN ELLY, Stirling

Celtic tune (to Ally's Army)

Who's that team we call the CELTIC?
Who's that team we all adore?
They're the Bhoys in emerald green
And the best you've ever seen
And you won't go wanting anymore.

Who's that Bhoy in number seven?
Who's that Bhoy that always scores?
Yes it's Larsson through and through
He's the best you know it's true
You can always count on him to change the score.

Celtic's the best you can't deny it
We've had success for many years
We'll win the Euro Cup
It'll shut the others up
And we'll send them all away in floods of tears

We've won the league we're top again
We've won it twice and going for thrice
Cause we're at the top to stay

And that's all I've got to say
And we'll win it in Celtic's Paradise.
CARLY MILLIGAN AND ELEANOR DICKSON, Holyrood Secondary, Glasgow

The man who found Paradise and brought it to Heaven

Some may say the greatest of heroes must share your own roots
Yet we know race, colour or creed matters little when you are wearing the Hoops
From the four corners of the land we welcome them from all over
To play for the famous green and white jersey, bearing the four-leaf clover.

For it was a man who once wore orange that ensured our future was bright
When from his homeland he captured Swede Henrik
to wear the green and white
From a debacle of a debut at Easter Road we witnessed
a miraculous resurrection
As the Bhoys, inspired by Larsson, prevented them
adding the 10th to their collection.

The loss of King Wim for the Doctor was a bitter pill to swallow
After all the great promise of '98 the future once again looked hollow
In a season of woe even the arrival of the evergreen
Lubo could not stop the rot
Apart from the heroics of a certain Players' Player,
the year is best left forgot.

Summer of '99 sees Barnes and Dalglish become the new managerial team
Yet after a bright start, a dark night in October spelt the end of the dream
When displaying the bravery of the Lisbon Lions Henrik fell in Lyons' Den
Yet flat out on his stretcher he stood shoulder to shoulder
with those great men.

Summer of 2000 and we welcomed a man who pledged to
bring us back past glory
Yet it was the return of King Henrik that proved the season's
most remarkable story
Who could have imagined winning the title and
twice celebrating at Hampden in the sun?
It would not have been possible without the 53 goals that
made Henrik Europe's number one.

A year on and the Bhoys are still Champions by
retaining the trophy that mattered
With a massive 100-points won in a season

46

they ensure yet another record is shattered
Not to be outshone, a certain number seven scores
the goals that also see him hit the century mark
While the fans can enjoy another summer knowing
the flag is still flying over Celtic Park.

It will be with great sadness that we'll greet the day
when Henrik gives up his hooped number seven
Yet with great joy we'll remember the Swede who brought
Paradise many a moment of heaven
Like all the great former Celtic servants, may Henrik remember
that he will never walk alone
For in the East End of Glasgow there stands an un-foreign field
called Paradise, he can forever call his home.

SEAN TULLY, New Southgate, London

MY dad was taking me to Parkhead one morning to watch the players go in for training. I had my camera and I had my photo taken with all the players except Henrik Larsson and he's my favourite player.

We were just going to the car when we heard a commotion, so we turned and looked and Henrik had just turned up. I ran up to him and said: "Please can I have my photo taken with you?"

He was really nice and said "Yes."

It was just after the demolition derby - the 6-2 game against Rangers - and somebody came up to Henrik and said: "What's the difference between a black cab and Stefen Klos?" Henrik laughed and said: "I don't know."

The man replied: "A black cab only lets five in!"

Henrik burst out laughing and said: "I have to get in now, but it has been nice meeting you all."

That was my dream come true, meeting Henrik Larsson, and I hope to meet him again.

KAYLEIGH DEVLIN (age 14), Corby, Northamptonshire

Henrik, Henrik, he's the best
Better than all the rest
Scores the goal, lifts the cup
Well, that's just Larsson luck.
Henrik, Henrik, takes the ball
Round the players and into the goal,

Celtic, Celtic, win the league
By 18 points, ahead of other teams
Celtic, Celtic, everyone loves
Celtic, Celtic, from Earth to Above.

NADIA HARVIE (age 11) Glasgow

My best footballer is Larsson

He came to Celtic Park for very little loot
Anywhere on the park he would be tempted to shoot
He is a genius when he puts on his striking boots
For any other footballer I could not give a hoot

He pulls on the Celtic jersey as he is the player other teams want to stop
This is Henrik Larsson he will take us to the top
He is the man to catch you on the hop

They call him the genius sent from God above
To play for Glasgow Celtic Football Club, the team he grew to love,
Now is the time that everyone should keep their loot
Because Henrik is a genius with his golden shooting boots.
JOSEPHINE McGARRIGLE (age 11), St Francis Primary, Gorbals, Glasgow

Larsson

ONE day not like any other day I walked into the phone box to phone my mum and tell her that I was on my way home, but this time the phone box looked different, it had boxes with the headings YEAR, MONTH and DATE. There was a funny looking pencil so I picked it up and wrote in the year box 2021 in the month box July and in the date 10th, the lights started to flash and I travelled into the future and started like this.

I was in my kitchen making something to eat; I stopped so suddenly the doorbell rang so I went to answer it. It was Henrik Larsson he said "Hello you entered a competition and you won" I went nuts I was so excited I won the competition that I had entered weeks ago that I had dreams about of winning and I did. Later on that week he turned up again and said "I am here to take you for the time of your life".

That day we went to the beach and went on a boat ride in Henrik's beautiful silver boat. That night we had lamb chop for dinner that was made by a professional chef and it was beautiful. Later on that night we looked at the stars and about one o'clock we headed home he drove me right to my door in his Renault Megane sports car. I had had a lovely night the best night ever until I woke up and found out that it was only a dream.

MICHELLE DOUGAN, (age13), St Luke's High, Barrhead

Henrik Larsson's on the ball
Watch the mighty Rangers fall
The Rangers fans are feeling blue
'Cause it's CELTIC 6 Rangers 2
VICTOR SULLIVAN, Buckhaven

Seven

S   is for a SPECTACULAR STRIKER
E   is for an EXCEPTIONAL footballer
V   is for a VERY skilful player
E   is for the way you put in the EXTRA EFFORT
N   for NUMBER seven your lucky NUMBER.

AYSHA MIR (age 9), Glasgow

The Goal Machine

Larsson, Larsson, our wonderful king,
Can make a goal from anything,
Pancake mix, bread or cheese
Henrik Larsson scores with ease.

Henrik's reaching to his peak
He's getting fitter by the week,
He's got the magic golden boot,
To fit his magic, golden foot.

Henrik's always full of class,
And is married to a lovely lass,
But little Jordan stole the show,
'Cos he's the reason he's gotta go.

Back to Sweden full of joy,
But Henrik will always be our Bhoy,
We'll love him to the very end,
So, till then, our love we send.

EMMA TORRANCE (age 13), Glasgow

Henrik Larsson 7

Goals, Goals lots of goals
But yours is the best of the rest.
So that's why I'm saying
This little poem
That reminds me a lot of YOU!

Larsson Larsson
Aw the Henrik Larsson
He gets the baw
And scores aw the goals
Aw the Henrik Larsson

EMMA HOPE (age 10), Glasgow

49

The Bhoys

MY favourite hobby is football but I have others but I only have one team I admire Celtic. I admire Celtic because ever since I was four they made me set eyes on football and ever since I have been Celtic mad.

Ever since I became a real Celtic fan I have collected Celtic books, Celtic footballs, Celtic strips and everything else. My family are all mad about Celtic and they go to every match. When Henrik Larsson broke his leg against Lyon I was heart-broken, and I didn't think it was true and ever since he was off his team dropped points but proudly when he came back they got better and in 2000/01 he became best goal scorer with an amazing 53 goals in that one season.

I prefer Henrik Larsson with short hair just like me. And I would love to take a day visit to Celtic Park and train with him on my own. Henrik Larsson is my favourite footballer, when I feel upset I'll go to my room and if there's something wrong I would think what would Henrik Larsson do and then it would go into my head and I would do it. Henrik Larsson is my favourite and I want it to stay that way.

SEAN PAUL COSTELLO (age 11), Coatbridge

The Green God

Henrik Larsson is the King of Kings,
So the Parkhead crowd sings,
Week after week he scores whatever the scene,
He's Glasgow Celtic's Goal Machine.

You are my Larsson, my Henrik Larsson,
He makes you happy when skies are grey,
Out of nowhere he scores,
And yet again lightens up your day.

When he came to Paradise,
We thought he was a zero,
But when he started to score the goals,
He soon became our hero!

He's No. 7,
And sent from Heaven,
What more can I say?
Every time Henrik Larsson plays
He puts the supporters in a daze.

When the day comes that we have to part,
He'll leave behind 60,000 broken hearts,
Scotland's loss, Sweden's gain,
The likes of Larsson, you'll never see again.

NICOLA CONNELL, Hillington, Glasgow

Larsson

There is a man called Larsson
He's the best player around
The fans all think he's God
And the player should be crowned.
Henrik is the best
The best in every way
He is always training hard
He's gets better every day

He broke his leg one season
He was out for half a year
It was a sad, sad night in Lyon
Many shed a tear
Larsson recovered well
And soon was playing the game
And Celtic were glad for him
He would soon win back the fame

It was his first game back at Celtic Football Club
The fans were so delighted
He scored a brilliant goal
Against Dundee United
Larsson is still so brilliant
The best I've ever seen
He'll also be remembered
In the Hoops of white and green

When Henke's headers hit the net
It feels like we're in heaven
We really are so proud of him
He's our magnificent seven

KIERAN FERRIE (age 13), Wishaw

The Celtic striker I admire

THE Celtic striker I admire is a great man - some call him a legend - but all I can say is, the famous man signed from Feyenoord in the year 1997/1998, in his first year at Celtic he scored an impressive 18 goals. In his amazing second year he scored an astonishing 38 goals. In his horrifying year of sadness he scored 14 goals as he broke his leg in two places in our 1-0 defeat in Lyon in 1999/2000.

In the Treble-winning year of 2000/2001 he scored an unbelievable 53 goals and won Player of the Year Award, the Golden Boot Award and top goal scorer award! Have you guessed who my favourite player is yet? Of course, my favourite player and the person I admire is... HENRIK LARSSON No.7

ALISON WATERS (age 10), Warrenpoint, Co Down

Henrik Larsson

H is for Hero. The Magnificent 7.
E s for every shot he takes, every time it's a goal.
N is for never missing a chance.
R is for Rab Douglas his favourite goalie.
I is for intelligence the skill and the aim.
K is for kicking the ball on target that always gets the goal.

L is for Larsson the best of them all.
A is for accuracy he's deadly from the spot.
R is for running all the way down the pitch.
S is for seeing the ball coming right to him.
S is for the speed he runs at, he's right down the field.
O is for O'Neill the best coach ever.
N is for the narrow shots he takes and never misses.

GRACE SWEENEY (age 9), Glasgow

A story on Celtic

ONE day I was in my house listening to the radio. It was Celtic v Rangers on. My remote was by my side I grab it to turn up the volume. It was so exciting it was two each and 10 minutes to go. I listened and listened waiting for that vital goal to be scored by Celtic if they scored they would win the Scottish Cup. I was hoping Larsson would score it as he is the best and my favourite.

As my mind started to drift away I hear the commentators shout, "He's done it, Larsson has scored Celtic win the cup."

I am ecstatic and think YES! They've done it. My dad comes racing in screaming and shouting. He gave me a hug and to celebrate we're going to a posh restaurant your choice." I say " Dad off to Brewster's then."

He says "Right, honey get the car we're going to Brewster's." Mum says "Fine." We get our coats and start our celebration.

TERESA FALCONER, St Luke's High School, Barrhead

Henrik Larsson

IS there a better player than Henrik Larsson you may ask, and I would have to say no. Henrik Larsson is one of the best players Celtic have ever seen, and I know he's one of the best I've ever seen!

I mean is there a player with more skill, speed and accuracy than Henrik Larsson? Some people may say that the likes of Pele or Maradona are better than Henrik Larsson but I would have to disagree, I think Henrik Larsson is the best player I have ever come across and he is the best in the world!!

People may say that David Beckham or Michael Owen are better than Henrik Larsson, but I think that, and many people would agree with me when I say this, that Henrik Larsson has more skill than both Beckham and Owen put together! That is why I think that Henrik Larsson is the best soccer player in the world.
EMMA-LOUISE O'DONNELL (age 12), Mullingor, Co Westmeath

Watching Larsson score!

He had a dream that
Everyone was cheering on him!!
Number 18 had passed to him,
Relying on him to run.
In and out of Rangers,
Keeping the magical ball!

Looking for
A player to past to, still
Running with the ball nearer the goal, then he
Shoots and
Scores!!!
On their feet are the
Numerous amounts of people

WATCHING LARSSON SCORE!!!
GILLIAN MURPHY, Holy Family Primary School, Kirkintilloch

Larsson's bad day

Larsson's running down the pitch,
When suddenly he falls down a 6oft ditch.
He emerges from the ditch glad he's not dead,
When a bird comes by and leaves a present on his head.
He takes the ball and passes it to Boyd,
And who would have guessed it, Larsson is hit by an asteroid.

He stands up and looks at the crowd,
To see his mother who doesn't look proud.
She says to him in a voice the stings,
"You're a disgrace to you family and your football mings."
After the match Larsson thinks about his day,
And wonders how all this bad luck could come his way.

He returns home to his wife and kids,
Who all tell him how terrible his football is.
DANIEL MAXWELL (age 13), St Luke's High School, Barrhead

Larsson, Larsson

Larsson Larsson is the best
Larsson Larsson runs rings around the rest
Larsson Larsson is the test.

Larsson Larsson is the man
Larsson Larsson is better than Zidane
Larsson Larsson is loved by the fans

Larsson Larsson is my hero
Larsson Larsson would never be rated zero
Larsson Larsson plays better than Rio!

Larsson Larsson is better than Mols
Larsson Larsson would skip by Scholes
Larsson Larsson scores many goals!

Larsson Larsson plays with pride
Larsson Larsson makes his opponents hide
Larsson Larsson makes the ball glide

Larsson Larsson is a joy
For every fan, man or boy
Larsson, Larsson we hope and pray
That you are at Parkhead to stay.
KEVIN McGRANAGHAN (age 13), Holyrood Secondary, Glasgow

Henrik Larsson

L is for his looks, according to the woman
A is ability to beat every player.
R is for his runs when he nutmegs Numan.
S is for the six two game when he scored a double.
S is for the simple goals he scores every time he plays.
O is for his outstanding free kicks on and off the pitch.
N is for the noisy crowd singing you are my LARSSON!!
JAMES BYRNE (age 11), St Francis' Primary, Glasgow

Chapter Five

I Wish

"ARE you alright, son?" The stranger's massive hand easily swallowed mine as he helped me up from the floor of the tunnel leading to the pitch. "I didn't see him, boss," the man behind me said. I hadn't noticed him until then. My head was buzzing a bit, the way it does when you come round in the dentist's chair after having gas, and my eyes were blurred, but they were getting clearer. "I just opened the door and he must have run into it," explained the younger man, apologising.

The older man hunched down in front of me and held a couple of fingers up. "How many can you see?" he asked. "Three," I replied. He tousled my hair playfully. "That's alright, Bobby, there doesn't seem to be too much wrong with him." I heard Bobby sigh with relief. "Away out and join the other lads warming up. I'll look after the Bhoy."

Bobby smiled at me as he left. He was massive, nearly filling the whole mouth of the tunnel as he entered the sunlight. I rubbed the lump on the side of my head as it throbbed. It felt the size of a football. "So what has you down here? Children aren't allowed in this part of the stadium."

I told him it was my 10th birthday, and that my dad had taken the day off work to bring me to Celtic Park. It was my first time at the stadium. I'd seen it on the television hundreds of times before, but this was miles better. We'd had something to eat in one of the restaurants, got loads of autographs from the players, and best of all we got to see round the trophy room, even had our pictures taken with the Treble cups. Then I went to the toilet and must have taken a wrong turn somewhere and got lost. Next thing I knew I was lying on my back seeing stars.

"Your birthday," the big man, who looked a little like my grandda, said. "It doesn't do to have doors flying in your face when it's such a special day." He stood up. He was even bigger than Bobby. "How long have you supported Celtic?" "Since I was a baby," I told him. He smiled a smile which seemed to push his cheeks up higher than normal and close his eyes into little slits. "Well, then, how would you like to come out onto the pitch and kick the ball about with the team?"

How would I like it? Was this guy joking? What a birthday surprise. I'd be the envy of the class, of all my friends. They'd all be jealous. Great! "Sure," I said, eyes wide open. "But I've no boots with me." "No problem. I'll get one of the lads to grab you a new pair from the shop. It'll be your birthday present from us. Will that be alright with you?" I was dumbstruck. New boots as well. Magic! "Did you get any toys?" he asked as we made our way out onto the pitch. "A gameboy and some games." "A gameboy? And what's that when it's at home?"

I thought he was joking, but the mystified look on his face made it clear he wasn't. "Have you never heard of a Gameboy before?" I asked. He shook his head. "It's just like a computer game, only you can carry it about with you and play it whenever you want," I explained. He rocked his head once more. "What will they think of next."

The sun had dried up the pitch completely, which was some going, seeing as it hadn't stopped raining the previous night, and the sky had been well overcast when we had arrived at the ground about an hour or so earlier. But that was only something I realised much later. As we walked together out to the centre circle I took a good look round me. It didn't look the same as it did on the box. Everything was shiny, new, big.

There were seats and signs and screens. Standing there in the middle of the pitch, I could see none of that. The place still looked massive, yeah, but dilapidated, as bad as some of the old places that used to be around our way before the council pulled the factory shells down. Dad told me there used to be thousands of men working there in the days when Celtic won the European Cup. My dad must have a good memory.

Before I had time to ask the old guy what the craic was, he called over some wee guy who was dribbling the ball at the time, who wasn't much bigger than me, and asked him to go find someone to fetch me a pair of boots because it was my birthday. "And, Jinky," he added, "don't be long 'til you're back. You owe me two more laps." A wavy-haired player, wearing a T-shirt and the bottoms of some kind of fleece tracksuit, ran past us chasing a loose ball. "Stevie, this is…." he turned to look down at me. "The birthday boy and we don't even know your name." "It's Tom."

"Take Tom with you and let him limber up with the rest of the lads until Jinky brings his boots." "I know you," I said, the man's face suddenly clicking with my memory. "You're in the big photos in the hallway, inside. You're all heroes for winning something for the club, aren't you?" This Stevie character blushed a little. "Heroes, is it?" He chided me as we walked over to a bunch of the other players. "Getting a few shillings like heroes would be nice. Not the most important thing, mind you, but it would be nice. Do you have a favourite player, yourself," he inquired. "Magic Moravcik." His lips turned down at either end, totally bemused with my answer. "Lubo," I said. "Moravcik. The greatest player in the world." Still nothing.

"Are you sure you play for Celtic?" "Last time I looked at the shirt we played in, I did." "And you haven't heard of Lubo Moravcik. He's brilliant. He can beat a dozen players while she reads the *View* and has time to go make the tea. He's great." Stevie laughed aloud. "If you say so, wee man. If you say so."

"Who's he?" I thumbed over my shoulder, perhaps a bit too cheekily, at the granda guy still standing in the middle of the pitch where we had left him. "The Big Man? He's our gaffer." It was my turn to be flummoxed. "He's the Boss. He's Jock Stein. You haven't heard of Jock Stein? Are you sure you're a Celtic supporter?" Touché.

But I had heard the name, in stories my dad told about the old days, while he was growing up and coming to roar his head off at the games, it just never clicked that this guy was the same person and he was still about. Hey, I was only 10. What did I know?

Pretty soon though all the little things that didn't appear right soon slipped me by. The red-headed player they all called Jinky returned with a brand new pair of boots, with a name on them I'd never seen before, or since. A perfect fit, despite me not recalling having given anybody my correct shoe size. Lucky guess, I expect. We were soon into a bit of passing the ball around, a lot of push-ups, running up and down the stands, leap-frogging (God knows why), and jumping jacks. My favourite part was playing shooty-ins against some auld lad who really must have been a grandda. All the rest of the players were calling him Da. He was good, though. Not many got past him. That old keepers top he wore must have been as old as himself. It fitted him more like a comfy cardigan than a football shirt.

And then it happened. Always, whenever you are right in the middle of something that seems so good, fate conspires to wrench the moment from you. I know that sounds corny, but I think I heard it on a video I watched. Anyway, it's true in this instance. The ball was being knocked in from the right by a player named Bobby Lenaxe or something like that, and I went to jump up to head it. Two steps, ready to rise, stand on my own laces, fall flat on my face…

Next thing I know, it's my dad's voice, and I can feel the rain on my face. My vision slowly begins to sort itself out. Two other people are huddled about me along with Dad. "Tom! Tom! Are you alright, son? Can you hear me?" "Yeah, dad, I'm okay," I muttered a bit groggily. "I think I just stumbled over on my feet when I was going for the ball, that's all."

Dad glanced at the men to his left, Brian Scott and Roddy Macdonald, and shrugged his shoulders. Scott held his fingers up. "How many fingers can you see, Tom?" I blinked. "Three."

I wondered if they always put three up. I held my hand out to catch the droplets. "It's raining again." "It hasn't stopped all day, son," Dad informed me. "No. It stopped while I trained with the team." I looked past dad and the two physios who, by this time, were throwing puzzled looks of concern between each other. "Where have they gone? Where's Stevie, and Jinky and Bobby? And Jock Stein? And how did they get the place looking like it did on television so quickly?"

Scott helped me out of the seat and up onto my feet, just as Jock had done earlier. "That's a quare bump you have there, Tom. Why don't we take you down to the physio room and give you the once over, show you how we get the lads off the sick table and back onto the pitch." A bit out of sorts, all I could do was go along with them. "How did you get a shiner like that, Tom" Dad asked me. "I was lost in the tunnel, when Bobby – Murdoch, I think you called him – opened the door and slammed it against the side of my head. Accidentally. He didn't see me coming." All three men just smiled kindly at me.

I tried to make them see I wasn't making it up. I told them everything that had happened to me during the time I was separated from my dad. The practicing, running, shooting. They stared at me as if I'd lost my marbles. Half way back up the tunnel, my Dad stopped me. "Tom, where are the trackshoes you were wearing?" On my feet I still wore the new boots bought for me by Jock Stein. My birthday surprise. We turned as one to face the pitch. "There," I pointed. "Where the guy Lenaxe helped me change them."

And there they sat, side by side on the far touchline, one to the left, one to the right of an old and slightly used orange leather football. So, who's jealous now?

LAWRENCE MERVYN, Belfast

Ghirl Power

THE year is 2052 and Glasgow Celtic have just completed their record-breaking season by winning the Inter-European Championship for the 10th year in row, under the guidance of their manager Peter O'Neill, grandson of the legendary Martin O'Neill.

My name is Christine O'Neil, although no relation to the manager. I am captain of Glasgow Celtic, the first female captain in the club's history. Things have changed in the last 50 years.

Football was once a male-dominated sport, but the equal rights changed all that for women. In fact, just the other day Pope Catherine the Second remarked that the world seemed a safer place to live in since the President of the USA and the President of Russia were both women.

I was born and brought up in Glasgow and lived at 416 Kinnear Road which, as everyone who follows Celtic knows, faces on to the main car park at Celtic Park.

I attended St Helen's Primary School in Bishopbriggs and then went on to study Inter-Galactic Communication at Glasgow University of Science. After passing my exams in 2042, I was all set to captain Scotland's first space shuttle, which was set to take off from the launch pad in Govan on the site which was formally the home of the now, long defunct Glasgow Rangers.

The weather was bad so we could not take off. Luckily, there was a sports centre nearby so we decided to go and play five-a-sides. That night the Celtic scout was there and saw me playing football.

He asked me if I would like a trial for Celtic. I said, "Of course I would."

A few days later the Celtic manager, Mr Peter O'Neill, telephoned me and asked if I'd come over to Celtic Park to take the trial. I took part in the trial and the manager asked me to sign for Celtic. I played my first game three weeks later and scored four goals!

In the newspaper the next day - the *Daily Planet* – it was reported that I was the best player since the legendary Henrik Larsson.

I have had many highlights in my football career, like last week when we were playing Venus Rovers with the World Select and I scored the winning goal.

That was a great feeling, but it does not compare with the thrill of running out at Paradise while everyone singing *The Fields of Athenry*.

CHRISTINE O'NEIL (age 11), Bishopbriggs, Glasgow

THIS incident happened back in the 1950s. My father, a staunch Celtic supporter, was flying over to Ireland to watch his cousin, Hugh Kelly, playing in a Northern Ireland international. Hugh Kelly was the goalkeeper.

On the plane coming back from this game sitting next to my father was Charlie Tully. In the course of the flight they chatted and Charlie, when offered, took one of my father's cigarettes.

For many years later that same cigarette packet sat up on the mantelpiece in our family home.

TERRY GOW, Linwood, Paisley

I'M tossing and turning, can't sleep for the excitement, may as well get up and get prepared for the league decider today against Rangers after light breakfast, make my way to the ground pop in to see physio. I feel slight strain, but I say nothing, I ain't missing this one. As kick off gets nearer the gaffer gives me some last minute instructions; the lads know what's required. Standing in the tunnel the noise is amazing. "Walk on, walk on, with hope..." The butterflies are flying in my stomach. Get on to the park we have the Huddle. Can hardly hear the skipper. The game kicks off. Here comes my first touch; phew, I've skinned their full back and won us a corner.

A very tight tense match of few opportunities is into its last five minutes here comes the ball again I summon my last energy I'm round the full back again I'm tripped...PENALTY! The skipper is walking toward me with the ball he's giving me the chance to win the title, I pick a corner, run up hit it low and hard the net bulges all I hear is cries of "Fogginess! Feggans!" from the north stand, But wait, aw naw it's the missus shaking me. "Feggans, are you no going to work this morning?"

PATRICK FEGGANS, Linwood

Genie in Paradise

I had a visit the other night
And a genie came to say.
"I'm granting you three wishes son,
So whit would you like tae dae?
"Well I'd like a Celtic season ticket
It would really make my day
So I can go to all the games
And watch my heroes play"

The genie put his hands together
And said this wish was given,
I can't explain just how this felt
I think this must be heaven.
So the genie bowed his head to me
And asked for wish number two.
Well it didn't take me long to think
I knew what I had to do.

I want to go to Celtic Park
And meet the boys I love,
And let them meet a fan that's true
To Celtic Football Club.
So wish number three was waiting for me,
But I couldn't decide what the wish was to be.
When I finally decided the genie was screaming
"Get up for school David" it was my mum ...
I was dreaming.

DAVID FERGUSON (age 14), Pollok, Glasgow

From despair to God knows where!

IT had been an incredibly long, tedious day at the office the first time I came across Tony Dornan, the infamous Celtic striker who gifted Rangers 10-in-a-row in season 2020 / 2021.

He was busking on the London underground and at first I walked right by him but something about him made me glance back and even then I wasn't convinced. He looked the same as every busker and beggar I walk by every day, staring straight ahead not daring to make eye contact inexplicably wracked with guilt for not giving him or her a single red penny. Even through the dirt and patchy facial hair his trademark cheeky grin lit up his face. That's what made me look back, his smile.

The same smile that beamed from every poster on my bedroom wall when I was a kid as he celebrated goal after goal for Celtic as they reigned over both Scotland and Europe. His meteoric rise to the top was every schoolboy's dream. Plucked from the youth ranks in his native Ireland after impressing Celtic's scout he went to Glasgow for a week's trial and so impressed manager Martin O'Neill he was signed there and then.

My dad raved about Tony Dornan right from his first game, comparing him to Celtic legends such as Jimmy Johnstone, Kenny Dalglish, Charlie Nicholas and Henrik Larsson. Dad was like an excited child when he'd wax lyrical about the good old days and his heart rate would increase with the mere mention of Tony Dornan. The young kid who had the weight of expectation on his shoulders being compared to every Celtic great from the dawn of time. Dad said he took it all in his stride and lived up to every comparison and took all the plaudits like a man who'd been around the world 10 times and not a kid fresh from a farm in the country.

Tears well up in his eyes when talk turns to Tony Dornan's fall from grace and not because he gifted Rangers 10-in-a-row and the all-time record but because his status of legend was tarnished and he vanished without trace soon after. I sat in Starbuck's nursing a coffee when I convinced myself it was Tony Dornan strumming away on his guitar. I was dying to confront him. To shake his hand and a warm embrace to say thanks for all the memories. All those feelings of sheer ecstasy he brought Celtic supporters the world over as he shot the Bhoys to European glory not once but three times in an eight year spell.

I watched Tony's first European final in 2008 with my dad in the local club and he unashamedly wept with joy at the final whistle, changing in my eyes forever that night. Here was my dad, the toughest man on earth crying his eyes out in front of all his friends, who could well have been crying too but all I could see were dad's tears. I never felt closer to him than that glorious night. I was only 13 and had been with dad at many Celtic games and he never ceased to amaze me. He'd leap and bound all over the floor, jumping for joy with every goal scored and throw his arms high above his head in despair whenever one was conceded. Even the loss of throw-in was greeted with contempt.

Mum hated it when dad watched Celtic games in the house and would hide the remote controls before kick off as he had this nasty habit of hurling them across the room when things went against the Bhoys. One particular game she recalled, the Sky remote obliterated when it hit the front of the video recorder, inevitably putting it out of commission, and the telly and VCR remotes came off second best when they smashed into the wall by the fire. And that was a game Celtic won.

Mum always teased he was the biggest kid in the house, only sometimes I think she wasn't teasing but speaking the truth. I got into so much trouble at school when I was about five or six because of dad's sense of humour. He had me convinced Henrik Larsson was God and each time I resisted his version of events he'd try harder to persuade me otherwise. I was getting along well at school and religion played a major role being a Catholic institution but dad wasn't much of a churchgoer and would fool with my young impressionable mind.

He was forever singing "Henrik Larsson is the king of kings…" to the tune of Sing Hosanna and trying to show off my schooling I'd point out that God was the king of kings. "That's right son" dad would say, "and Henrik Larsson is God."

"No dad, God is God."

"Yes son, God is God, but God's real name is Henrik Larsson."

"Daaaaad. God is just called God."

"Calum," he'd say in his most sincere voice, "what's my name?"

"Dad" I answered him.

"No. My real name? What mummy calls me?"

"Babe," I answered again.

"No, my real name, what granddad calls me?"

"Sean" I said. "Sean what?" "Sean Kelly."

"Yes, my names Sean Kelly, but you call me dad. God is everyone's dad but we call him God so as not to confuse the other dads in Mass, but his real name is Henrik Larsson."

To a five-year-old kid it seemed plausible and I got a severe bollocking when I put this to the classroom. Dad still laughs about it now when I ask about the time the school headmistress demanded to see him for teaching his son to blaspheme.

2008 made dad's life. He was born in September 1967 so wasn't even born when the Lisbon Lions became the first British club to lift club football's number one prize, but when I was growing up he and granddad would talk for hours about that great team. Pictures of them adorned every wall in the house so it was hard for me not to support Celtic. When Martin O'Neill hoisted the giant trophy high above his head in Madrid's Bernabau stadium on that never to be forgotten night the early comparisons with the late Jock Stein were now complete.

Even when Rangers wrestled the SPL championship from their arch rivals in 2012 and went on to win it six years on the spin it was glossed over because Celtic were so dominant in Europe, winning the Champions League in 2008, 2010 and 2014, whilst finishing runners up in 2012 and 2013 and falling at the semi final stages in between. Tony Dornan was the world's most coveted player but he was settled in Glasgow and couldn't envisage playing for anyone other than his boyhood idols. He had it all. Two great feet, lightning pace, was strong in the tackle with an eye for goal like no other. He was Dennis Bergkamp, Zinedine Zidane, Luis Figo and Roy Keane all rolled into one.

But the attribute that earned him acclaim the world over was his work rate. Even if his team were six goals to the good he'd still be tracking back, defending at corner kicks and chasing every lost cause until the final whistle blew.

The fans loved him because despite the dominance on the continent he made all the right noises about being hurt by the fact they couldn't win the domestic Championship, even if most around him were content with the Champions League. Tony wanted to win every game and hated being left out of the side, even for much maligned League Cup games. His stance was you couldn't win a domestic Treble without lifting the League Cup, so fielding weakened sides cheated the fans. If he chose to run for public office during his heyday he would have won at a canter.

Even Rangers fans would have voted for him, mainly because despite all the goals he scored against them he never went overboard celebrating them. He'd just run into the back of the net, pick the ball up and place it on the centre spot. It wasn't until 2019 when Rangers won the SPL for the eighth consecutive year and Celtic crashed out of Europe at the second group stage did Rangers upper hand domestically arouse the concern Tony had being screaming from the rooftops for years. Rangers were boldly predicting they'd win nine-in-a-row again only this time go one better and make it 10, claiming the record for themselves rather than sharing nine in a row with Celtic.

Dad would tell me the tales how Celtic supporters in the 1970s, 80s and early 90s would taunt their Glasgow rivals with nine-in-a-row and when Ranger's equalled it, it was like the death of a family member. If Wim Jansen's side hadn't stopped them from winning the coveted 10th successive title, dad said there would have been mass suicides across the globe. As all around me gloated about Celtic's European success whilst Rangers won all before them at home, I kept quiet. These things can have a nasty habit of turning around and biting the arse off you. Those who taunt loudest often bear the brunt of the retaliation.

I mean it wasn't as if they were quiet on the continent either winning the revamped UEFA cup twice and reaching the semi finals of the Champions League three times themselves dispelling the myth Scottish clubs couldn't mix it with the big guns. The day Tony Dornan gifted Rangers 10-in-a-row is one I'll never forget.

Nursing my coffee in Starbuck's it's still fresh in my mind. As the ball came over from the left in the final quarter of a finely balanced goalless game, Tony Dornan, as ever was back in his own box defending a corner kick. As the ball dropped to him eight yards out 80,000 packed inside Ibrox expected him to volley clear with his right foot, but he adjusted his stance and smashed an unstoppable shot high into the top corner of his own net. For a split second a smile lit up his whole face until the severity of his rush of blood dawned on him. It was the eeriest few seconds I've ever experienced.

The players, match officials and ball boys along with 80,000 spectators looked on in disbelief as Tony Dornan sunk to his knees with his head in his hands. Then the roar went up, a little muted at first but as the crowd realised they weren't dreaming and the goal stood they went into raptures. The Rangers players too didn't know whether to celebrate wildly or just prepare for a Celtic onslaught in the dying minutes. As it happened the onslaught never came. The players were too shocked to mount a fight-back.

Tony? He just walked of the pitch, head bowed with the hint of a tear in his eye. His parting shot to a reporter in the tunnel was "if they listened to me five years ago they'd never have got close to 10 in a row." That was it. He just vanished without trace never to be heard from again yet there I was just yards from him with a head full of questions for the man I'll never stop idolising.

All I can think of though is his smile. The smile beaming from all my posters now illuminates the squalid platforms of the London underground. He looked at peace with himself and I couldn't bring myself to dredge up the past but I couldn't let the moment pass without a word with the man who replaced Henrik Larsson as my God. I drew £500 from my bank and handed it to him in between songs, "Can you sing *The Fields of Athenry*?" The smile he flashed me before bursting into song warmed my heart forever more.

MARK O'SULLIVAN, Coventry

Parkhead catering - circa 1960

WE owe a great debt of gratitude to the quality marketing and attention to customer needs of the Parkhead catering operation in the early 1960s. Few people appreciate the subtly different nuances in the sales pitches aimed at the diverse market segments, nor the vast resources expended on research and training to bring us the ideal winter fuel for the terraces of Parkhead – the macaroon bar!

A brilliant concept! A touch of exotic splendour brought to the East End of Glasgow. It is one of life's great calumnies, the assertion that a consortium of Glasgow dentists funded the operation.

In the 'downmarket' Jungle, the sales pitch was a simple: "ERRA-MAHA-CAHA-ROONAH-BAHARAS-AH!" No selling problem but the need to be heard above the crowd was paramount.

For the 'middle-market' West Terracing, a more sophisticated: "HEERZA-MAC-CA-RRON-ABAR" was required.

Note the distinction: "ERRA" implying "take it or leave it; "HEERZA", meaning "I've travelled night and day across five continents, almost losing my life on eight occasions, to bring you this."

For the 'genteel' East Terracing, an almost subliminal approach was used: "ERZA-MACAROONBARANDA-CHEW-YING-GUMMBB."

Can you spot the two main differences in this approach?

1. "ERZA" implies "it's for you" but not quite so 'in your face' as "HEERZA", but much more "I'm here to please" than "ERRA."

2. For what some would term the 'miserable sods' in the East Terracing who wouldn't give you what they were throwing away, it has been argued that the 'package' of macaroon bar and chewing-gum was needed to clinch the sale. Rubbish! The chewing-gum was added because these gentle, sensitive souls would require gum to chew in the event of exciting goalmouth incidents.

Ah, the macaroon bar and a cup of BOVVERELLE-HAH! Nectar. The food of the Gods. It's up there in the pantheon of haute cuisine alongside the classic creations – coq au vin, soup in a basket, crispy pancakes.

Why can't we get macaroon bars at Celtic Park nowadays! I pray for their return. Nay, I demand it!!!

CHRISTINE BREMNER, Elgin, Morayshire

The Paranoia Poem

Persecution of the green and white ranks
Mistrust of the men in black
Those faceless ones in suits can't hide
The conspiracy stretches far and wide
A Spanish archer [El-bow] from the giant Balde
The goal that never was from the balding Hartson
Let's get away, leave the SPL
To the rest we hold no malice
North America would suit us well
Sunshine, no hidden agendas in a town called 'Dallas'

PAUL MACKAY, West Drayton, England

The Bhoy's Day Out

THE crowd bustles into the stadium, in a flurry of green and white cheers. The familiar aroma of pies and brew swims through the ecstatic fans. The crowds murmur as *The Celtic Song* roars through the open stadium. The sun is shining, it's a beautiful day for a game, here at Celtic Park.

As we take our seats, the fans roar as a green and white blur flows through the tunnel. Through the loudspeakers, the team is called out, with a cheer from the crowd after each name. Then more cheering from the fans as Celtic gather for the Huddle.

They take their positions on the pitch. It all goes quiet for a moment, with only the one or two whistles and jeers. And then, the ref brings the whistle to his lips, and ... "Preep!" Yes! They're off. The ball pings from player to player, feet to feet. A wee turn here, a great run there. Intercepted, no intercepted again! The crowd is going wild.

And after two near misses by Henrik, and a storming shot off the woodwork by Petrov, the teams leave the park goal-less, as the half-time whistle sounds. The never-ending lines for the snacks grow longer. Out steps the half-time entertainment, but all is no match for what comes after the next 15 minutes.

So again, finally the teams emerge, and again the match gets off to a flying start. Here's a great break from Celtic. Lambert a great through ball to Agathe. He's on the run at an Olympic pace. Past one, past another, then a phenomenal high cross, the crowd is on its feet. Over one head and another, then up jumps Larsson like a moth to a flame. He connects with a blinding header. The keeper is left stranded, and the ball's in the back of the net. GOAL!

The crowd roars, as the final whistle blows after another winning performance from the Champs. They shake hands and shirts are swapped. What a match. A great goal, a great game, another great day out at the winning stadium, that is Celtic Park.

ANDREW STEVENSON (age 13), Newton Mearns, Glasgow

Chapter Six

The Lea Field, Mulroy Stars and Jimmy McGrory - a remarkable Celtic Story

THE Rosguill Peninsula in Co. Donegal is a truly beautiful part of the world. You cannot help but be awe-struck by the picturesque scenery you encounter as you travel north from the town of Carrigart towards Downings and the Atlantic Drive. Many who visit the area – including even the most knowledgeable football fans – however, remain oblivious to the significance of the plateau of land, known locally as The Lea Field, which stretches from the roadside to the shores of Mulroy Bay on the outskirts of Carrigart.

The Lea is now overgrown and any pitch markings are long since obliterated, but 70 years ago the field was home to local football team Mulroy Stars and regularly hosted matches between the Stars and their rivals in the Donegal League.

On a summer's evening back in 1930, however, it provided the venue for a rather special match, which was to live long in the memory of those who witnessed it. Mulroy's opposition on that evening? None other than the famous Glasgow Celtic.

While these days it is not unusual for Celtic to make regular trips to Ireland to take part in friendlies , back then a visit by the full first-team squad was a rare occurrence. Even rarer was their participation in an organised match against the likes of Mulroy Star, who were, after all, just a bunch local lads who enjoyed playing a game of football.

The match had come about as the result of a conversation between Mulroy officials and a certain Jimmy McGrory. The Celtic legend had for years rented a holiday home in nearby Downings and was a familiar figure around the area. In the summer months it was not uncommon to see 'the big fella' strolling along the main street of an afternoon or doing the odd training stint in the nearby sand dunes.

Indeed such was his love for the place that he was eventually to build his own house on the outskirts of the village with the intention, it is said, of moving there permanently. However, family circumstances caused a change of plan and he was forced to sell it on - reputedly for the princely sum of £300 – to a local family who still live in it today.

It was during one of my own recent visits to Rosguill that I finally resolved to research the details of Celtic's famous appearance at The Lea, an event which had for some time engaged my fascination.

Since no official records of the match exist and given that all of 72 years have elapsed, piecing together what took place that evening was always going to be a daunting task. It was therefore with something akin to Stanley's reaction on encountering Dr. Livingstone that I greeted the news that two local men who had witnessed the momentous occasion were still alive and well and, more importantly, willing to offer themselves up for interview. As young boys Charlie Friel and Joe Sweeney had attended the match with Joe's uncle, Paddy Sweeney.

Sitting in his front room overlooking Muckish Mountain Joe eagerly takes up the story.

'I remember the day well. Uncle Paddy came down to the house and asked myself and Charlie if we would like to go along to see Mulroy playing. He never told us who they were playing mind you. No, never let on until we arrived. Lord save us and bless us, the size of the crowd. You could hardly get near the place. There must have been about eight or nine hundred people there.

'We made our way to the front anyway. It was then we saw the green and white hoops. Paddy turned to us and said, 'Do yous know them boys then?' He stood there pointing out this one and that one. 'Yon's Jimmy McGrory. And yon fella over there. That's Jimmy McStay. And yer man Johnny Thomson.' I'd seen pictures of these fellas and now there they were a few feet away. It was just unbelievable.'

'Wasn't Johnny Thomson killed shortly after that?' Charlie asks thoughtfully.

'The following year in 1931. In a game against Rangers,' I respond, pleased at the opportunity to contribute a small fact of my own.

'Lord save us, that was a terrible tragedy. Very sad.' Charlie utters the words with a genuine feeling of sadness as though recalling the death of a close friend or relative. 'Aye, and he had a few fine saves against Mulroy that day. I remember him making one fabulous save. Mickey McGroddy hit a great shot in. Oh a certain goal. And Thomson just dived right across and turned the ball away. Ah, he was a great keeper altogether. And you know Mulroy were no slouches. They had some fine players. Alex Brown. George Friel from Carrigart and Charlie Ferry from out by Tirlaughan.'

'And there were some of the players from over Creeslough too,' Joe reminds him. 'The doctor from over that way played. What was his name?'

'Coll. Charlie Coll.'

'Aye, that's him.'

'Didn't he live in yon big house on the way out of Creeslough that yon English fella bought? It's all done up now.'

As Joe pauses to consider the accuracy of the details I act swiftly to bring the conversation back on track. 'And what about the score? I'd say Celtic won. Did they?'

'Sure they won of course. I think it was 4-2.'

Charlie, however, is not so certain. 'I doubt it was more than that.'

'I know that Celtic scored first anyway. At one point I remember it was two each.'

' Didn't Mulroy score with a penalty?' Charlie puts in helpfully.

'Aye, I think you're right, but from what I remember it wasn't much of a penalty. I daresay the referee was trying to give the Mulroy boys a bit of help.'

'What? A dubious penalty awarded against Celtic?' I ask in mock surprise. 'Was the ref's name Dallas by any chance?' (I am on the verge of querying if the linesmen were related, when I remember that virtually everyone in these parts is related to everyone else).

Joe laughs heartily 'Ah that buck. He wasn't around in them days.'

Charlie's bemused expression betrays the fact that he is not as familiar with the recent controversies of the Scottish game. Consequently, Joe spends the next few minutes explaining my reference, in rather colourful terms it has to be said. Charlie appears to appreciate the point.

'And what about Jimmy McGrory himself?'

'Jimmy McGrory. Lord, Jimmy was some player. I remember the goal he scored that day. We had a great view of it from where we were standing. The winger beat two or three men and then hit the ball over. And up jumped Jimmy, head and shoulders above everyone and headed the ball into the goals. I'm telling ye, it was as good a goal as you see any of them fellas scoring, like yer man that plays attack for Celtic now. What's yon fella's name? He used to have the long hair? What's this you call him?'

'Larsson', I volunteer.

'Aye, Larsson. As good a goal as Larsson or any of them boys score.'

Not having had the privilege of witnessing the goal Joe is presently exalting, I make no attempt to disagree.

'You know, Jimmy continued to play well into the 30s. I remember seeing him play years after that over in Scotland. I was over there doing some labouring out around Kirkintilloch and Falkirk and some of them places at the time. It was 1936. A Scottish Cup game at Ibrox . Two - nil they beat Clyde that day and Jimmy scored one of the goals. James Edward McGrory. That was his full title. Did you know that?'

I do, but the question is posed with such earnest authority that I feel obliged to feign ignorance.

'You never told me that you seen McGrory playing over in Glasgow.' Charlie's tone suggests that the oversight has caused genuine offence.

'Jasus, many's a time I've told you that story. I doubt you're starting to dote.'

I sense that this is a good time to steer the pair's thoughts back to their shared experience of The Lea. 'And you were saying that there was a big crowd at the match that evening?'.

'Aye, they came from all over. From Milford and Ramelton and all round.'

'How did they all find out about it? Was it advertised in the papers or what?'

'Damned the bit of it. Word of mouth. Sure, wasn't just the day before Paddy heard tell of it?'

Joe nods his confirmation. 'That's how it was in them days. You'd be in the shop or pub and somebody would mention it and then you'd pass it on to someone else and that's how it would go.'

'The local taxi firms must have done a rare trade ferrying all those people up and down'. I venture teasingly.

The two old boys wear expressions which say, are you mad, man? 'Lord save us, there were no taxis in them days and I doubt if anybody had a car. No, it was the oul' pony and trap. A few would have come down on bicycles and maybe the odd one on horseback.'

'Aye, and a good few would have walked it too,' adds Joe. 'You would think nothing then of walking five or six miles. Sure the young people now, some of them wouldn't walk from here to Biddy Duffy's yonder. I look out at the white house - which I presume to be Biddy's - 50 yards down the road and note the point.

'And were there any kind of facilities for the players, perhaps dressing rooms or a pavilion?'

'Not at all, the players just got togged out alongside the field.'

'You'd think that would be a bit of a come down for big name players like McGrory and Thomson.'

'No, they weren't the least bit bothered. I suppose to them fellas it was all part of the craic.'

The craic. Indeed. I am tempted to enquire about the post match craic, but a glance at the clock on the far wall tells me that time is pressing. Kick-off is in half an hour. I ask Joe and Charlie if they would like to come with me to watch the match, but they inform me that it is 'time for the te' and besides, Charlie's daughter will be down soon to take him home. I nod understandingly. I suspect that, having exhumed heady memories of The Lea, Mulroy Stars and one James Edward McGrory, a Scottish Cup semi-final by comparison probably pales into insignificance. I thank Joe and Charlie for their time and bid them a fond farewell.

'Take care now.' The words follow me as I make my way down the long gravelled drive.

On reaching the outskirts of Carrigart I pull over. The sun is setting on Mulroy as dark clouds gather ominously, casting a shadow over The Lea. I wonder if it was the same on that summer's evening all those years ago. As I look across at the deserted field, I try to imagine the ponies and traps lined up along the road, the players 'togging out', the cheering crowds, and somewhere in their midst, two young schoolboys, standing, incredulous at the sight of the famous green and white hoops.

Back in Downings the bar of the Beach Hotel is already packed with a large audience eagerly awaiting the evening's Sky TV game between Celtic and Ayr United. As Davie Provan's pre-match analysis booms out from a pair of twin speakers, I make a conscious effort to readjust to the contemporary ambience. Suddenly a familiar sight fills the huge screen and the room erupts in a crescendo of adulation. From behind me a voice cries out in a broad local accent 'Come on the Celtic'. Some things it seems just never change.

GERRY COYLE, Bishopbriggs, Glasgow

Celtic Fan

AH wis feelin bloo Ma giro didnnie come,
Ah sat aside the fireplace Lookin mighty glum
Then ah started laughin Ma heid wis foo ie cheer
Ah thought ie aw the games The Celtic won this year
Ah remembered aw the goals Crackers every wan
Ah remembered aw the cheerin N aw the songs we sang
Whit ie yi feelin doon fur Ah asked ma sel oot loud
Yur heid should be raised oan high Yi should be foo ie cheer n proud
Thurs nae team like the Celtic Yi can search the hale world wide
Ah m singing a song fur Celtic As ah walk alang the Clyde Ahm proud
tae live in Glesga N ahm a happy man
Life jist cannie be better If your a Celtic fan.

DAVID MARTIN, Stirling

THIS Celtic story is in part about my great aunt Grace Coll. Grace died a few years ago and at her funeral Mass the priest mentioned that Grace had three great loves in her life -her God - her family - and her beloved Glasgow Celtic. But as he went on to explain "not necessarily in that order."

Aunt Grace took my dad to see the Celtic from a very early age. One of his favourite aunt Grace stories is about a Scottish Cup final sometime in the 1950's. Celtic were due to play Clyde in the final. My great aunt knew a lady who worked in Ferrari's restaurant in Glasgow.

In those days the team would meet for lunch at the restaurant prior to the game. My aunt arranged with the waitress for my dad and her to be allowed to wait in the foyer for the team to arrive. My dad remembers that all the players were really nice, some more so than others. One player in particular stood out from all the others. When Sean Fallon arrived he asked my dad "what team do you support"

My dad who was no more than five-years-old and quite shy answered sheepishly "Celtic". Sean shook my dad's hand and said "Do not ever forget you support the greatest team in the world".

As I said at the beginning this story is in part about Aunt Grace but it is also about Sean and my dad. My dad has never forgot that Celtic are the greatest team in the world, and guess what? Neither have I. Our family has numerous aunt Grace stories ranging from her delirium at the 7-1 game, to the joyous tears of that great night in Lisbon.

I now live in New York, but when I meet young Celtic supporters I always ask them "what team do you support?" And when they sheepishly say "Celtic" I tell them "Do not ever forget you support the greatest team in the world".

TOM HENDRY, New York, USA

The Big Buzz

I'M on the bus, and on my way, everyone's singing loving the day.
My heart is now a hollow cave, with a pulsating beat, like in a rave.
My hands are sweating, my mouth is dry,
we've got to attack, and I know we'll try.
The ground draws nearer, the sound is raised,
and "THE GLASGOW CELTIC" gets songs of praise.
We're off the bus and down the hill,
the voices crying "one-each", "two-nil".
It's harder to focus, my bodies a shake,
I'm asking myself "am I really awake?"
I'm checking my ticket as I breathe, looking around in sight of a thief.
I get to the gate, I give them my stub,
I'm about to explode, for the sake of my club.
I go to my seat and soak up the sight,
the scarves are a glow, and they light up the night.
I look around, the place is a muddle,
but it all becomes sane with the sight of "THE HUDDLE".

DONNA LAFFERTY, Viewpark

"Human language is like a cracked kettle, on which we beat out tunes, for bears to dance to, when all the time we long to move the stars to pity…"

Gustav Flaubert

TRYING to do justice to what it means and has meant being a Celtic fan. One of the first times in my life that I became aware of how big a part Celtic played in my life was when I met an old school friend that I had not seen in about 10 years.

The first words he said to me were "howzit goan Terry still goan tae see the Celtic? That statement was simple but it gave me a sense of pride that he saw me in that light. Some of the following are extracts from my time watching Celtic- Going with my da on the Milburn bus with characters such as John McGilly the (rat catcher) who would sing Elvis songs on the way to the game. Dropping a bottle of vodka out of a duffle coat sleeve while going through the turnstile and miraculously it not smashing.

Telling someone to get up on their feet, that Celtic could still score (last minute Ajax in Amsterdam George McCluskey duly obliged). Hairs standing on my arms, tears in my eyes when Jinky threw his boots in to the Jungle. The 4-2 game a roller coaster of emotion that could never be matched by any other entertainment vehicle (I fell down a hole that night looking up at the stars with tired elation).

The train journey to Turin ('80s), waking up in the morning seeing the Alps and being silenced by their beauty. Turning round in a Chinese carry out shop and meeting a legend, Jimmy Johnstone.

Lying in the bath one September weekend wondering if my mate was going for a pint, a telephone call later and I was on my way to Glasgow airport flying with the team to play, Germinal Ekeren, courtesy of my old boss who could not make the trip.

Admiring guys who sing when all about are quiet and getting the inspiration myself. Finally the thing I love most about Celtic is the sheer diversity of our fans we cut across all styles from sophisticated to square, young and old and all willing us on.

TERRY O'NEILL, Bellshill, Lanarkshire

Celtic, the caring club

I SUFFER from mental health problems and in 2000 I was in a deep depression. I wouldn't leave the house and I was probably making life a nightmare for my family. Life was not good. Unknown to me, my wife, Margaret, wrote to Celtic Football Club asking if they could send me a signed photograph of Henrik Larsson and some of the other team members in the hope that it would cheer me up a little bit.

She knew I was a diehard Celtic supporter. Within a couple of days of sending the letter someone from Celtic's public relations department phoned her about the letter. They asked if she would like to be a guest of the club at the home match that Saturday, September, 2000, against Hibernian and bring me along as a gift from the club. I had known nothing about this and, on the Saturday, she told me what had happened and what the club had offered.

For the first time in months I agreed to leave the house and travel to Glasgow to the match. Instead of feeling depressed I got a major lift and was feeling very excited as it was the first time I had been to Celtic Park in years. We travelled to Celtic Park and on arrival we were given VIP complimentary tickets to the Grand Stand East. The steward looked at our tickets and said they were great seats, and he was right.

We entered the stadium, it was the first time I had been there since it was rebuilt, and I was in awe of my surroundings. The seats were in the best part of the ground and I was totally overcome with Celtic's generosity towards me.

To increase my pleasure Celtic went on to win the match with my hero Larsson scoring twice and Mark Burchill scoring in the dying minutes to seal an easy win.

We went top of the league that day and we stayed there for the rest of the season. It was absolutely magnificent to be there for that, and I have the caring side of Celtic to thank for that. To me that gift from Celtic was a turning point in my life.

My depression lifted and I have progressively got better since that day. I have not worked for six years but I am about to start a voluntary job soon to get me back in the way of work. This all started with a phone call from Celtic. What a great and caring club.

BRIAN MATHIESON, Kinross

Tuesday Wake

It was Tuesday and his wife was beneath the earth.
We hugged the bar in Casey's in all our splendour
as black as the Guinness we supped.
I watched his eyes moisten with tears
as we hailed the Celtic.
Fine days, Fine days
but who were we to know.
MARK BAINE, Stromness, Orkney Islands

WHY has a 41-year-old man who's lived all his life in the football hotbed of Newcastle such a strong affinity with The Hoops? Surely he should have stood in the Leazes End as a boy and have a comfortable season ticket in the re-developed St.James' now? Not me and I'll tell you why.

When I was six years old I watched my first football match on TV. I had read about the greats of world football such as Puskas, Di Stefano, Pele, Garrincha etc. and was just becoming aware of both the emerging stars of the world game and the superteams of the past and present. One team, for me at that time represented power and flair and a sort of sinister greatness. That team was the blue and black giants of Inter Milan.

This first match, however, just happened to be the 1967 European Cup Final between Inter and Glasgow Celtic. Mazzola et al looked confident and machine-like at the kick off, but it soon became apparent that the maverick and unorthodox style of the Scottish Champions was unsettling for them. Celtic would not be steam-rollered like many of Inter's other opponents on the way to the greatest final of them all.

The Bhoys were fighters and themselves had players who rose to world greatness that day. The image of victory which has stayed with me since then is that of Tommy Gemmell, green and white hoops, stylish white boots (30 odd years ahead of Beckham and co!), blond hair flowing, epitomising the Braveheart attitude of the team as a whole.

Glasgow Celtic were the machine. Glasgow Celtic were the victors. Glasgow Celtic were the first from Britain to hold aloft the famous trophy. That is the reason why.

MARK STOKER, Fenham, Newcastle-upon-Tyne

Being Celtic

Hesitantly confident thoughts flow throughout the crowd,
All wrapped up in a sheet of anticipation.
As we await our hooped heroes, green and white gods,
Endlessly deserving of constant adoration.

"Walk on, walk on, with hope in your heart"

We travel an unpredictable journey, with occasional strife,
Encompassing tradition and religion in the blood - a way of life.
The past, present and future all blend into one,
From Stein to O'Neill and legends more to come.

"And if you know the history"

Sixty-thousand voices synchronised in song,
Multitudes more in their homes sing along,
As an ocean of support floods all the land,
Dedicated and devoted, countless like sand.

"Over and over, we will follow you"

Being Celtic we're aware of the cost,
To revel in the victory and be devastated by loss.
A river of passion, we flow constant with pride
And regardless of the obstacles, we'll always follow our side.

"And the Glasgow Celtic will be there"

TRACEY NISBETT, Barrhead

A Love Affair

At the Walfrid for her birthday,
The photos, the autographs, my fish and her vegan meal,
She quips, "That was great, what more can I say!"
When asked the price, I wouldn't reveal.
Asking of her favourite treat,
Whilst drinking our wine,
She replied, "Just walking along Kerrydale Street!"
I struggled to pick mine.

A kiss for the afternoon, A kiss for the night?
There she goes in the colours of green and white.
Singing and smiling with joy,
Waving her scarf and hugging her Celtic toy.

Saturday afternoon at three,
There's the Celtic, the famous Huddle,
A great sight, a sure to see,
She remembers, "This top he bought me,
because he's not here and can't give me my cuddle!"
Fans belting out *The Fields* and *You'll Never Walk Alone*,
She tells me of her goosebumps,
With a message on my mobile phone.

Jackie, "Lubo" and Henrik, players she adores,
The team, the skill and the goals.
Then ultimate pleasure when one of her players scores.
Her only dislike is the strip so yellow
The score is 2-o, a double from her fellow.

4.46pm, she's off her seat, Searching for the keys to the Clio,
Car radio on, she listens for the "others" if they got beat.
Looking at her buys from the Celtic Shop visit,
Scores come through,
She thinks, "The game is back on later, I don't want to miss it!"

Looking forward to see her,
She phones, we get together, I'm at her side,
All she talks of is the game,
She's happy, smiling with pride,
Her show of love, something she just can't hide.

"Is this a fling?" and "Have I lost her?"
Questions she says annoys,
"Listen it's a love affair with my beloved BHOYS!"

BILL PAYER, Coatbridge

Thanks for the memory!

I FIRST met Celtic in the bad days of the 1950s when results were rotten and getting worse. Except for street football, the game was a closed shop to me but a new boyfriend suggested that we go to Parkhead 'some Saturday to see if you like it'. At that time, few females were daring enough to storm the male bastions and the lack of toilet facilities and uncovered grounds were enough to turn off even that few.

But I did go, and saw Celtic playing Queen of the South, which I found really boring stuff. As it was a case of 'love me, love my team, or you're long gone', I persevered and this brought rewards as I began to understand the beautiful game and admire Celtic. By October 1957, I was a convinced supporter and looking forward to the League Cup final against Rangers. We had seats in the stand (luxury – I wouldn't need to be escorted from the terracing to the stand at half-time by a policeman because there were no women's toilets in the ground. No running the gauntlet of cheers and jeers – half of the men hoping you'd been arrested, the other half – we won't go into that). However, fate intervened and I found myself in the Western Infirmary for an appendectomy three days before the big match. I didn't know the score until after 6pm that night, when a newsboy came round delivering papers.

The boyfriend had a Vespa scooter and we travelled all over Scotland to see Celtic play. Most of the football in those days was forgettable, but other things remain in the memory. At Stirling, we were standing close to a foulmouthed crowd, which had caught the eye of the local constabulary. At half-time, they closed in and arrested a quiet young man who'd hardly opened his mouth. I protested loudly and was told to 'shut up or we'll take you too Missus'. Whoever you are, I'm sorry for my lack of courage, for it cost you a weekend in jail and £20 at the Monday court for breach of the peace. Then there was the boy-in-blue who couldn't say where the women's toilet was, as he didn't use them himself. Funny how lots of my story revolves around women's toilets, isn't it?

There was a fatal accident in Stirling, when a bus killed a Celtic supporter. We didn't actually see the accident, but both of us had remarked that the bus was going too fast for conditions on a crowded street with a wet, slippery road surface and we constituted ourselves as witness to the road conditions.

Hilarious memories also abound. One Motherwell supporter was giving me stick for being at the match and even worse, daring to support Celtic. He advised me a dozen times 'away hame and make yir man's dinner'. The last laugh was on him when he screamed 'I widnae pay good money to see you, Celtic!'

Many folk will remember the old stand and enclosure before the Centenary Stand was built. In those days, newspaper vendors went around the park before the game. On a very wet Saturday, one came along from the Celtic end, jumped into the enclosure and landed up to his waist in rainwater. He got the biggest roar of the day. Since I now 'loved his team', we decided to get married in 1958 and by 1963 we had two small children. Having a great mother and mother-in-law who were willing to baby-sit for us, we managed to get to see Celtic whenever they were playing at Parkhead.

By 1962, some young Celtic players were making their mark and in September of that year, Real Madrid came to Glasgow. It was a memorable game, and we were beaten, but it marked the start of a long hopeful road which we relished.

November 1963 was marked by John Kennedy's death and the hush during the minute's silence at Parkhead the following Saturday was earth-shattering. We all felt that we'd lost a hero.

Finally the great days came and the European nights to enjoy. But 1967 brought its personal decision-making time for us. Not even the European Cup winners could keep us in Scotland and we moved to Geneva for the now-husband's career reasons. What anguish when we couldn't get the results till the Sunday newspapers arrived at the airport! We used to drive up into the mountains at 5pm on Saturdays to se if we could catch the football results on the radio. And if a European Cup game was to be on television, we sweated blood, hoping it would be Celtic's tie. Occasionally we'd manage to see a game while visiting the family in Glasgow, but it was meagre fare for us.

How things have changed. We (and our three grandchildren) are Celtic shareholders. On a visit to Celtic Park to witness the opening of the North Stand, our grandson Michael had the great privilege of standing in the centre circle at Parkhead with the Scottish Cup above his head. Both Michael and little John have had their pictures in the *Celtic View*. Allisia is still to make her debut.

We can now see Celtic on the Internet and on Sky Sports and have had the great privilege of attending some of their matches in Europe. When we appeared at our hotel reception in Luxembourg a couple of years ago en route to the match wearing our Celtic blazers, the receptionist remarked 'Que vous etes beaux!' 'How handsome you both are!' Bless her for her white lie but she made us feel a million dollars.

On April 6, 2002, we watched Celtic win two-in-a-row and joined in the party from afar. Our cup runneth over! Thank you, Celtic, for all you stand for and for the thousands of memories wound into my own life. Thanks for the memory!

ANN MARCHETTI, Geneva, Switzerland

MY name is Megan Ross and I am eight-years-old. Even in my mummy's tummy I was a Celtic supporter because I'm sure I could hear my mum cheering on the Bhoys. She is Celtic mad and I am pleased to admit I am too.

I watch them on the telly all the time because I haven't been to a match yet but my mum has promised me that I will go this season so I feel as if all my birthdays are coming at once. I can't wait to see the players. My favourites are Larsson and Lubo. I have even called my goldfish Lubo and I wanted to call my dog Larsson but my mum said no because I can't shout on it in the street, but I really wanted to because I love Larsson and I love my dog too. I have made a small poem and I hope you like it.

I love Larsson, he is the best.
He is so special, he is so sweet, he really is something else.
With his feet he is handsome and tall, and brilliant on the ball.
And Martin O'Neill, I love him too.
He has made the team what it is today
And I say a prayer that he doesn't go away.

MEGAN ROSS (age 8), Cumbernauld

No Conception

5.30am...

Rrriiinnggg! The alarm! Get up quickly, don't wash yourself, yet, get the kettle on, and make sandwiches for the supporters' bus trip. Will he fancy bacon 'n' eggs or cereal for breakfast? Oh hell, stick a banana under his nose, he'll eat anything on a Saturday morning.

5.45am...

Wake him up; put a cup of coffee carefully on the small bedside table. Tell him it's six-thirty and the alarm didn't go off, that'll get him moving.

5.55am...

Make sure he doesn't forget his green and white scarf, put the coach window board bearing the legend 'CELTIC SUPPORTERS' CLUB – NEWCASTLE BRANCH' near the front door. He almost forgot it last time.

6.00am...

He wants to know why I let him sleep in. As bus convenor (as well as being assistant secretary, deputy chairman and chief high punka wallah), the lads will be disappointed at being kept waiting.

6.05am...

"Did I remember to dry out the supporters' team strips in time for their match tomorrow?" he asks. I wonder if I should get Wimpey's in for a quotation to remove the ever-increasing amount of topsoil that the washed strips leave in my sink each week? I swear the back garden is about three feet higher because of it. I say nothing, though; humour would be wasted on him at this hour.

6.10am...

"It's Aberdeen at Hampden today, pet. Do ye think we'll win the cup?"

I wonder what he'd come out with if I said no. "By a barrowload," I reply. Harmony in the home is important.

6.15am...

"That's it, I'm off," he mumbles, chewing away at the banana and ramming his sandwiches into a coat pocket. "Give the weans a wee kiss for me." He wraps his scarf around his neck and heads at a steady trot along the street.

"Your coach board!" I yell. He runs back with a grunt of impatience, pecks me on the cheek and sets off again towards the meeting point.

"It's only quarter past six," I shout, a hearty cackle in my voice. "You've plenty of time."

The raised fist is a friendly gesture. I'm sure he would never do me an injury. Mind you, when Rangers won at Parkhead, that time I decided that discretion was the better part of whatsitsname. You never know when an innocent smile may aggravate him on those occasions. Better not to chance it.

6.20am...

I crawl upstairs. At least I might be able to manage another hour or so before the girls wake. Some chance! There they are in my bed, bright-eyed and bushy-tailed.

"Where's Portagil?" asks Glenda, my four-year-old.

"It's near Lisbon," replies seven-year-old Gail. "Daddy's going there, isn't he mum?"

Here we go again, I sigh. He's brainwashed the kids into thinking Celtic thoughts now. It's wee Jinky this and Big Billy that most of the time. They even know the words to 'Hail! Hail!' Mind you, I don't like it when they sing "What the hell do we care now!" It doesn't seem suitable for wee lassies. Still... what did I expect for marrying a young man who was born and raised in Cambuslang?

"So near to Paradise," he always says. "You Geordies have no conception of the sheer rapture we Glaswegians experience by supporting the Celts. It's a way of life."

Oh really, pet... no conception, eh? I've a house in Gateshead-on-Tyne decorated in green, white and gold. My daughters won't hear of a holiday anywhere else but Scotland and I launder the supporters' Celtic team strips. I arrange and attend supporters' functions and have even spent a terrifying Saturday at Hampden as he lost his reason for several hours.

Okay, so they won 7-1 against Rangers – it was my first ever match. Thank God we were newlyweds. If it had happened before the wedding I don't think I'd have made it to the altar. I thought I had married a lunatic. No conception. That's a good one, Ronnie.

Thirty-five years later...

My lunatic is a retired bank senior executive who is still enraptured by his beloved Celtic. The journeys are longer now. A five hundred-mile round trip from Leeds to the home games is "no problem." His cup runneth over because Martin O'Neill produced a magic Treble last season (Heaven forbid that is was an 'ordinary' Treble!)

During his two Hampden cup final trips, he had a wee blether on the coaches with the Lions ... Bertie, Boaby, Stevie and Faither Simpson ... players that my mature daughters recall with warmth and affection.

Still... I've no conception of what Glaswegians experience by supporting the Celts ... in a pig's ear sunshine. I'm knee-deep in *Celtic Views*, up to the ears in videos and I daren't go near the computer in case I accidentally delete a Jim Craig e-mail message. Oh well, maybe my wee five-year-old granddaughter will escape his brainwashing skills ... Oh God, is that her photo in the *View*?

The End?... I don't think so!

KATHLEEN CAMPBELL, Roundhay, Leeds

Celtic and Me

MY dad always said to me, "There's more to life than football." And it's only now as a husband and father I've begun to realise what he meant.

Celtic FC have been nudged slightly down my list of priorities, however there is still a tremendous pull towards them. If you are a Celtic supporter you will know exactly what I am talking about. The hairs on the back of my neck still stand up when 60,000 fans are belting out *You'll Never Walk Alone*.

Supporting Celtic is a bit like a marriage, it has its ups and downs, and highs and lows. When it is bad you think of the reason you first fell in love and yearn for the good times again. As a Celtic supporter man and boy for the best part of 35 years, I've experienced my fair share of highs and lows.

I've seen them lose a cup final to Raith Rovers, a semi-final in torrential rain to

Falkirk and, of course, the famous Inverness game where I came home and sat in stunned silence and couldn't sleep, hoping when I woke it was all a bad dream.

I've seen 5-1, 4-0 and 4-2 defeats from our old enemy, but for every humiliation there's been several highs. The Centenary Season, 5-1 and 6-2 v Rangers. The day we stopped 10-in-a-row, Martin O'Neill's Treble, back-to-back titles for the first time in 20 years. Henrik Larsson, great goals, great nights, great atmosphere, 5-1 and 6-2 v Rangers - sorry, I think I've already mentioned that. What is being a Celtic supporter all about?

It's about clutching your season book proudly in your hand as you head for the game. It's stomach-churning, nail-biting, goose pimples as you hear the first few lines of *You'll Never Walk Alone*, it's about the Huddle, it's about paranoia, it's about Jock Stein, Lisbon Lions, Nine-In-A-Row, great players past and present. It's about being part of an army of supporters all wanting the same thing. It's about getting married on a Friday to avoid missing the match on a Saturday - the 10-in-a-row match v St Johnstone (understandable really!)

But most of all, it is as the famous song says, it's about being 'faithful through and through'

Now, who was it that said, "There's more to life than football"?

GREGOR MILLIKEN, Rutherglen

For Dad

I learned about the Celtic
Upon my father's knee
He told me many stories
Of their famous history
He talked of Charlie Tully
And many folk besides,
And in his voice I recognised
An unreserved pride.

On growing up he took me
To watch his favourite team,
His heart was always full of joy
Amidst that sea of green.
It wasn't always easy –
When we lost he felt real pain,
But he was always there to cheer
The Celtic on again.

One sunny day in Lisbon
The 25th of May,
He watched and waited breathlessly
And silently did pray.
Of course his prayers were answered
And we lifted up that cup,
We were the Kings of Europe

78

And his heart was fit to burst.

The seasons passed relentlessly
Some good and sometimes bad,
Watching players like King Kenny
Among the best we've ever had.
When Charlie Nic
Played for the 'Tic,
It was a wondrous time,
But still something was missing
And we waited for the sign.

He came along quite recently
And brought with him a gift,
A dream that once again in time
That famous cup we'd lift.
He'd brought tremendous players
And some were quite a steal,
Yes, we've got to count our blessings
For the man they call O'Neill.

These days I watch my heroes
Each one his own talent
Mjallby, Joos and Balde
They are absolutely brilliant.
Lambert, Lennon, Stan the man,
And Didier with his pace,
Thommo, Sutton, Hartson
Bring a buzz about the place.

Big Rab in goal is awesome
For a clean sheet he's hell-bent,
And Henrik Larsson 'King of Kings'
Is surely heaven sent.
There's many more to mention,
And they will all surpass,
But Lubo stands out from the crowd
'cos he's a different class.

My father's not around today
To shake his hand in mine,
I miss him, not just Saturday's –
They say it fades in time.
But one thing that I know for sure
Each match day as I rise
He's right behind me cheering on
The Bhoys in Paradise.

EDWINA DOCHERTY, Hamilton

Over the barriers

Introduction: 'Over the barriers' is a short story about myself being nurtured as a young fanatical Celtic supporter growing up to face everyday dilemmas which would try to deter me from going to the game.

AS a young lad growing up in a football crazy, working-class community of Paisley, an ambition grew inside of me, a great desire to play football at the highest level. Surrounded by many other enthusiastic players', games would take place between the lampposts in the street on an everyday basis for hours on end. Fantasising about playing for Celtic, all the Bhoys would passionately claim the names of Doyle, Provan, and McGrain, whom I'd soon be taken to watch by my father, even though his advice would have emphasised the importance of concentrating on my own game if I'd wanted my dreams to come true.

Residing from a broken home, my father, who lived in Maryhill, would only have had access to visit me at weekends. As Saturday morning arrived, routinely my father made his way through Paisley to watch an early morning match with my under-10 Foxbar United team.

Afterwards I always had the option to do whatever I wished to do, should it be Tiffany's roller-skating hall or the pictures, though I soon found my preference was to head for Paradise.

Grasping my father's hand, I skipped along side him listening intensely, being educated on the Lisbon Lions and the Quality St Gang, as we made our way up the Gallowgate to my first match. The feelings I had of great excitement, I will relish sharing with my own children. Approaching the Celtic End, among the hordes of fans, you could not forget the man on the corner of Janefield Street, playing the accordion to the tune of *Sean South*, punters selling hats, scarves and badges. In the ground you had the macaroon, tablet, chewing gum, Morton's pies and Bovril going round. Caught up in all the atmosphere, I am left with a vague remembrance of the match, but not the scoreline, St Mirren were on the receiving end of a seven one thrashing.

After the match, it became customary to return to Maryhill to visit my late grandmother who originally resided from Castle Blaney in county Monaghan. Faithfully she'd have listened to the Radio Clyde commentary and was able to depict the injustices dished out by McGinley, Syme, Valentine and company. A whole clan of other Celtic mad grandchildren would also visit after the game for what would be a family congregation, reminiscing about Ireland, and singing Celtic ballads.

Returning home to Paisley after Sunday Mass left you with a depressed feeling that you try to sweep away by boasting about having seen the Celtic and how great they were, in the school playground on Monday. The rest of the week seemed like a prolonged wait, anxiously counting the days until Saturday.

It was one Wednesday evening; Celtic would face Sporting Lisbon on the return leg with the task of overcoming an away defeat. Through the youthful love I had developed for my team, determination would take me to this match without parental supervision. During school hours I planned on how I'd be able to get to Celtic Park, rushing home while my mother was still at work, I proudly changed into my colours and mischievously took money from my savings bottle without fear of chastisement.

I quickly made my way to Gilmour Street train station knowing I'd have to catch the 61 bus once I arrived in Glasgow. With the experience of travelling every week, I knew to look out for the famous old floodlights, towering beacons in the Parkhead sky. My enthusiasm had brought me to the Gallowgate with a few hours to kill; I wandered up and down the long road, as the thought of what I had done crept into my head, though more impatiently waited on the crowds to arrive.

As the time drew near to kick-off, thousands descended towards Paradise, where I would mingle among those queuing up to enter the turnstiles for the Jungle. Looking up at the experienced regulars, without a ticket, I had to pluck up the courage to ask a friendly face, if he'd lift me over the turnstile.

As I did the fellow shared a laugh between his mates and replied 'nae bother wee man'.

As he hoisted me over, a curiosity, which had accrued, because of my father's precautions on taking me anywhere other than, the Jungle had been contended.

My daring actions were to be consolidated in memory forever. Celtic wearing an all time favourite away strip, the light green top with dark green shorts, hammered Sporting wearing our beloved hoops by five goals. The performance of Tommy Burns on that night stands clear as one of his best. Dashing moments of flair were ones you tried to portray in your own game influenced by his deftness on that night. Travelling home I worried about repercussions for my escapade, though the magnificent Celtic display was more prominent in my head.

Remembering correctly my punishment was no more than a clip around the ear, well worth it for that glorious European night. A diary consisting of many occasions, when nothing could deter me from following Celtic had begun. One Saturday afternoon an arrangement made with my father would bring us to Fir Park. On the way to meet him I heard the Glasgow-bound train approach the station. In haste I went to the wrong platform. Panicking, I about-turned then raced back downstairs.

With a great leap I tried to clear the last flight, but unfortunately I landed awkwardly. In sheer agony with extraordinary perseverance I narrowly made it aboard. Unable to hold back the tears a lady passenger showed some concern. Though embarrassed by it all I removed my shoe and sock to reveal an immediate swelling developing.

Hobbling off to catch the football special, my father tried to persuade me to go to hospital, rebelliously I would persist that we made our way for the low level train to Motherwell. Watching the game through a severe pain barrier, I vaguely remember Charlie Nicholas had a super performance during the four-goal victory.

Endurance had to be prolonged due to my father's weekend custody until Monday morning's visit to the Royal Alexandra Hospital where I was diagnosed with a broken bone in my left foot and put in plaster for six weeks.

A disastrous family crisis saw my mother and I uproot, to be exiled for three years in Manchester. Unable to adapt to a hostile culture, we eventually returned home. It wasn't' soon enough though, missing the incredible '84-85 season and the following year's Centenary Scottish Cup Final, were torture. *Sunday Mail* reports and brief television highlights was a pitiful diet, having a massive hunger for Celtic.

On that miraculous day in Paisley, I was to find out the news by a Rangers fan in despair, that we were crowned champions. Walking towards me, along Blackpool's promenade. Wearing his colours and I was wearing mine, with a sneer, he said "A see you'se b*****s won the league". Peering into a radio rental shop window, in disbelief the two sides of the story were being televised. Albert Kidd breaking Hearts, and the five-goal heroics performed at Love Street. Wishing I was there brought feelings of anguish and jubilation, Mancunians were oblivious too.

Manchester United versus Everton took prime television coverage on cup final day. Only highlights again would provide the historical cup winning moments of Davy Provan's beautifully curled free kick and Frank McGarvey's spectacular diving header. Watching those jubilant celebrations on the slopes of Hampden, I felt in isolation amid arrogant Englishmen.

Qualifications to the Cup Winners' cup, would prescribe a controversial rendezvous with Rapid Vienna at Old Trafford. Although it was unjust, Celtic's presence in Manchester was a much-needed cure for depressive homesickness. Obtaining a ticket was like receiving your best ever Christmas present. Guarding it like a lottery winner until the night I was reunited the largest ever-travelling support for a European tie.

As the faithful arrived in droves, the natives gazed in awe, as a massive Celtic army occupied their city. For me it was the reunion I had pined for, in all my time away from home.

Entering the stadium sent shivers down my spine, the place was awash with green, white and gold. The atmosphere being pumped up as the Wolfetones band marched around the pitch. Voluminous decibels ringing around the ground must have been an inspiration for the player's.

Though with bad luck, Celtic went a goal down. Losing to Rapid infuriated supporters at UEFA's dubious decision. Ugly scenes started spilling onto the pitch as an over passionate fan assaulted the Rapid goalkeeper. The anti-climax was horrendous, we were out of the tournament, and I remained in Manchester as the coach loads returned north.

Immediately on return home to Paisley, I would resume following Celtic. It was the beginning of the Souness era at Rangers big money spending led them to reign superiority in Scottish football. Unused with their dominance, confidently I went to the League Cup Final at Hampden Park.

Teaming up with new schoolmates. I was relishing the old firm atmosphere, I'd bragged about in England. In the last five minutes, a harsh decision by referee Syme handed Rangers a victory.

Billy McNeill's departure from Manchester and his reinstatement as boss put the brakes on the cavalry charge of Rangers progress. No 12-man force would be able to overpower these gallant Centenary Bhoys. Fighting tooth and nail to the last minute, throughout the season was the nature of every game. Towards the end of a match some fans would leave early, disappointed without the points.

As a member of St Peter's CSC in Paisley, I witnessed each fight to the death, watching in confidence, anticipating the winning goal. Whispers of fate with it being the Centenary season, became much talked about the terraces. Happy Birthday dear Celtic, celebrating the first 100 years of the club, became a regular chant as the points accumulated. Adding fuel to the talk of Centenary omens, Andy Walker's chested ball over the line at Ibrox, sending us on our way to the Championship, Chris Morris opening the celebrations against Dundee, and the Scottish Cup semi-final, were all played in glorious sunshine.

The last taste of success before the domestic drought came with another day at Hampden in the sun. The year 1989, we retained the Scottish Cup. Stealing the ball from Stevens, Joe Miller poked the ball in the top corner. In my first year of employment, though, still underage, celebrations procured a mighty hangover.

The long suffering years of the '90s were brought to a halt for a short period, quenching the thirst for silverware, it is none more deservedly than Paul McStay who would lift the trophy.

Following Paul throughout his career, ability in abundance had Italian vultures hovering with multimillion-pound bids for the Maestro. Showing great devotion to the club, his unfashionable ideology makes him a martyr in the club's history.

A record number of managers reigned at our club through the '90s. Fan power brought the McCann revolution. The long promised stadium had been erected, a new Dutch Manager was in the hot seat to bring us glory, completed under a five-year schedule.

McCann's plan gave me an experience of a lifetime. Now living with my own family in Belfast, I travelled with Erin go Bragh to see Jansen's hero's defend our nine-in-a-row status. Expression's of young Hoops fans remains in my mind, having never seen their side as champions brought sentimental tears to my eyes. Dancing with a steward on the pitch was just the start of a party, which carried on for a week back in Belfast, finding it difficult to contain euphoric feelings.

The dawning of a brighter future had begun, now marching with O'Neill; I continue to practise my faith from Ireland.

DAVID GORMAN

But why Celtic?

I AM frequently asked this question. Is it my English accent? My Portuguese ancestry? A bit of both, perhaps.

Growing up I supported, or 'followed' might be a better word, Liverpool, but about 10 years ago, at a Jack Charlton evening in Hong Kong I was fortunate (or otherwise, some might say) to be seated next to a Celtic supporter who could not squeeze on to the Celtic supporters' club table.

He introduced me to the rest of the Bhoys later on and one asked why a good convent girl like myself was not supporting Celtic. So then began the brain-washing and the start of my trek to Paradise. And I am convinced that if the Jesuits could convert as well as Celtic supporters, they'd have conquered the world by now!

The process took time, though, with being so far away and it was not easy to relate to Celtic when, apart from the odd televised game, we had to watch tapes sent over from Scotland days after the match.

When I decided to leave Hong Kong I first went to live in Leeds but after less than a year moved to Harrogate. I joined both the Celtic and Liverpool supporters' clubs in Leeds as I was still a little partial then, mistakenly, to my childhood team. If Celtic, as a club, had not convinced me of where my allegiance lay, then the supporters certainly did.

They took me in and they became, for me, my new family in Yorkshire. The reception from the Liverpool sector did not come remotely close and soon I drifted away from them and from Liverpool as a club and gave Celtic my undivided attention and devotion.

I began to read about Celtic's history and was so moved by everything connected with Celtic that I wanted to find out more. I bought all the CDs and subscribed to the *Celtic View* as well as Scottish papers to get the latest on Scottish football. Then the day at last arrived... my first game at Celtic Park.

I can remember looking around me in awe with tears welling up and feeling, for the first time ever in my life, that I was in the majority. And it is a feeling that still stays with me at almost every game.

I started to attend games regularly and then became a season-ticket holder, which really meant 'no way back'. I work in Harrogate still but travel up to every home game and every away game that's not broadcast. Then finally, I succumbed to becoming a Celtic shareholder to satisfy that need to own a bit of Celtic. The best way to equate my feelings for Celtic would be to compare it to someone who's converted their faith. They do so by choice so they do it wholeheartedly and having seen it from other angles before.

I cannot explain to my English friends the difference between the supporters of Celtic and the supporters of any other club. I have tried on numerous occasions to put my feelings into words but unless they have actually tried the Celtic experience, they will never really know what it's like to be so moved by the atmosphere. And this includes everything from our songs of *Fields of Athenry* and *You'll Never Walk Alone* to drinking in Baird's Bar, Saracen's Head and Brazen Head, to name but a few of the true Celtic bars.

Then there are the other Celtic bars in the Merchant City, city centre and the West End which, although do not blatantly display the green and white, are our strongholds as is evident before and after every home game. It always makes me feel part of a very special club.

How do I explain the Huddle? And it's not just watching the players on the park doing their Huddle, but to be actually drawn into one in a bar somewhere, or even on the street when celebrating a victory. To explain also that, whenever I go on holiday I always take with me, either my Celtic shirt or cap because through these I have made many friends, not just Celtic supporters, but supporters of other clubs have come over and spoken to me.

When I wore my Celtic scarf to a Leeds/Chelsea game at Elland Road several months ago, it prompted many smiles and conversations, as well as a few verses of Larsson's Song. Which other scarf is so distinctive, so well know and, more importantly, so well liked?

As far as Celtic supporters' clubs in the world go, it seems that almost every city in the world has one. And everyone says Manchester United have the largest support in the world! A support as fervent as ours? I would doubt this very much indeed.

During the Dalglish and Barnes era (one best forgotten) I grew tired of shedding tears on my own in numerous pubs in Harrogate so decided to place at advertisement in the *Celtic View* and the local paper in the hope of finding others to cry with. (Little did I know what was to follow the next season!)

So was born the Harrogate Hoops Celtic Supporters Club, where we even witnessed Eddie Gray joining us to watch an Old Firm game, and to have founded just in time to witness Celtic's resurrection under Martin O'Neill's leadership made it even more memorable for me.

I've followed my team to Europe, and usually on my own, secure in the knowledge that I will be surrounded by Hoops who will befriend me wherever. I have stood in the middle of Parkhead Cross sharing a bottle of Buckfast. I've danced to Charlie and the Bhoys and I've sung in a number of supporters' clubs, and I've sat beside some of the most famous names in Celtic's history, looking out for the prawn sandwiches which Roy Keane was talking about (and which I still haven't seen!) … And through my own Celtic experience I have made many, many new friends.

But even if Celtic were to tumble backwards in the future, and I had to revert to tears again, I would still be there, in Paradise, along with the thousands like me who know what it's like to be a part of the greatest football club in the world.

And that's why I'm a Celtic supporter … through and through.

ROWENA SMITH, Harrogate

Tic Talk

Time ambles on, relentlessly ticking away, relentlessly ticking away
Nothing is surer than night becomes day
My years melted together in Castlemilk grey
One highlight each week, Celtic, Saturday!

I watched in admiration, wished the 80s away,
To be out there on merit, beside Paul McStay.
The Maestro, Champagne, T.B and the Bear,
Alongside Big Packy, No Team could compare!

Proud to be born, the green 'n' white way,
I could have lived in the Jungle, forever and a day,
Anywhere was comfortable watching Mick McCarthy play,
Celebrating our Centenary, that very special way.

Time keeps on going, the Jungle came down,
Up went a stadium on Parkhead like a crown.
Martin's in charge, I'm happy to say. One thing
Won't change, I love to see my, my Celtic play.

JOHN DEANE, Cheshire

The real thing

JOHN LENNON wouldn't budge! None of them would. All four signatures, not a smudge. I rubbed them, scraped them, even wet them. Nothing.

I'd joined The Beatles Fan Club in 1963. I couldn't believe it when I received a signed photo. To actually have their autographs. I was star struck.

Then my mother burst my balloon. "They're printed on the photograph." Fakes. Mass produced copies. They'd conned me. But I'd caught the bug.

Around this time, football was becoming more and more important. However, living in East Kilbride and with no car in the family, Parkhead seemed inaccessible to an 11-year-old.

School friends, who seemed to attend every game succeeded in making me very jealous. So when my pal Sunny suggested I went to Celtic Park with him and his dad, there was no stopping me. Well his dad did have a car!

An upcoming game against Airdrie was the agreed first visit to Paradise and so I joined their ritual. The ritual of 'Gawnty the Gemme.' Firstly this involved Sunny's dad finding the perfect place to park the car.

Inevitably this seemed miles from the stadium. Later, this apparently would enable an easy escape from any possible traffic jam. Next, the paying of local kids to watch over his car, half now, half later.

While this was taking place, Sunny and I quickly made our way to Kerrydale Street. We would only meet up with his dad much later for the journey home.

Next on the agenda was how to gain entry and not spend any money. This involved loitering at the turnstiles accosting anyone older who looked strong enough to lift us over the gate.

I was assured this ploy had always worked for Sunny and indeed was common practice for smaller kids (wonder what the crowd figures really were!).

This would enable us to afford a programme, which of course would contain hours of fascinating reading (aye right! Really makes you appreciate the excellent quality of matchday programmes we're now accustomed to).

Meanwhile back at the turnstiles, Sunny was now inside the ground and slightly perplexed as to why my pestering of strangers hadn't met with success. Now I'd always been a big lad for my age, not fat you'll understand, but apparently very heavy.

This meant any request to be lifted was met with incredulous laughter. Worse still, any actual attempt to hoist me up induced cries of suspected hernias.

The game itself, well, what an introduction. What a walkover. Celtic won 9-2 and in the last few minutes of the game there was a defining moment to a wonderful afternoon.

A penalty had been awarded to Celtic. I didn't know if it was common practice but the crowd began chanting the goalkeeper's name. Celtic's goalie. Haffey! Haffey! Haffey!

As everyone else in the team seemed to have scored, I guess the crowd just wanted the goalie to get in on the entertainment.

Amazingly, he ran the length of the pitch to get on the scoresheet. The fans were laughing and cheering. Frank Haffey was lapping this up. It was party time and he was obviously loving every second. As he approached the penalty spot he was clapping and waving to his adoring audience.

He missed!

It didn't matter. The crowd just laughed and cheered again. What a first game. I'd definitely caught the bug.

Around this time, Sunny and I began attending high school in Hamilton. This led to making some new friends from the surrounding area. Most were Celtic fans but some did follow Hamilton Accies.

One wee lad, though, was from Motherwell and he was fanatical about his local team. His name was John Boyle and he could not be separated from his beloved Motherwell scarf.

Always wearing it to school and forever berating us for not supporting his team from just down the road. I've often wondered what became of him!

For the Bhoys among us, the agreed meeting place on a Saturday afternoon was a certain barrier on the terracing, now known as the Lisbon Lions' Stand. We knew it only as the Rangers End.

It was quieter and easier to find each other before the game began. Just before kick-off, we'd make our way through the Jungle.

More atmosphere. Better view. Better patter. And the singing was great. Although we had to beware of dropped cans. Their contents were dubious and usually questionable.

You see, Ewan McGregor got it wrong. No way was that toilet in *Trainspotting* the worst in Scotland. Half-time, back of the Jungle, was the time and place to regret the lack of a pair of wellies!

It's no wonder female fans were almost non-existent in those days. Obviously, through the years, facilities have been upgraded but compared with today's wonderful stadium, well, it's rosy specs off, and thank you Fergus.

European games followed. New teams, exotic names. Winter evenings, dark and freezing. That precious cigarette to heat my hands 'til 'the Bovril Break'.

I remember looking to the packed Celtic End and fascinated that never a second passed without seeing several cigarettes being lit. A constant flickering of sparkling lights appearing haphazardly in the darkened crowd. Strangely mesmerizing.

One night James Bond appeared! For some reason, Sean Connery's name was announced in a half-time garbled message. In the distance, a wee guy in a bunnet appeared from the tunnel, waving.

He received a big cheer from the crowd as he made his way to the touchline for a lucky draw. He seemed miles away and I couldn't make out his face but it didn't matter. I'd just seen James Bond! The fame was continuing.

My grandda was the source of great Celtic stories. Tales of the Bhoys from way back when. Faceless icons of the past became familiar names. Great goals from Jimmy McGrory; "Three goals in three minutes, McGrory's delight" he'd sing.

The amazing skills of Patsy Gallacher. Chatting to Jimmy Delaney in Caledonia Road (we lived in the Gorbals when I was much younger). He would recall stories of his two pals from Oatlands, who just happened one time to be standing in the Vatican's St Peter's Square enquiring, "Who's the wee fella up on the balcony wi' Charlie Tully?" All perfectly true of course!

Fast forward now to '66 and 'The Season of the Lions' had begun. I'd dream of being spotted by Neilly Mochan or Jock Stein. Just by chance they'd be passing the lock-ups at the end of our street.

They'd be stunned by the dazzling ball control on display. Amazed by my 17 goals in our 17-16 three-a-side victory. Pleading with me to play in this week's team. Celtic seemed so near, yet so far.

Then we discovered where they trained! Early one weekday morning, it was bikes out and we were off to Barrowfield. Strangely, no-one else seemed to be off school that day!

All the players were already out and limbering up when we arrived. Luckily no-one seemed to mind our presence as we sat on the grass mound.

There was my hero, big John Hughes, training just yards away. A mini game was arranged. Celtic v Celtic. We felt so privileged. All the big names were playing just for our benefit.

Stein shouted orders. McBride passed to Chalmers. On to Lennox. Jim Craig attempted a tackle on the wee Buzzbomb but his speed was only halted by a diving Fallon.

Quickly up to Bobby Murdoch. Touched back to McNeill. Over to wee Jinky on the wing. Gallagher and Cushley both tried to pounce, but with a deceptive feint and some dazzling runs, Johnstone gave the ball to Bertie Auld.

As John Clark blocked his way, it was time to 'Feed the Bear'. Big Yogi swept past Brogan and O'Neill to hit a thunderous shot. Unbelievably, it was saved by a flying Ronnie Simpson. Surely the greatest goalie ever.

Then came my moment. The ball was kicked up the length of the field to Stevie Chalmers. He clashed with big Tam Gemmell and it bounced free. As this was happening near to where we were standing, everything seemed to go in slow motion.

None of the team could reach the ball in time and it rolled straight to me! The precious seconds. The game momentarily halted. All eyes on me - Lisbon Lions to be. Don't mess it up. I thumped the ball. It swerved high, over to John Hughes. Perfect. A few raised hands in grateful acknowledgement. There was even a smattering of applause! Play continued. The moment was over.

The players eventually trooped off (I think Celtic won). We grabbed our bikes and attempted to follow the squad as they were driven back to Celtic Park.

The following hours were spent patiently waiting at 'The Gates of Paradise' (also known as 'The Car Park'). At last the team emerged in groups of twos and threes, only to disperse every which way to their cars.

This was our signal to swoop. Dementedly we attempted, in turn, to block each player's exit. The souvenir magazine we clutched contained individual pages and photos of everyone in the squad.

However, with the short time available as they made to depart, finding their allotted page became mysteriously difficult. We were all finger and thumbs.

Instead, several players ended up autographing their portrait within the big group poster on the middle pages. No matter, as long as they signed.

As Billy McNeill was on the front cover, I definitely had to have his signature there. When he finally appeared, he was talking with Jock Stein! Bonus time.

Caesar duly signed his photo and suddenly it was to for:- 'My Big Conversation With Jock Stein.'

I held out my book and pen, said "Please?" and Mr Stein replied, "Aye son."

Much later, when the entire team, (reserves too) had left their mark, literally it was time to compare our treasured magazines (Wow! I got Wee Jinky's twice!). They bulged with autographs. Real ones!

The crowning glory. He emerged like royalty (well, in my eyes anyway). It was Jimmy McGrory. I stood in awe of him. This was superstardom.

No-one turned as, unceremoniously, he made his way from the hallowed entrance of Celtic Park to his waiting transport. I only had a few seconds.

I remembered seeing a tiny black and white photo of him in my magazine. Quickly I fumbled to the relevant page. But the little picture just seemed inadequate. I had an idea. I closed my book. On the front cover was the simple title in large bold, light green letters; C E L T I C.

I asked him to sign his name right across the title. He smiled and obliged. It seemed most fitting. My day was complete.

One last thing. I looked at his signature. Quickly, and on purpose, before it could dry, my finger smudged a tiny part of his writing. Now it really looked genuine. I may not have had my favourite Beatle's autograph, but there was no disputing, this was 'The Real Thing.'

ANTHONY BRANNAN, East Kilbride

What does it mean?

CFC ... what does it mean?
Is it the sound of the ball
Thrusting into the net?
Is it the final whistle
Declaring a victory?
Or is it when Celtic
Win 7-1 over Rangers?

CFC ... what does it mean?
Is it the atmosphere as soon
As you gaze among Paradise?
Is it the banter of frolicking supporters?
Or is it the shimmering
Thousands of flags uniting as one?

CFC ... what does it mean?
Is it the glistening image
Of the team emerging from the tunnel?
Is it the shine of a newly won trophy?
Or is it the Huddle,
Forming like a dedicated team?

CFC ... what does it mean?
It means, Celtic Football Club.
Passion. Honour. Glory.

GARY DONLIN, St Luke's High School, Barrhead

Helen

HER impulsiveness was one of the great things about my ma. I must have been only about eight or nine, off sick from school. She came up with a pretext of going to town for something. After a brief excursion she shot us off up London Road and there we were at the front door of the old Celtic Park.

After some exchanges between ma and someone, the next thing I knew I was in the entrance hall. A huge wooden panelled thing with the best piece of lino I've ever seen – the biggest Celtic badge in the world at your feet. And, my God, was I frozen solid to it. Billy, 'the' Billy McNeill was stood there chatting to someone. The next minute he was towering over me talking to us, me and my ma. He spoke to US.

It was a moment of pure gold. Of total awe. Vaulted away in a part of my brain that'll never let it escape. Nearly 30 years on I took my ma out for lunch, finding an excuse to call off at the Celtic Superstore on one of my regular forays up from my home in Sheffield. She knew it would be her about her last trip out. The pain was becoming unbearable and her energy ebbing away and she knew she would soon die. Her spirit, though, was unchanged. And she worked her magic again on the people at Celtic Park. For the second time ever, there we were stood – inside the entrance to Celtic Park. Thirty years apart and brought about by her impulsiveness we were kindly allowed to look around and the memories of that special visit as a boy returned stronger than ever. This second, time was special though, we knew it would be a last special moment together and two months later she was gone from us.

Unquestionably there are utterly innate reasons for being a Celt, running through our veins and ingrained within us but the connection between that place, the not knowing - as a boy – the significance of standing in that place at that time 30 years on would have and of the importance those memories would symbolise for me are just beyond explanation. It is beyond definition. My ma and I will always be close because we shared two special moments, on quiet mid-week afternoons, 30 years apart, because of her impulsiveness and because Celtic is Celtic. That rash moment of madness from my ma, when I was a boy, created an experience that not only bonds mothers and sons together but also sons and Celtic. And then, back in the '70s, we were oblivious to the fact that that's where we'd share our last experience together. Walk On.

JOCK WAUGH, Totley, Sheffield

The Rush

Rush, I have the need, it creeps upon me every week.
I feel the power, the sense of pride, as I watch the "Hoops", I beat inside.
My body tingles, I'm drawn to my feet, he pulls the trigger, the ball and net meet.
There's a deafening cheer around the ground, I live each week just to this sound…."Rush"

STEPHEN KILDAY, Glasgow

Chapter Seven

Rocket Man

"… AND don't read the headstones because I know what you're like."

So ended the final instructions from the late Joe Moore to his grandson, Michael. That statement told him more about how his grandfather saw him than the entire letter and he read it over at every opportunity presented to him by the constant stream of red lights.

He registered the latest churn of stomach-based moroseness as he drove through the Gallowgate and passed Baird's Bar. He was all too aware of the journey's now eerie familiarity, but slightly startled at an unexpected sense of embarrassment felt that at 35-years-old, this was the first time he had made it alone.

It took him 10 minutes to find a parking space at the Forge Shopping Centre. He grabbed his sports bag and crossed the road into Janefield Street Cemetery. It was one of the three beautiful evenings you get in Glasgow each year as he slowly made his way through the vandalised headstones, stopping occasionally to look at the liberal sprinklings of withered flowers. Three teenagers disappeared behind a tree with a bottle when they saw him, then quickly reappeared when they realised he wasn't part of some Council-funded covert operation set up especially to nail under-age drinkers.

He found a reasonably spacious spot at the back of the cemetery and gazed up at the magnificent structure that dominated the East End skyline. It's hard to believe a human being could harbour such affection for concrete and iron. There wasn't a moment in his life when he wasn't aware of its existence. Images of Celtic Park looming in the distance like a proletarian amphitheatre, struggling to contain the exuberance of the hooped warriors enshrined within, littered his childhood memories like tiny nuggets of euphoria. Where other childhoods were the copyright of Disneyland and Uncle Walt, his was enchanted by Glasgow Celtic and Joseph Daniel Moore.

His grandfather made a day at Celtic Park seem like a timeline in Heaven. How could you fail to be mesmerised by someone who could make direct comparisons between Patsy Gallagher and Lubo Moravcik, or who would glaze over in visible delirium when imagining the devastating power of a Jimmy McGrory/Henrik Larsson strike partnership.

His arguments ranged from the plausible "Jimmy McGrory's international strike rate of six goals in seven games makes him the greatest ever Scotland striker," to the outrageous "If Gene Kelly's family had not moved to America he would have been a Celt. Born in 1912, the man was a natural athlete and he would have played in the same team as Delaney and McGrory.

"I'm tellin' you, son, watch him if you ever get to see *The Pirate*, he's got legs on him like Bobby Murdoch." From the age of 12, when he first heard the 'Gene Kelly Theory', Michael had begged his grandfather not to repeat it to anyone else.

At that moment he would have given anything just to hear it one more time. Joe Moore had died two weeks short of his 90th birthday. He had now been dead for six days. Michael wondered how long it would be before he stopped counting them.

The blast of a car horn made him get up and he waved to the driver and pointed to the Forge car park. He watched three figures get out of the car and slowly make their way into the cemetery. A couple in their late 50s were sharing the controls of a shuffling octogenarian who, from the movements of her head, was talking incessantly. As the trio moved closer to Michael, he could just about make out what the little homunculus was saying.

"Whit we daein' in a cemetery? He wiz cremated last week. Ah didnae know they wur still buryin' folk here."

When the little party eventually reached him they each wore expressions of such complete bewilderment that he could feel the muscles in his face contorting with the strain to keep it straight. He embraced them individually.

"Hi Mum."

"All right, Dad?"

"How are you, Aunt Mamey?"

He was more than a little surprised with their funereal attire.

"What's with the outfits?"

"None of us knew what the dress code was for dilapidated cemeteries on a Friday night," snapped his father.

This was the man who had fallen in love with Joe Moore's only daughter and had married her in 1967. The wedding costs had prevented the father of the bride attending a little pilgrimage to Lisbon, a tragic episode that the late Joe Moore never really got over and one for which he held his son-in-law personally responsible, using it as the main evidence in the regular character assassinations of the man that only Michael was privy to. His father was, by decree, apparently "from the soles of those flat feet to that big, glaikit napper, a 'Blue Nose'." Michael's father actually had no interest at all in the beautiful game and, to his son, that was even worse.

"I hope you won't keep us here too long, son," said his mother. "Your Aunt Mamey's tired."

He glanced at Aunt Mamey. She his grandfather's youngest sister so that made her a grand aunt to him, or something, he never could figure it out. She was now the family's representative of her generation, sharp as a tack, feisty and whom his grandfather referred to as the "Tweed Piranha."

"Okay," he began. "Well, first of all thanks for coming out here this evening. You must be anxious to find out the reason why, so..."

He fumbled around in the inside pocket of his jacket and pulled out a piece of paper that looked as if it had just been exhumed from one of the graves. His father raised an eyebrow, his mother shifted her weight from one foot to the other and Aunt Mamey released a tut that exploded from her mouth like an exocet missile and ricocheted off several headstones before it detonated in his face. Unfazed, he continued:

"It was grandda's wish that I read this poem out to you exactly as he's written it, but if you don't mind, and believe me you won't, I've edited a couple of the words.

Man and boy, ah've watched the 'Tic,
Told folk stories 'til they wur sick.
Tales that relieve ye of aw yer cares,
Like puttin' seven by the teddy bears.

Patsy an' Jinky, ah've seen them aw,
You wouldnae believe whit they could dae wi' a baw.
Liam an' Lou, ma eyes ah'd rub,
Couldnae believe whit they fumblers nearly did tae ma' club,

Peacock, Tully, Johnstone and Dalglish,
Couldnae wait to see who they would next unleash.
Macca, the Maestro, Larsson and Lubo,
Were as welcome to Rangers as a bloated bubo.

Thought ah'd seen it aw until the 4-2 game,
Took me three days 'fore ah finally made it hame.
Seen so many strikers quickly come and go,
Honky, Cadete and that wee fumbler, Mo.

Had ane fit in Heaven the night the Lions roared,
Had baith feet in there when we got rid o' the board.
And now ye're here to watch the remains o' this auld relic,
Light up the sky around his beloved Glasga' Cellic"

Michael looked at them apologetically. "It's not Shakespeare," he said.

"We know," snarled a distinctly unamused Aunt Mamey.

"Okay," his voice was really beginning to falter now, "as you know I took grandda's ashes away because he wanted something quite unusual done."

He reached into his bag and carefully took out what looked to them like a psychedelic cruise missile. Eyes widened and mouths opened.

"What have you done now, son?" asked his father, the incredulity in his voice almost tangible. Michael closed his eyes and went for it.

"Grandda asked me to have his ashes mixed with gunpowder, put into a big rocket and let off in this cemetery so that it could explode over Celtic Park."

He thought that if he just came out with it, then that would lessen the shock for his unprepared relations. He was wrong. His mother put one hand over her retching mouth while heroically attempting to keep Aunt Mamey upright, whose legs were beginning to wobble violently. His father felt his stomach shoot through the top of his head, slap him around the face a few times then re-enter his body through his backside. He grabbed Michael by the arm and turned him away from the quickly disintegrating women.

"Tell me that again," he said. "No, don't. I can't believe I'm hearing this. Are you serious? The last memory your mother and Aunt Mamey are going to have of your grandfather is of him skiting through Janefield Street in a dud firework."

"It's not a dud. It cost an absolute fortune."

"You're not too old to get a belt in the mouth, son."

"It's what he wanted, dad. He had already arranged it with the firework company and paid for it. I have to do this. I'm going to do this."

Michael's father didn't say any more. He turned away and led the two distraught women out of the cemetery.

"Luk et the size o' that madman's rocket, man," shouted a member of the teenage drinking party who had been observing them and watched his family leave. He took a makeshift launch pad from his bag, quickly erected it and searched for his matches. He searched for them again. And again. He didn't have them. He had come all the way up here and he didn't have any matches. Just as the despair was beginning to descend, a shrill voice spoke behind him.

"Want a light there, Rocket Man?" The teenage drinking party was only a few feet away from him now. The smallest member was trying to whisper into his mobile phone but Michael could just make him out.

"Ah'm tellin ye, man, there's some bam in the graveyaird wi' a mad rocket. Tell Jasper we'll be doon as soon as he lets it aff."

The one who addressed Michael threw him his Zippo lighter. "Fire it up, big chap," he said.

"Thanks, man," said Michael in a pathetic attempt at 'Ned-speak'.

He lit the fuse of the massive rocket and stood well back. The teenage drinking party watched him and did the same. Seconds passed that seemed like minutes when a banshee-like scream replaced the sound of a hissing fuse and the remains of Joseph Daniel Moore were sent hurtling into the pale, blue dusk sky. A cacophony of enthusiastic teenage profanity had accompanied the launch. What followed next had them convulsing in amazement.

The first explosion coloured the sky above Paradise in emerald green with an almost ethereal light. The second followed a second later in an eruption of incandescent white. The third and fourth erupted simultaneously with the same visual magnificence and breathtaking colours. The teenage drinking party started bouncing around the cemetery when the patterns formed into a perfect four-leaf clover, crackled wildly and hung in the sky for several seconds before they slowly dimmed and disappeared.

"Aw, man, that wiz pure ace, man," screamed the owner of the Zippo lighter. "Ye gote any mare?"

It was a while before Michael answered.

"No," he said, through a perpetual stream of tears, "that was the only one."

MARC ORR, Glasgow

MINE is only a wee story, but I think it is worth recording. In 1953, after Celtic won the Coronation Cup, our local priest, Fr Lyne, persuaded Sean Fallon to bring the cup to our little primary school. I was picked to present Mr Fallon with a posy of flowers for his trouble, and spent the previous week being taught how to curtsey.

When the great day arrived, I was ready for my five minutes of fame. Unfortunately, Sean Fallon was not the only Celtic representative who was there that day and I duly did my little bob, and presented the posy to the wrong guy. Nobody had thought to tell me which one was Sean. Shamed my whole Celtic-loving family that day!

To this day, I wish I could do that presentation over again!

ANNE HEMPHILL, Chislehurst, England

Playing for the jersey

SO there we were ensconced in one of the glitzier hotels in Las Vegas, my husband Dave and me. To us, not exactly affluent, it was going to be the holiday of a lifetime. We were big Bette Midler fans, she would be performing a special Millennium concert at our hotel and so it seemed the perfect anniversary present to ourselves.

"Dave, why don't we wear something cheerful tonight when we go out? I've packed our Celtic tops" Dave agreed.

We headed down to the hotel lobby wearing the tops with a strange mixture of pride and trepidation, obvious pride in the jersey which I always wore to the game, but also that niggling doubt that since I am hardly in the first flush of youth and we were in a strange country, people might think "Mutton dressed as lamb" or "She looks fat in that", you know the kind of thing.

My fears seemed to be confirmed in the hotel lobby. This young chap, one of the desk clerks, kept eyeing us up and down with that look people have when there is something dirty under their fingernails!

"We're probably imagining it" reassured Dave.

But over the next few days, even when not wearing the tops, we could feel those eyes piercing into us whenever we walked through the hotel.

"It's not imagination," concluded Dave, "that young fellow has a problem with us. You don't suppose he's a Rangers fan, do you?" We both burst out laughing.

The next day at the desk this young guy come over and said "Not wearing your top today, sir?" "Here comes the sarcasm," I thought. He leaned forward and whispered into Dave's ear "I'll give you $100 for your top." Dave and I burst out laughing. But this sent the wrong signal to the clerk. "You drive a hard bargain. Okay, $150" Dave declined. "Well, if you change your mind…"

Back up in our room I said to Dave: "Don't be such a cheapskate. Give the lad your top if he likes it that much. You'll easily get another one when you get back home."

I was right, I know, but it did actually conjure up another little niggle I had in my mind. Buying another top would not be a major hardship but as well as that I had promised my nephew that I'd buy his season-ticket for him for his 21st birthday next month and Vegas was stretching the finances a little. However, I was determined to forget about money worries and enjoy my stay.

So I gave the chap, Eddie as it turned out to be, the jersey and I must say it was worth it just to see the look of delight on his face.

As I waited for the lift this deep, gruff voice behind me said: "No wonder you gave away that rubbish top." I turned angrily to be met by a tall, well-built fellow in his late 50s who was wearing a very broad grin. "Only kidding", he added. "Seriously I thought that was a very nice gesture."

He introduced himself as Big Hugh. He was originally from Coatbridge but had lived in Toronto for about 30 years and as an ardent fan tried to get over to Parkhead a couple of times a season. What a pleasant surprise.

It was the night of the Bette Midler concert. The tickets had been on sale for $100, $500 and $1000. We had "pushed the boat out" for two $100 tickets and arrived at the entrance to the arena.

"If you wait here, ma'am, an attendant will take you to your seats" said the guy at the door.

"Where is it?" I enquired.

"Over yonder", indicating the farthest seats from the stage.

I was thinking that I wasn't going to see anything when:

"I'll take care of these folks, Jack," said a steward. "Follow me ma'am".

I looked. It was Eddie, doing a bit of overtime. I hardly recognised him all formal in his tuxedo. As we made our way through the arena I asked: "Are we going the right way Eddie?"

He just winked.

He was taking us right to the front $1,000 seats.

"Your seats folks. You've just been upgraded. Enjoy!"

And we certainly did. Thanks Eddie.

The last day of our Vegas trip had arrived. With a couple of hours to spare before catching the plane, I decided to have a go on the slot machines. And why not? It would have seemed rather odd not to avail myself of the ubiquitous slots. As I sat at a "quarters" slot, I heard this voice from behind me, now recognisable, it belonged to Big Hugh, whom I hadn't seen since I gave Eddie the top.

"Any luck, Betty?" I shook my head.

"Try that one" he almost commanded, indicating the next machine along the row. I took his advice. Just as I was thinking what a waste of time it was becoming, a bell in the machine went off.

A jackpot!

I turned to thank Hugh but he'd gone.

I cashed in the dollars, made a quick mental conversion into sterling, and was amazed to discover I had won almost exactly enough to buy that season ticket present for my nephew and a new top for Dave.

This is a true story. It really happened. Was it a fluke? Just a coincidence? I don't know.

I'll leave the reader to draw his or her own conclusions. But all I want to say is: "Hugh, wherever you are out there, thanks for your part in making our stay in Vegas that little bit extra special and helping me "play for the jersey".

BETTY BREMNER, Elgin

The No.1 team

I've loved them since I was three years old.
They're the ones in Green, White and Gold.
When they win a game it's always the same.
Celebrations going on everywhere.
Celtic are always the team who play fair.
So remember always to support your team.
Especially when they're wearing the Green.

KAREN McCAFFERTY (age 13), Glasgow

My Celtic dream

I want to play for Celtic
The best team in all the land,
I want wee Bobby Petta
To smile and hold my hand,
I want to go to Paradise
And feel the grass beneath my feet,
I want to score the winning goal
That would be so sweet,

I want to wear the famous hoops
And play in Number 7
I want the crowd to chant my name
That would be like heaven
I want Martin O'Neill to watch me play
And send his mind into a whirl,
Enough for him to shout "Hey lads"
I'm gonna sign a girl!!!!

I want the Bhoys to shout yahoo!
And with pride shed a tear,
When every footballer in the land
Votes me player of the year!!!

STEPHANIE CORBETT (age 12), Glasgow (Celtic's first female signing!)

The day I missed Celtic

SINCE I was eight my left eye has been becoming progressively more near-sighted. I was told that if nothing happened to my right eye I wouldn't need glasses until I was 18. Easy enough, just keep my right eye in order. No problem!

Not for me! No, I had to go and stand in the path of a large flying stone! It all began on an ordinary day, in my ordinary life at my (almost) ordinary school, Turnbull High. I was discussing the future of our 5-a-side team with Patrick in the yard. One of our players had quit (and as we all know, 5-a-side teams tend to do better when there are in fact five players). I turned to collect my bag. Then it hit me.

I just stood there, wondering why Paddy was staring at me like that. Then it hit me, a pain so great I could hardly stand. Blood was gushing from my eye (not surprisingly my right eye!) Suddenly, the sky was pink, the ground was green (not the normal colours by the way) and people were just orange lights, gradually fading. I was losing my sight and I knew it.

I didn't know if it would ever return but that didn't matter, it was going now and all I could do was watch (though not literally as my vision was impaired). Luckily, my left eye soon regained vision and I was able with the help of Paddy to make my way to the school office. From there I was escorted to the medical

97

room and told to lie down. Mr McKenna walked in, he was a family friend so I immediately felt safe. He cleaned my eye and stemmed the blood. He then placed a bandage over my eye and told me I was lucky.

"What?" I asked him (before remembering that to have a rock smash into one's eye is the epitome of all the joy in the world). He told me that it was not too serious and I would likely be allowed leave from school for a few weeks.

I, just a young lad, without any care over my education, jumped at that. My mum came and took me up to casualty. I waited around half-an-hour (not bad for an 'inconsequential' injury), the wait, of course, doing wonders for my nerves. I honestly thought I would require major surgery (touching my eye is bad enough let alone cutting it open). I was then taken into the treatment room and was 'given' some yellow drops. I didn't like these as they were inserted directly into my eye and stung quite severely.

The doctor looked at my eye and cleaned it thoroughly. I the made a short trip to the eye department. I was extremely worried, I thought if it had to be referred to a specialist then it was quite serious. I was thirsty and asked if I could buy a hot chocolate, but was told I would be seen soon, so no. Indeed, I was seen a mere two hours later, by a friendly doctor who put more drops in my eye, these ones weren't as painful for some reason.

I was told they were called 'minims' for all I could care. I took my seat in an electric chair, the purpose of which was not to kill me, the electricity merely helped it move so the doctor could examine me closely. There was an eye examination unit attached to the chair, the doctor could move either independently (what a fine health service we have in Britain!). An extraordinarily bright light was shone into my eye. After a procedure of movement and cleaning I was told to return home. Upon leaving I asked if I could go to the Old Firm game that weekend and was told, "I don't see why not" and in truth he didn't, my mum was outside! I had to give my ticket to my sister's friend, Kirsty O'Brien.

I watched it on Sky Sports Extra as digital TV had just been installed in my home. I had really wanted to go to the game, it was the game where we could prevent Rangers winning the league. I was sure that we would lose now that I was not going. Sure enough, we lost and they clinched the league title at Parkhead.

I was very annoyed for about three weeks, not least because I wasn't there. Every cloud has a silver lining (supposedly) and luckily I was fine, no permanent damage. We (Celtic) have certainly came out on top, beating the Gers left, right and centre. I've been able to go to all the games since then, we have triumphed in nearly all of them, and won a Treble since then too, which was nice.

MARTIN CONNOLLY (age 15), Bishopbriggs, Glasgow

PICTURE the scene…Saturday 2.30pm Celtic are playing Rangers at Celtic Park. Three friends (John, Pat, and Gus) enter Ladbrokes bookies at Parkhead Cross which is full of supporters placing their bets. A voice from the crowd shouts, "Gus, how are you doing?" A chap dressed with a green and white hat, a Celtic jersey, a scarf on each wrist and holding the biggest flag you can imagine appears from the crowd, cuddles Gus and says, "Long time no see." Gus replies, "WHERE ARE YOU GOING?" Every punter looked at us and just burst into fits.

WILLIAM FLYNN, Milngavie, Glasgow

Celtic View

From page one to page sixty-four
From the start to the end
I can't take my eyes off those glossy pages.

Celtic View, that's the book for you!

From the facts to the interviews
From the posters to the pictures
From on competition to another
I can't take my eyes off those glossy pages.

Celtic View, that's the book for you!

Junior View is so good
For all fans under 16
From the crosswords to the drawings
Competitions that could win you prizes!
I can't take my eyes off those glossy pages.

Celtic View, that's the book for you!

Adverts that say all sorts of things
From birthday to bands
I can't take my eyes off those glossy pages.

Celtic View, that's the book for you!

I take it everywhere I go, into school,
To the toilet, and even into school.
I can't take my eyes off those glossy pages.

Celtic View, that's the book for you!

When it gets near to the end,
My tears start to come,
I hope I can hold on till the next issue comes,
I can't take my eyes off those glossy pages.

Celtic View, that's the book for you!
All I can do is read the next issue of the *Celtic View*.
OVER and OVER and OVER again......
MEGAN McLAUGHLIN (age 12), St Luke's High School, Barrhead

The big kicker

A breath-taker
A no faker
A goal maker
A nerve-wracker.

A noisy manager
A tense player
A goal swayer
A net shaker.

A heart breaker
A blood stopper
A frantic shooter
A left footer.

A shy thrower
A face glower
A horn blower
A magnificent kicker.

A typical football match.
ROBERT KEAN, Corpus Christi Primary, Knightswood

MY story goes back almost 30 years when I was engaged to a girl called Mary who I am now glad to say is my wife. In those days I was Celtic daft and that has not changed one bit but Mary was not all that bothered about soccer. I talked her into going to see the Tic play Aberdeen at Pittodrie one Saturday.

After boarding our train we reached our destination but then had to board another train which was Aberdeen bound. We tried to get a seat but most of the compartments were full so we kept on walking till we arrived at a compartment where I saw big Yogi Bear standing outside.

I remember him saying, "Can't you find a seat?" and then led us into his compartment which, lo and behold was full of players.

With Mary having long blonde hair and looks to match she was asked by Jimmy Johnstone to come and sit on his knee, which she gladly did to the roar of the rest of the players I think it had something to do with the miniskirt she was wearing.

We all had a good laugh as Jinky began to tell us a few stories but sadly to say it came to a quick end when King Billy McNeill came in and asked us to leave. It's a memory that will live with us forever especially for me as I was standing close to my hero the dear departed Bobby Murdoch.

JIMMY KERR, Forest Lakes, Perth, Australia

Chapter Eight

The Lion Sleeps

Bobby Murdoch was his name, a Lisbon Lion they could not tame
The man was class when he played the game, his like we will never see again
When Bobby Murdoch got the ball,
there was always another lion waiting to maul
Bobby was the first lion to go,
but will always be remembered as a lion who stole the show
Sleep tonight oh Lisbon Lion, for your Celtic will never stop trying.
JOHN BURNS, Roslyn, Pennsylvania, USA

John Hughes

MY abiding memory relates to the most famous match in our history. As someone who was there, my story is not related to either of the two goals. Nor is it the celebrations, or big Billy (forever Caesar) holding the European Cup aloft. It is an emotional Ronnie Simpson crying with shear joy. How well we understood it, because many of us were joining in!

I saw those tears; I was there on the field after the final whistle – along with a couple of thousand others who were unable to contain themselves.

At the final whistle Ronnie had collapsed into the arms of some of his team-mates. He was unable to contain himself – and his tears of joy flowed. Without shame, without embarrassment and without any vestige of self-conscience. Because they were tears of pride.

I had been 'introduced' to Celtic some years earlier by some mates who had talked me into attending a couple of European matches. Up to then, my dad had regularly taken me along to see Clyde. I went from the staid surroundings of Shawfield with an average attendance, in those days, of about 5,000 to Celtic Park with in excess of 50,000 committed and dedicated fans. I was hooked! Later, so was my dad.

In 1967 I was working for the Inland Revenue in Glasgow. Up until two weeks before the match, I had resigned myself to watching the match on TV. Then one of my colleagues was told by his dad, who owned a car business, that he could borrow a car if he wanted to go to the final. The idea was born. We had no shortage of others who were willing to share (we even had to knock back a couple of Rangers fans!) and we soon had a total of five who were desperate to squeeze into a Morris Oxford for the trip to Lisbon.

We set off on the Monday from the old Tax Office in Waterloo Street and broke down before Carlisle! We lost an exhaust in France and spent a very enjoyable couple of days in Nantes (we had beaten their team on the way to the final). The attractions of the local university students who "wanted to practice their English" further delayed us. Five young guys cooped in a car for a couple of days meant that in the heat of south west France we had to smash open a side window which had become stuck. When we climbed the Spanish Maseta, that broken window meant we froze at night. Our delay in Nantes meant we had to drive through the entire day and night before the match. We almost crashed in the orange groves between Spain and Portugal. But we made it – half-an-hour before kick off! The stories of the vast number of fans who made it to the final are NOT exaggerated. It beggared belief. Especially when you take into account that the majority would never before have been out of the UK. The stories about the guys in their working clothes (having come straight from a shift) are not just legend. I saw more than one.

And we saw some sights. Two silver-haired old guys in Lisbon City centre teaching a crowd of bemused Portuguese the Celtic Song. "We'll dae the words first, then the tune. After us now boys – sure it's a grand old team to play for." Their rosy cheeks were more down to inner refreshment than the sunshine earlier in the day! And the locals loved it. I remember we were treated as honoured guests in a local restaurant. It was a holiday (the feast of Corpus Christi) and the restaurants were packed with local people who readily offered up their seats to the Celtic fans. I saw the "Cairo Celtic Supporters" bus. Not full of ex-pat Celtic fans, as you might expect, but packed with swarthy types in full Arabian regalia!

Looking back, I don't remember any feeling of over confidence. But neither was there any trepidation. In any event, we had made it to the final and we were there to show the world what Celtic was all about. The behaviour of the fans was impeccable. The locals took us to their hearts and we reciprocated.

The match was a blur. I honestly remember two incidents, the penalty for Inter Milan and Ronnie's back pass to beat an Inter striker well outside the Celtic penalty area. All of my other memories are based on the subsequent TV footage.

But I remember the final whistle. I remember the Portuguese fans crowding around to shake our hands and to ask for a "Celtic souvenir". I remember the five of us being in a sense of disbelief then erupting in celebration which lasted until well after we returned some days later.

And I remember Ronnie Simpson's tears.

The team called him "Faither". His public persona was professional and undemonstrative; a taciturn character who had seen it all and had the scars to prove it. He had played with many teams and had won two FA Cup medals. But the enormity and achievement of that evening in Lisbon, the sheer cheek of it, the gall, the fact we had no right to be there: it suddenly hit him - as it did us.

Eleven peely wally Scotsmen ambled on to that field to challenge the tall, tanned proponents of the infamous Catenaccio. (This word described a system of defence in depth, which was strangling football in the late 1960s) we were confronted by the footballing aristocracy and were given no chance by anyone outside Celtic Park. We then proceeded to give them a lesson in open, attacking and exciting football. We played football the only way we knew how. We played it the way it should be.

Years later I met Ronnie and reminded him of his (in) famous cheeky backpass when he confounded what had been, until then, the best team in Europe. It was an astonishing demonstration of skill and confidence and it rattled them. Ronnie confided that he would still occasionally wake up in a sweat at the thought of what could have happened if it had gone wrong! But it didn't, and it inspired his team-mates.

The poet Iain Chrichton Smith said it best. "It is very important to me in my poetry that I should be professional in my attitude – and I think MacDiarmid was and Celtic Football Club was". He was, of course, linking professionalism with a poetic and cavalier approach. That was the Lisbon Lions.

Those 11 men became immortal that day. In a sense so did the fans.

But the tears of Ronnie Simpson made him more of a man than most. In that moment he exposed his emotions. He opened his heart and he didn't care who saw inside. The proof was there. I saw it. I am a witness to the man and his emotions. And it will never leave me.

JOHN HUGHES, Bearsden

The case of the missing goal

"GO----AL!", roared close to 60,000 people, as that man Larsson knocked in number three with five minutes to go. That's three more points in the bag. The euphoria was quickly followed by the noise of seats being tipped up and a general exodus form the ground. "Grandda, why are all those people leaving? Celtic might score again, sure they might, Grandda?"

Young Bobby was perplexed. "I tell ye later, son. Wait till the game's over, " said Bobby's grandfather.

As they walked up the London Road, Bobby, decked out in his Celtic scarf and tammy, to protect him from the cold, according to his mother, was intent on his chips. He really looked forward to the homes games, which he was allowed to attend with his Grandda Jim. His mother worried a lot about her only son and did not want him to be going to the away games just yet.

"Maybe next year," she said. The old man, he wasn't really old, but just appeared to the wee boy, remembered the look in Bobby's eyes when he received his birthday present last year – a season ticket!

Jim enjoyed the wee fella's company and Bobby was happy to listen to his grandfather's stories, as long as they were about Celtic! He had heard all about the great games and the great teams of yesteryear – many times. He could recite the team that won the European Cup in Lisbon on May25, 1967. He had even made up a little tune to accompany the litany, "Simpson, Craig, Gemmell, Murdoch, McNeill and Clark, Johnstone, Wallace, Chambers, Auld and Lennox".

He knew all about the other wonderful night when 136,000 people crammed into Hampden to watch Celtic triumph over Leeds to go into another European Cup Final. He never tired of hearing about that goal scored by George Connelly in the 4-0 Cup Final against Rangers or the magical night when the Bhoys won the league in the last game of the season against Rangers with only 10 men!. His Grandda was a great man with the stories.

"Ye were askin' about why a' those folk leave before the end of the game", said Jim. "A lot of people have tae leave early, son. They come from all over the place and they have tae get home." Do they come from England?". Wee Bobby managed to say between munches. England was obviously a long way away. "England?

103

England?" said Jim, "They even come from America tae see the Celtic. We won't leave early, son, don't worry about that. Oh no. I made that mistake once. Never again." Bobby continued digging into the bag of chips, knowing that there was probably a story coming. "I remember, oh aye, I remember alright. It was 1967." Oh yes!it was a story about how Celtic won the European Cup, and maybe Granda's part in the glorious triumph!

"I attended all the home games that season," Jim went on, warming to his theme. "they were great. Henrik would have been lucky to get on the bench in that team".

"Och away, Grandda," complained wee Bobby, quickly coming to the defence of his hero.

"Aw well, maybe no," Jim conceded. "Anyway, what was ah sayin'? Oh aye, whit a team! We won everthin' that year. Ah remember the first Old Firm game that season. We won two nuthin'. Bertie Auld scored in the first minute! Aw, it was just great. I was at all the European games at home. We beat Zurich in the first round. Zurich's in Switzerland," said Jim, who was not entirely convinced of modern educational method.

"Then we beat Nantes home and away," Jim went on. "But it's the quarter final ah was thinking about. It gives me nightmares even yet. We went tae Yugoslavia to play Vojvodina. That's near Russia." Jim liked to show off occasionally. "We got beat there one nuthin' but it was close. They came to Parkheid. What a game that was. There were 75,000 people packed in that night, all roarin' their heads off for the Celtic.

"They Yugoslavies must have been dead scared but they played well. Half time was nuthin' each and we were a wee bit worried even though we had been attackin' all night. Anyway, early in the second half, Stevie Chalmers scored to even things up on aggregate. We kept on at them for the rest of the half but it seemed as if we were goin' to have taé play a third game somewhere neutral. That was the rule then. There was only aboot five minutes tae go an' I thought that ah better go an' get ma bus because there was so many people: it would have been difficult to get home with the big crowd. So, out ah goes and hops right on a bus nae bother. Ah was home dead early an' ah waited up tae watch *Scotsport*, or whatever it was called then.

I can remember the moment clear as day. The game was nearly finished and we got a corner. Charlie Gallagher went to take it.

Now, jist before ah left, I had seen him take a corner, so I said to my mother, that's your great grannie, but you never knew her. Ah she was a great wumman. Anyway ah says, 'oh, I seen that.' And then, miracle! Charlie pops a perfect ball over. Lubo would have been proud o' it.

Big Billy McNeill gets up over everybody, just like in the cup final in 1965 against Dunfermline, and he heads it straight intae the net. Well, ah went crazy, so ah did! We'd won! We were in the semi-final o' the European Cup! And ah had missed the winnin' goal!

Bobby had finished his chips by this time and was agog. He had heard many stories from his grandfather but never before had this dark secret been revealed, and somehow Bobby felt closer to him for revealing this human frailty.

"So ye see, son," Jim went on, "that's why ah have never leave before the end. You could miss somethin' important. C'mon lets get you home for yer tea."

JOSEPH CHALMERS, Roma, Italy

Lions Rampant

Celts wha hae wi' Wallace bled
Celts wham McNeill had often led
On fields across Europe, and Parkhead--
And to victory!

Simpson was there to make the save
Clark and Auld pinpoint passes gave
Craig and Murdoch made runs so brave--
They were sights to see!

The Celtic faithful, their hearts would sing
To see Lennox blazing down the wing
And Johnstone doing the Jinky swing--
Defenders turn and flee!

And now's the day, and now's the hour
See the final battle lour
Down one-nil, but it's no ower--
These Bhoys would never die!

All Scotland's voices sang Hail, Hail
They knew their sons would never fail
The European Cup, the Holy Grail--
Won't be going to Italy!

So see proud Herrera's Catenaccio sour
As we keep comin' at them, ower and ower
Then feel the wrath o' Gemmell's power--
A helpless man, Sarti!

Just one more goal would do the trick
The pressure's on, then a Chalmers flick
The cup is ours! 2-1 Celtic--
The Team of Destiny!

Every cup they entered was clearly theirs
Beating Inter, Partick, the Dons, and Gers--
The Lisbon Lions under big Jock Stein
The greatest team the world's e'er seen!

ALEXANDER D. CARMICHAEL, Denny

A trip of a lifetime

EARLY May 1967 and like all Celtic supporters my thoughts were focused on the forthcoming European Cup final on May 25. Would I be able to see the game on TV? Would I be off duty?

As a Detective with Edinburgh City Police I was not certain what I would be doing in the next two or three days never mind the next week or two.

While reading through the morning papers before going on duty for the afternoon shift, one headline stood out in the *Daily Express*:

'LAST CHANCE TO WIN A TRIP TO LISBON'

I read through the competition details, which offered a three-day expenses paid trip to Lisbon with match ticket courtesy of the *Daily Express*.

With little thought of getting the necessary holiday time off, I filled in the competition form and sent it off.

On reporting for duty that day I said casually to my Senior Officer that there was a possibility I was going to Lisbon and would require the time off.

He replied cynically "You'll be lucky". Little did he know how true those words would be.

Some days later I received a visit from an *Express* reporter who informed me that I was one of 12 lucky readers going to Lisbon.

To say I was ecstatic was an understatement. This only happens to other people.

However, my exuberance was soon to be dealt a mighty blow.

I was informed by my Senior Officer that due to holiday commitments, sickness and court appearances it was very unlikely that I could be granted time off, but he would give it some consideration.

I then thought 'court appearances' OH NO!

I checked my diary and there on May 26, the day after the final, I was due in court as a witness in a major trial. I would still be in Lisbon.

This had completely slipped my mind in all my excitement. Lisbon seemed a million miles away and the trip of a lifetime was almost gone.

But this WAS a 'Trip of a Lifetime' and I was not prepared to give up without a fight.

I approached the Procurator Fiscal and told him of my predicament. He was very understanding and pointed out that I was an important witness but he agreed to look over the case notes and let me know if I could be excused.

My prospects looked brighter when I was advised by my Senior Officer that I could have three days off duty. But what about my court appearance?

The big day was approaching and I had little time to advise the *Express* if I was going to Lisbon or if I would have to pass my prize to a friend.

I again contacted the Procurator Fiscal and he advised me that as he had such a strong case, he was prepared to excuse me from court.

"LISBON HERE I COME"

I travelled to Glasgow and met the other winners in the party, one whom was a Glasgow police officer with a dark secret - he was a Rangers supporter!

His wife had won the competition but being the only female winner she passed the prize to him. I give this Rangers supporter 10 out of 10 for rallying to the cause and his dedication to the green and white, even though it was probably tongue in cheek.

Archie MacPherson, who was on our flight, soon cottoned on to this scoop and mentioned it in his column in the *Daily Mail*.

On arrival at Heathrow we were transferred to the Lisbon Terminal. While standing on a packed airport bus taking us there, I heard a voice BOOM out from the back of the bus.

"Hey Lofty, I know you." The conversation on the bus went quiet. I knew the voice immediately, as would most older football supporters.

I turned round and there sitting beside Kenneth Wolstenholme, one of many media personnel on our flight, was the legendary Bill Shankly.

I had met and befriended the legend on holiday some three years previously. He engaged me in conversation for a few minutes reminiscing about how we played together in the same holiday football team with some success.

The excitement I felt was almost as good as winning the trip to Lisbon. Here was a footballing legend talking to ME in front of the nation's media personnel.

I was honoured and delighted that Shanks had remembered me and spoken to me, could things get any better?

I had won a free tip to Lisbon;

I had met a footballing legend;

They say events come in threes; could Celtic win the European Cup and make it a Treble for me? Well the rest is history.

Celtic won the cup and I and thousands of Celtic supporters partied the night away in the bars and clubs of Lisbon.

On returning to Glasgow I was greeted and congratulated by complete strangers just because I was wearing green and white.

The traumas and excitement of this great event will forever be a highlight of my life and I hope and trust that under the guidance and management of Martin O'Neill and all at Parkhead, another generation of supporters can experience what I can only say was; "A TRIP OF A LIFETIME!"

CHIC O'MALLEY, Penicuik, Midlothian

Lost in a dream

THIRTY-FIVE years ago, in that famous year of 1967, my wife Madge and I lived in a room and kitchen with outside staircase at 11 Blythswood Terrace, Condorrat, an area known in the village as 'The Culsh'.

We were incomers, Madge being originally from Glenboig four miles to the south and myself, a Crojan, being a native of 'The Holy City' of Croy, two miles to the north. Being a fanatical Celtic supporter I was, at the time, lost in the dream of going to the European Cup final in Lisbon. We had only been married for three years and were already the proud parents of two-year-old John and one-month-old Marcella.

My dream revolved around the expected tax rebate for the birth of our new baby daughter; either that or the long shot of winning a competition, together with Jim McGinley's cheap market-niche price for the Lisbon trip.

At the time I was working as a joiner with JB Bennet in Lennoxtown and, on-site, was regularly ribbed about my total fixation about attending 'The Final'. Several on the site already had their arrangements made and insisted on giving me a hard time with the kidding as I was nowhere near managing the trip.

They would bring in all sorts of newspapers containing competitions relating to the Lisbon game, for in my desperation I was trying everything. It went on for weeks.

"Hiv a go at this yin, Sammy."

"You're bound tae win this yin, Sammy."

Time was running out. The beginning of May arrived and one day I had just got home from work as usual and having divested myself of working boots and jacket, I was downstairs at our outside coal-cellar filling a bucket with coal, when I was startled by the approach of a couple of strangers behind me. One carried a camera and the other a little case.

"Excuse me," I said, "Who would you be looking for?"

"Could you tell us where Sammy O'Neill lives?" asked the cameraman.

My heart did a couple of back-flips. "I'm just dreaming," I thought, "I'll wake up in a minute.

"I'm the man," said I, "What's is about?"

"Well," replied the guy, as cool as you like, "don't panic, but you're on the short leet for the *Daily Express* Lisbon Competition."

Now, Madge had already told me that the tax rebate cheque had just arrived and had hardly been worth the posting. She'd been kidding me, for it would, in fact, have covered the cost for two on the McGinley flight to Lisbon.

Anyhow, my heart still thumping like a bass drum, I took the cameraman and reporter upstairs to our wee room and kitchen. As we climbed the outside stair I told the pair.

"Never mind the leet. I'd better be on that plane or your *Express* will have a death on its conscience."

I introduced the visitors to Madge. The cameraman proceeded to snap off a few shots and the reporter took some notes regarding my fanatical support for 'The Tic'. I was very obliging.

Their interview ended with their telling me that the results would appear in the *Daily Express* in a couple of days, then they left.

Although Madge had the dinner ready, I couldn't eat a bite and could hardly contain myself. I asked her how much cash we had, mindful of the fact that this was Thursday, the day before payday.

She delved into her purse and came out with a threepenny bit and an old penny. The rebate cheque could not be cashed until next day. There was only one thing for it.

All I wanted to do in my euphoric state was to exchange my wildly exhilarated mood for a mildly intoxicated mood.

Off I went across the road and tapped my uncle for a few quid before setting off for my mother's house, via the pub, of course, although Madge didn't know the half of it.

The reporter, by the way, had impressed upon me the importance of keeping the whole thing quiet meantime. That would be right! I told everybody in the pub, on the street and at the bus stop. In Croy, the whole clan and all the neighbours were alerted.

On the Saturday morning, I made my usual trek by bus from Condorrat via Croy to Kilsyth for my lift to work in Lennoxtown. All the way, I reveled in the photograph and the list of competition winners in the *Express* under my arm.

At work, my mate, Jim Millar, asked me for a look at the paper. After a bit he looked over.

"Hey Sammy. I see there's an O'Neill among the winners."

I burst out laughing. "Aye, that's moi." I shouted.

After that there were congratulations from all the workmates, Rangers supporters included. In the intervening days, the only talking point, the only reality, was 'The Final'. The prize included flights from Abbotsinch via London to Lisbon and return with three days full board in a good hotel.

The day finally came. On the flight from London, I discovered that co-passengers included Bob Shankly and Kenneth Wolstenholme. We landed at Lisbon and a coach whisked the 12 winners off to our hotel which was situated directly across from Lisbon Cathedral.

As rooms had to be shared, I teamed up with a namesake, Jim O'Neill, from Blantyre. We spent the first day sightseeing and exploring Lisbon hostelries in anticipation of celebrations for the expected victory the next day.

Game day. The 12 Apostles, well-watered, so to speak, boarded the coach to the National Stadium. We had reserved seats and I happened to find myself beside a coloured Hawaiian American of Portuguese extraction. In our ensuing conversation I learned that my new friend had played soccer while in Germany with the US forces. Unfortunately, a broken thigh sustained in one match had put him permanently out of the game.

I will not bore you with a poor personal account of a historic match that has been relived and replayed a million times. Suffice to say that my new mate, Frank Acameda by name, reacted to that infamous Italian penalty goal with his assurance that the game was over and Celtic would now be contained until the final whistle.

That view could not go unchallenged and I proceeded to enlighten Frank about Celtic's renowned resilience and never-say-die attacking capability. Of course my faith was rewarded. The European Cup was going home to Parkhead.

When the final whistle sounded, I mysteriously found myself transported on to the pitch and found myself beside none other than the captain himself - Big Billy.

A photograph in a national daily later provided incontrovertible proof of this. Just as incredibly, I was able to make my way back to my seat where Frank the Yank stared at me.

"How in God's name did you manage to get across that big moat to the pitch Sammy?"

"Whit big moat?" says I, "I never saw any big moat. Hey Frank, did you see me on the pitch beside Big Billy?"

I invited Frank back to the hotel, assuring him that everything was on the house for us. So there was Frank, an obviously coloured gentleman with an American accent among us 12 pasty-faced Scots, sitting down to a free dinner.

The headwaiter could not have helped but notice and pointed out to his junior that there appeared to be a rather obvious extra body at the table.

Well, hands up Guv. Fair cop. Frank agreed to pay up (which he had insisted all along was what he must do). After the meal, Frank waited while we changed clothes, then, accompanied by Tony Barret from the Southside and Frank, I made my way to the reception desk where Tony and I changed a fiver each into escudos.

The bold Frank pulled out his wallet and produced a wad of notes that made our eyes pop. He then proceeded to order a taxi and, en route to his hotel (the best in the city, by the way), he explained that he was in a business partnership in Germany and was worth a few bob.

After he had changed his gear at the hotel, we hit town. Frank took us to a local traditional nightclub where he ordered champagne by the bucketful. We had a fantastic evening such as I am never likely to experience again.

After a few hours we went our separate ways. I was never to set eyes on Frank again, although I still have his business card to this day. Of course, I lost Tony as well, but found many others of the Bhoys with whom I continued to celebrate the night away.

Back at the hotel, I hardly slept a wink, talking and reliving the game with Jim O'Neill. Next day we had some more sightseeing before preparing for the late afternoon flight home.

We arrived back in Glasgow too late for the Parkhead celebrations, but not too late to head into a city pub for the last hour or so.

Only later did I find out it was a Rangers stronghold - but it didn't matter. I caught the last bus home to Condorrat and as soon as I reached the house I was met with the question, "Where's the duty-free from the airport?"

"Whit airport?" says I, "I never saw any airport. Hey Madge, did you see me on the pitch beside Big Billy?" Talk about being lost in the dream!

SAMMY O'NEILL, Condorrat, Cumbernauld

I AM a lifelong Celtic supporter and I am enjoying our current run of form very much, but it would have to develop into something spectacular to outshine my memories of when I was an early teenager. You've probably guessed by now, the period was mid to late '60s...

Saturday at noon and my mum would have pie & beans ready for my dad and me, pies seemed to taste better then. Dad & I would get on the supporters' bus in the centre of Bathgate to the banter of the Bhoys in a sea of green scarves. I don't remember any of the supporters wearing the Hoops then; maybe they were too expensive or just not readily available.

Then it was time to spend a tanner on your sweep ticket for the first goal scorer, oh, the excited anticipation if you drew out Bobby Lennox or Stevie Chalmers! I won first prize of 10 bob two weeks in a row courtesy of those two heroes and was secretly worried in case I won it the next week again as the crowd might turn nasty!

When we reached Paradise, I used to get "lifted ower" the turnstile, but that was only in the very early days, growing up does have its disadvantages. The first thing I would do when we got to our regular space on the terraces was to hunt around for a couple of empty Tennent's Lager tins. These were not particularly comfortable to stand on, but they did raise me high enough to see.

Trouble was that when we scored the crowd swayed so much that I often lost ma tins and I was on the search again! The atmosphere was electric and I loved the songs from the Jungle.

"He's here, he's there, he's every f***ing wherr, feed the berr, feed the berr"…. Big Yogi Hughes, whit a player and the crowd would show their delight when he ran out on a winter's day wearing his gutties (sannies/tennis shoes) as he didn't seem to be affected by the slippery conditions.

Then there was the spectacle that I feel privileged to have witnessed the most amazing ball control on the planet by Jimmy Johnstone. He would dribble past defenders one after the other, and then go back and do it again to shouts of "Ole!" from the crowd.

He would take the ball to the by-line and still manage to get a cross over for Bobby Murdoch or Willie Wallace to nut into the net. Although probably my favourite header of the time was Big Billy McNeill's bullet that gave us a 3-2 win in the 1965 Scottish Cup final against Dunfermline.

I was there! On the Corpus Christi school trip in 1967 I was in Burntisland with my other 14-year-old schoolmates. We knew the European Cup final was going to be on TV, so we summoned up as much courage as we could and went into a pub on the corner of the main street.

After initial disdainful looks from the barman he at last relented and let us watch the match with lemonades and orangeades. The rest of that story you know and we were blissfully happy on the bus home. Our joy must have been intoxicating as we each swore that the barman must have been putting alcohol in our drinks!

ALLAN LAWSON, Edinburgh

Lisbon Lions washed out!

IT was 1967: a year of the highest glory and of the utmost tragedy. I had become engaged the previous Christmas and, as if to celebrate my engagement, the mighty Lisbon Lions turned on a succession of glorious performances culminating in that memorable European Cup win!

Yet this glory and my personal happiness were to combine in an event of unimaginable tragedy. My fiancée's aunt Cissie was in the fortunate position of having vacational employment at Seamill Hydro and often came into contact with the Celtic team.

Knowing of my fanatical devotion to Celtic, she managed to obtain the signatures of the entire team and managing staff on a souvenir Celtic tea towel. So where's the tragedy?

Shortly after our marriage, my new wife was doing the dishes. With no clean dish towel to hand, she searched through the drawers and found – you guessed it – the Lisbon Lions special! Still not disastrous, but my wife was a nurse. No clean towels means a washing was due and the once-used Celtic towel went in with the rest.

The signatures did not survive, fortunately our marriage did. Despite this early setback, we're still happily together 35 years later.

MICHAEL STANNARD-TAYLOR, Mount Eliza, Victoria, Australia

The ballad of the Lisbon Lions

In the capital of Portugal
In the year '67
Many of the Celtic fans
Felt they were in heaven
They came to see their heroes
In the final of the Euro cup
Against Internazionale Milan
Who were sadly one goal up!

They travelled many days and nights
To see the Glasgow Bhoys
When Gemmell found the back of the net
You should have heard the noise
Twenty minutes later
Steve Chalmers hit the spot
We'd already won two other cups
And now we had the lot

Our team was mainly local lads
Like Johnstone, McNeill and Clarke
Wallace, Craig and Lennox too
And Simpson the best keeper on the park
Bobby Murdoch, Bertie Auld
And the big man Jock Stein
No wonder these Lisbon Lions
Were the best there's ever been

About twelve thousand Celtic fans
Were there on May 25
To see the first British team
Lift the cup that day
Then homeward bound to a gala night
Held at Celtic Park
Where even more support was gathered
To party through the dark

The big man and his followers
Couldn't believe their eyes
At last the European Cup
Was home at Paradise
It was a great achievement
How could it ever be beat?
Beating Rangers to win the league
Would be a wonderful feat.

A very short time later
That's exactly what they did!
That year they won everything
And their pride has never been hid
It took almost eighty years
To get to this great place
The pride and the joy on the whole squad
Was on every Scottish face

William Wallace at Stirling
Couldn't invoke such pride
It was a pleasure to be a Scot
Not something you can hide
For every single Celtic fan
The hope is always there
That one day it'll come again
And that feeling's his to share

But, remember dear listener do not forget
We won the European Cup
BUT
Like England in 1966
We will keep bringing it up.
ANDREW CHESHIRE (age 15), Murieston, Livingston

Lisbon, my part in the victory

I RECKON that I was born just at the right time to be a Celtic supporter. I was too young to remember the '50s but suffered enough in the early '60s to really appreciate the good years that were soon to follow. Up till then I had only ever gone regularly to home games although I had been to Ibrox, Hampden, Firhill and even as far as Fir Park! However, in Mr Stein's first full season I started going to every game, home and away. The league Championship was won for the first time in 12 years and soon an exciting European Cup campaign was underway.

It was incredible to think that just a couple of years earlier I had been over the moon at Celtic qualifying for the knock-out stages of the League Cup, something I had never experienced before. Now, here we were on the verge of a European Cup final. I had been to every game played in Scotland that season and I knew that without me in Lisbon, Celtic would not have the same chance of winning. I just had to be there.

The problem was I was still at school at the time and the final was scheduled to play right in the middle of my Highers. As my father was a teacher, I daren't have asked to be allowed time off school for a football match, or so I thought.

May 25 is a date that is etched on every Celtic fan's heart, yet that is not the date the game was originally scheduled for. It was supposed to have been played on Wednesday, May 24 but was switched to Thursday as it was the feast of Corpus Christi, a public holiday in Portugal. That meant it was a holiday of obligation for us in Scotland and no school for me. However, on Friday 26, I was to sit my Higher Spanish. How could I be allowed to go to a game hundreds of miles away the night before such an important exam?

The second leg of the European Cup semi-final against Dukla Prague was played on a Wednesday afternoon. At that time my father was lecturing at Coatbridge Technical College across the road from St Patrick's High School where I was studying. As was often the case, I got a lift home in his car and we had the radio on listening to the game. As the game progressed it was apparent Celtic were going to get through. I can remember clearly where we were when he said to me, "If you are going to Lisbon you better book the flight quickly!" I was allowed to go! It was important that someone from our family would be there and it would be me.

The following lunchtime I went down to the public phone down the road from our school to contact Holiday Enterprises and arrange the flight and ticket. A school colleague, Alex Owens, was also going. A group of our friends were hitchhiking from Baillieston to Lisbon but as Alex had an exam the day before the game, he had to fly like me. He was a year older than me and had just passed his driving test so he would be able to drive us to the airport.

Looking back in time tends to make everything seem wonderful but as I think back to that May morning in 1967, I know it was a bright sunny day. Our first stop was St Andrew's Cathedral in the city where a special Mass had been arranged for those flying to Lisbon. Outside the church, the non-Catholics waited patiently while their mates said their prayers which no doubt included many requests for a favourable outcome in Lisbon. To add to the excitement, this was to be my first ever flight on an airplane. I am sure I was not the only one person in that category. In those days, overseas travel for the ordinary working man was still a novelty.

Lots travelled in suits, shirts and ties, presumably in deference to the importance of the occasion. The flight went quickly and I was soon looking out on the red roofs of Lisbon. After landing I thought I had gone I had gone deaf as my ears were blocked from air pressure on landing. Instead of thinking about the greatest day in Celtic's history, I was worried about losing my hearing. Then from somewhere, I remembered about pinching your nose and blowing. Bang! I could hear again and started thinking about the game.

First of all was a look around the city centre. To someone who had only ever seen cities and towns in Scotland, the place was breathtaking. Wide, clean streets with gardens in the middle of them. There were even flamingos in the park. Soon however, hunger set in and we looked of a place to eat. We certainly had no idea of foreign food, so what should we do? Fortunately, the café owners in Lisbon had done their homework on the visitors from Scotland and we were soon sitting down to a plate of chips washed down with beer.

Then off to the game. We got there early and the first people we met were the hitchhikers from Baillieston. As they told us of their fun on the road I was quite envious but I was glad that my trip home would be more comfortable than theirs. Then the game was underway. Usually, I am very cautious but I just couldn't see Celtic losing this one. That was until Jim Craig pulled down Capellini in the box and Inter were awarded a penalty. There were many who thought it was a bad decision by the referee but I felt it was a penalty.

For a few moments, thoughts of the long journey back to Glasgow and the Spanish exam waiting for me the next day filled my head. Not for long though as the Bhoys took over and threw everything at Inter. At half-time we changed ends and had a great view as Tommy Gemmell smashed in the equaliser. Then, as everyone knows, with just seven minutes left, Stevie Chalmers struck the winner. I could scarcely believe it. The remaining minutes passed in a daze. Celtic were going to win the European Cup. At the final whistle, my companions raced on to the pitch. I was in a daze and stood there trying to take it all in.

After a few minutes I thought I should try and find my mates but when I got to the barrier, a smiling Portuguese policeman, with a gun, 'suggested' I should stay on the terracing. Fortunately I caught up with the others at the side of the park a few minutes later and was given a piece of the turf they had acquired as a souvenir (that was proudly planted in a plant box at my parents' house).

Then the bus trip back in to Lisbon. All along the route we saw locals waving green and white colours. The Portuguese obviously enjoyed the result too. Back in the city centre we grabbed a taxi to the bar where we had arranged to meet the hitchhikers. I had never been in a pub before but as soon as we walked in a pint was thrust in my hand and the atmosphere was one of unconfined joy. Well almost. I can remember seeing two guys sitting at one table looking rather subdued. It turned out that they had experienced transport problems en route and didn't get to Lisbon 'til after the game!

Apart from that however, the place was rocking. I met an Australian who had arrived in Lisbon earlier in the week as part of his overseas experience. He was amazed at the enthusiasm of so many people who were prepared to travel so far to support their team. He was joining in the celebrations as if he had come from Shettleston instead of Sydney!

We couldn't stay long as we had to head back to the airport for the flight home. The bus to the airport was surprisingly very quiet. Possibly because most people were strangers to each other but I also suspect that there was a feeling quiet elation and just trying to take in what had been achieved.

The Portuguese driver tried to get some singing going by offering a microphone but only a couple of people took up the offer and after *Galway Bay* and *Kevin Barry*, we were at the airport. While waiting for the flight I stuck up a conversation with a local in a mix of broken English, Spanish and Portuguese. He had a fair bit of knowledge of Scottish football, particularly the difference between the fans of Celtic and Rangers!

He signed the ribbons on my flag and somewhere in a box in Auckland, New Zealand is a ribbon with 'Celtique 2 Inter 1 25/05/67.' We didn't leave Lisbon until after midnight but at no time was I concerned about my looming Spanish exam. I managed to get to bed three hours before heading for school. As I walked along Muiryhall Street, someone spotted me and soon scores of pupils were at the window waving to me. My brief minutes of fame.

At lunchtime, which consisted of the traditional Scottish fare of Irn Bru and cake, I was surrounded by other pupils eager to hear about my trip and to try and get one of the programmes I had brought back. That night I went to Parkhead for the welcome home party and eventually got to bed early on Saturday morning. Even then I could hardly sleep and the next morning the phone was constantly ringing with friends and relations wanting to know what it was like to have been there. Years later I bumped into a former teacher at Central Station in Glasgow. I remembered his name but I didn't think he would recall me. Then he said, "Yes, you were the one that went to Lisbon."

In the following years I travelled to many more European games but obviously nothing could ever equal the experience of 1967, even if Celtic had been more successful in Europe. Incredibly, it is now 35 years since that wonderful day and my own kids who were brought up in New Zealand still ask about it.

Names like Jimmy Johnstone, Billy McNeill, Willie Wallace, Jim Craig and Bobby Murdoch are as well known to them as Henrik Larsson and Stilian Petrov. They know all the Lisbon Lions who took part and hopefully they appreciate in some way the contribution I made to the victory.

MICHAEL MAHER, Auckland, New Zealand

The winning goal

MY dad told my brothers and I a story of when he was a little boy, both him and his friend went to his auntie's to watch the European Cup final, as he did not have a television. They were both seven-years-old in May 1967. They sat down to watch the most exciting game of their lives, he kicked every ball and saved every goal.

Even the sound of the ice cream van couldn't tear them away from the television. They were given a treat of a glass of coke, no sooner than when they poured it Celtic scored the winning goal. The coke ended up on the ceiling and for 20 years they painted round the coke stain on the ceiling to remind them of that great day.

JENNIFER McMAHON (AGE 10), Greenock

They're coming home!

MUCH has been written, as it should have been, about Thursday, May 25, 1967 and not so much about Friday, May 26, 1967. This was the day reality set in. Yes, we had actually won it. This was the day for the ones who couldn't go; the mothers who were left to watch the children while their husbands were on a mission; the guys who couldn't travel for whatever reason; the 10-year-olds like myself, too young to go but old enough to know this was special.

At 10 I knew time was on my side. My turn would come. This was the day when the rest of us got to see a team return. Our team, the Celtic team formed from homegrown players who 24 hours earlier had held, kissed, drank from, cried over but in the end had won the ultimate club prize. The European Cup was ours and it was on its way to Glasgow. They're coming home and that cup is coming with them.

Friday was a special day. There was no trouble getting up that morning. Couldn't wait to go to school. The sun was shining through the bedroom window. God was happy and why not. There were no video replays, or Sky Sports to show the goals time and time again until you were absolutely saturated with replays from every conceivable angle. No, these were the times when we were working from pure memory and it was in glorious, granular black and white. I had yet to see Stevie get the final touch, for in my mind Bobby had struck the ball and it had flew in. The courageous Sarti was finally beaten into history. I met Gerry McCabe and James McIvor on the way into school. We grinned; you didn't have to say anything. Gerry would go on to play against Bayern Munich in the future but today we were wee boys trying to make sense of what had happened.

It was the effect on grown men that was difficult to comprehend. We had witnessed a range of emotions that West of Scotland men had never displayed in front of us in our short 10 years. Shouting, laughing, crying, hugging, kissing, hollering, random distribution of monies for sweeties, massive evacuation of carry-oots from the Ranche Bar. All on the same night.

The rest of the morning was a blur. School work was not of paramount importance but I'm sure we managed to catch up on the adventures of Dick and Dora. Early in the afternoon there was a knock on the classroom door. A hushed conversation and then teacher said my mum was here to collect me. God what a day to go to the dentist! As usual she never mentioned it in case I done a runner. With a bit of luck it would only be a check up and none of the old gas and blood that I dreaded at that age. Into the sunlight I went where brothers Stephen (seven) and Michael (four) were waiting. It definitely wasn't the dentist, as Stephen at this stage had not attached himself to the school railings. No it was better. Dad had been in contact and the law had been laid down. "Mary, get the boys out of school and take them to Parkhead for the team coming home. They may never see anything like this again." There was no change of clothes, or a Happy Meal at McDonald's. We headed for Celtic Park in school uniform on a red double-decker, the 62 for Killermont St in Glasgow stopping at the DER television rental shop at Parkhead Cross.

We arrived probably late afternoon. I can't be certain but I know we were among the first. We walked into the front row of the old main stand, at no charge, and found a position approximately where Billy Connolly now parks his bum when he manages along nowadays. It is worth remembering that it was a standing enclosure in front of the stand in those days. In other words we had the view!

My mother must have brought something to eat because I don't think we were booked in anywhere for hospitality and I also don't remember passing out from starvation. Slowly but surely the place started to fill up. A BBC camera was set up not far behind us. The legendary George Davidson was shaking hands with anyone who came within touching distance. He seemed a nice old man. In the years to come the actor who played 'Smithy' in *Please Sir* would remind me of George. He seemed a sight more pleasant than that of Peter Thomson who hosted *Sportscene* in those days. I bet he wasn't shaking many hands at Celtic Park.

In the years to come, entertainment would be a common occurrence before the main event and often at half-time. Did David Essex really do the Paradise Windfall one week? That night a fan who had probably drunk his breakfast, lunch and his dinner kept us all engrossed as he climbed a floodlight to tie his scarf around one of the lamps. No bother at all. It was never going to be a night for an unexpected tragedy.

Twilight entered the stadium with the hordes. Some came straight from work immaculately dressed. Some had awoken from the night before and arrived on autopilot in the clobber they had witnessed history being made. I reflected much later in life and wondered if any ordinary fan had left the stadium in Lisbon on the Thursday and made it to Celtic Park on Friday evening before the team arrived. Anyway the atmosphere was building as an accordion band warmed up and a big ugly lorry dressed up for the occasion entered the stadium. I dwelled on these accordion players a while. My father was an accordion player. What he would have given to have led that party around the ground that evening. I looked up and the stadium was bursting with people and anticipation.

Soon… A man who was behind me in the stand and who did not know me from Adam gave me a Celtic top to put on. I instantly grew twice my puny size and it was with no disrespect to the Cadzow St Anne's school uniform. This was seriously the real deal. I wish my dad could see me. Then it happened, an almighty roar from outside the stadium. Jesus they were here! There was no Tony Hamilton for a countdown, no big screens to allow us monitor activities outside the ground. But we knew they were here and the prize was with them. As sure as you knew the presents were downstairs when you woke up on a Christmas morning. The prize had arrived!

Watch the tunnel! Keep your eyes on the tunnel! The Jungle roared and roared as they caught first sight of the team. An explosion of photographic light bulbs illuminated the tunnel area. Waves, salutes, hugs, grinning faces, I looked for the prize but in vain. John Fallon's red hair caught my attention and then it was there in the sky. No doubts about it. Ladies and Gentlemen, for one season only the one and only European Cup held aloft for all to see. I was welling up and I couldn't help it. I dare not look left or right in case mum or the brothers spotted I was gone. But even at 10, I knew I wouldn't be alone.

So they climbed on the ugly truck and paraded the cup and themselves around the stadium in absolute triumph. I don't remember if Big Jock was in the lorry or not. Big Billy at the front with Bobby at his side. Wee Jimmy beside the other Bobby, as you would expect. Wee Bertie in the thick of it and was that Tommy Gemmell or Danny Kaye? Who could tell from here? There were no favourites that night. Simpson, Craig, Gemmell, Murdoch, McNeill and Clark. Johnstone, Wallace, Chalmers, Auld and Lennox They were all special. Guys like Willie O'Neill, Joe McBride, John Hughes Charlie Gallagher and John Fallon had every right to be up there as well. We cheered them around the ground with pockets of fans erupting as the truck passed them and eye contact could be made with someone on that truck. All too soon it was over and it was time to go home. The man took his strip back. I'm sure I said thanks as we glided down the wooden stairs to look for a 62 or 63 bus to Eddlewood. I have no memory of going home probably because my heart and brains were still in Celtic Park.

I look back on that night and ponder. It is never discussed in the context of great Celtic moments because there was simply no game that night; there were no goals to discuss just the chance to say thanks and celebrate something utterly remarkable. But it still stands alone as a unique occasion because we were first and we have never again had the chance to repeat such an evening. I am now 45-years-old and I still wait for my turn. Time is still on my side. I am lucky in that although I wasn't there when they won it in '67 but I was there when they came home. It's not the worst consolation prize that was ever handed out. But, oh how I yearn for my turn to see them win that cup again.

JOHN McGURK

Chapter Nine

Jock Stein

MY story is not really my story, but one of which I will always remember until I die. It all start's in a little mining village on the outskirts of Glasgow a few years ago. My grandfather at the time was a young man who played football in the public park with all the other miners from the town. They had their own teams and had competitions like most small towns of that time. The village I'm talking about is Blantyre, a busy little place with all the mining work going on in and around that whole area.

On a bitterly cold Saturday morning, his team was getting together for a game but they were a man short. At this time in the morning there was only one guy in the park waiting for the game to start, he was standing by the line. My grandfather says he was a big man so the put him in goals as he had no strip and my grandfather who was the goalkeeper played in defence. The game finished with them being beaten 2-0.

After the game the big guy who was I goals come up to my grandfather and introduced himself as Jock Stein.

HUGH ROONEY, Bromley

DID you know that Jock Stein handed over the Celtic team in 1974 to a man called Danny McGalpine from Dumbarton? Danny McGalpine is now dead 18 years. While he was alive he looked after Dumbarton teams such as the Phoenix, the Dumbarton Castle Rovers and Dumbarton United. He put in 35 years of his life just to see young guys play football. While he was alive there was a fire in Bellsmyre, Dumbarton, when a whole family - the Dowds - were killed.

Danny McGalpine wanted to do something to help in this terrible tragedy so he phoned Jock Stein and asked if he would help to raise money for this family. Jock wanted to know what he could do and Danny asked if Celtic could come and play Dumbarton. Jock agreed. The Celtic team came to Dumbarton FC and played that night. This shows you what kind of man Jock Stein was to bring the Celtic team to Dumbarton and help a family he didn't even know

The next part of my story is the part that I love. Danny said to Jock, it's time to get your team ready to which Jock replied, "My job was to bring Celtic to Dumbarton. The Celtic team is yours tonight, Danny. You go and get your team ready." I believe Bertie Auld and Danny got the team ready for their night in Dumbarton. To this day, there's a testimonial played in Dumbarton every year called The Danny McGalpine Testimonial.

With your permission I would like to say that Danny McGalpine looked after Celtic for one night. This would be a great way to think back on his dedication to Dumbarton football. I have the photo of Jock Stein and Danny McGalpine on the pitch that night and I believe there should be a place in Celtic Park for everyone to see the kind of things that Celtic are prepared to do, to come to Dumbarton to help the Dowds family.

DANIEL McGALPINE jnr, Benoni, South Africa

The Big Man

FORTY-EIGHT years ago, whilst a young student at the Glasgow College of Art, I procured a Saturday morning job with a large art store, delivering packages of materials around the city. One Saturday morning as I staggered along the busy Argyle Street laden with dozens of parcels, I tripped on the kerb, scattered my unbalanced load all over the pavement. Many passers-by enjoyed a good giggle at my predicament. Red with embarrassment, I began to gather the assorted shapes and sizes, laying them in a position from which I might be able to lift and carry them.

A massive shadow blocked out the sunlight above my head, and in a soft, gentle voice, a giant of a man said: "If you stand up and hold your arms out, I'll stack them neatly for you."

I stood in open-mouthed awe as the big man, with a calm efficiency, interlocked the packages into a tight, manageable unit, suitable for carrying. He smiled warmly, asked if I was now "alright", patted me on the shoulder, winked and then strolled away. Hardly able to croak a "thank you", I blushed a brighter scarlet as my hero departed. The big man was Jock Stein, captain of Glasgow Celtic, the team I supported with fervour bordering on mania. I would cheer him later that day and on many an occasion thereafter.

For a few moments, I had been close to the man who would one day revolutionise football, and experienced the first of my opportunities to appreciate the warmth, courtesy, compassion and intelligence of a person who would be known world-wide as 'The Big Man'. As an impressionable youth, I carried the memory of that incident with me for a long time; 13 years later I would return the compliment, but I mustn't get ahead of myself.

A year or so after our 'meeting', Jock sustained an ankle injury that ended his career as a Celtic player, but not before he captained Celtic to win the Coronation Cup, the competition held between the top teams of England and his beloved Scotland in honour of the new queen, Elizabeth. The fortunes of Celtic declined after he left, with the club and its supporters yearning for a return to the glory days. The years passed and success continued to elude us. It seemed to me that I would have to sustain myself with dreams of the famous Celtic teams of the past, that fate had decreed we would never again be among the trophy winners.

But fate had decreed no such thing; indeed, fate was about to deliver us with a veritable deluge of trophies and, in my opinion, the greatest team manager in football history – Jock Stein. The big man had spent some years in the wilderness. No longer able to play among the elite, his passionate love of football eventually took him to play for a minor team in the Welsh Valleys among the mining fraternity, people who had so much in common with his own Lanarkshire mining family, a heritage he was immensely proud of. All his life he had studied the many facets of the game – its basic moves, its tactics, the variety of skill factors required to produce a balanced team and, importantly, how to motivate individuals into 'team' players.

At last the time was right for Jock to test his theories, to put into practice those valuable lessons he had learned as a player. He returned to Scotland as manager of Dunfermline, an unfashionable 'little' team from Fife. In a matter of months, he had moulded them into a team capable of competing with the best. Suddenly the players had a belief in themselves, a belief that took them to Hampden where, before a crowd of over 100,000 spectators, they won the Scottish Cup for the first time in their history; their opponents – Celtic.

I stood in the Celtic End of the stadium, stunned at the quality of Dunfermline's play. How could a team devoid of any 'real' stars outplay the mighty Celtic, a force expected to sweep them aside and add to their record collection of Scottish Cup wins? I knew the answer, of course, as did every spectator present – The Big Man was back and his influence was startlingly obvious.

A year later, Hibernian beckoned and Jock moved the few miles from Dunfermline to Edinburgh. Again, his management skills shone like a beacon, lifting his new team to heights they could only previously have dreamed of, including a win over the legendary Real Madrid, five times winners of the coveted European Cup.

My jealousy knew no bounds; Jock was a Celtic man, why wasn't he weaving his magic at Parkhead? Well... destiny called him home and I yelled for joy at the news that he had returned to manage the club he once captained. I knew his previous triumphs were but rehearsals for the greatness that fate had decreed for him. He was back where he rightfully belonged – at Paradise. The change in the club's fortunes was instant and dramatic, the attitude among the players and fans changed from hope to belief, a belief that The Big Man would restore Celtic to its pre-eminence in world football.

History shows that he took a squad of local boys and moulded them into one of the greatest football teams the world has ever known. They had skill, flair and the competitive hearts of lions, but they lacked discipline and leadership. Jock provided that leadership, he made them believe in themselves, made them believe that they could compete with the world's best and defeat them.

On May 25, 1967, I stood on the slopes of Lisbon's Estadio Nacional. My beloved Celtic had won all four of the domestic competitions they had entered that season but this was the 'big one', this was the European Cup final, the world's premier football competition. No British team had ever won it; indeed, no British team had ever reached the final. Could Jock Stein outwit the vastly experienced Helenio Herrera, manager of their opponents, Inter Milan, twice winners of the trophy? Could he find the tactical blend that would breach the infamous Catenaccio, Inter's ultra-defensive 'closed bolt' playing system that was strangling creative play throughout Europe? The answer was 'Yes!'

Celtic won convincingly and with a display of attacking football that was almost frightening in its intensity; they proved to a watching world that negative defensive play could be overcome, that intelligent attack really was the best method of defence. As I celebrated with my friends later, we raised a glass in honour of Big Jock – tactical genius, the man who had led our team to European glory at the first time of asking.

Unbelievably, in the Lisbon Airport departure lounge, I found myself sitting next to Helenio Herrera. He willingly autographed my match programme and told his dejected team to do likewise. Back home, I knew I could obtain the autographs of the Celtic players and, hopefully, Big Jock. What a unique memento that would be of the greatest match in the club's history.

It was the measure of the man that, despite managing a world-class club, he took his side to play in a fund-raising game for Ashington, a non-league mining village team in north-east England. There, I was to return the compliment of so many years before.

As his players showered in the tiny, makeshift dressing room after the match, I saw him struggling outside with a massive hamper containing the team strips. As I helped him carry it on to the team coach I spoke to him of the incident when he helped me. Not only did he recall the event; he even remembered the street corner where it took place. After a brief chat, he signed my Lisbon programme and I shook hands with my boyhood hero, now a legend in his own time. As the coach departed, I marvelled at the humility of the great man, who I was privileged to meet on a few more occasions.

At a football function a couple of years later, he recognised me and came over to chat. We discussed the forthcoming two-leg European Cup semi-final that Celtic would soon play against the English Champions – Leeds United. By then he knew that my love of the club matched his own and he listened intently to some observations I had made about the Leeds style of play that could be exploited.

He asked me to put my suggestions in writing and send them to him at Parkhead. Once again we shook hands as he winked, patted my shoulder and moved back to rejoin the function organisers. Proudly, I watched Celtic win both semi-final matches. Again, The Big Man had won the battle of tactical wits, this time against Don Revie, manager of Leeds and soon to be manager of England. During those games, my observations were accommodated on the field; whether or not Jock had been aware of them anyway, I shall never know, but I would like to think that I might have contributed in some small way to those victories.

Jock led Celtic to a world record-equalling nine successive league titles and many other trophy wins before accepting the ultimate honour – the task of managing Scotland. That he took our small nation into the World Cup finals twice came as no surprise to anyone. Sadly, he died during that second great achievement, right there in the football arena with his players.

Perhaps destiny had decreed it as a fitting end to the man who had contributed so much to the game. In this, the 35th anniversary of our famous European Cup win, when his Lisbon Lions swept all before them, my mind goes back 10 years, to May 25, 1992.

Then, I was selected as the only fan to appear on the BBC programme 'One Afternoon in Lisbon', released to honour the memory of that great occasion. I also featured in the club's official 'Lionhearts' video that year, when my Lisbon match programme containing the signatures of both teams and their managers, was highlighted. I was proud, indeed honoured, to pay my own personal tribute then, to my boyhood hero and 'secret' friend – Jock Stein, master tactician and Big Man in every way.

RONNIE CAMPBELL, Roundhay, Leeds

THIS story is one of my best and worse memories of visits to Celtic Park. It all started on a Saturday Morning in August 1976, when as a boy of 13, I was round at my mate's house to find out the day's itinerary. Big Gowser was our leader and what he said went, and what went that day was him and another of our gang going to Parkhead with Gowser's big brother Frank. I was devastated...why not me?

We'd been to many, many games together, but this other guy, Martin, had a big cousin on the same supporters' bus as Gowser's bruv, the All Saints (far from it!) which left from Govan every Saturday. I was well bombed out. Returning home, slightly miffed, I was met by the usual "Where's your mates? Why are you hanging about the house" This brought on a deluge of tears and tantrums when I explained I had been "Benched".

Now my Dad was not a regular at Parkhead, but after hearing my tale of woe, decides, "I'll take you! gimme peace!" "Gimme peace!" I would have given him a kiss but I was 13 you know! So striding back round to where the boys where gathered I proclaimed "am gone to the gemme way ma da, you can stick the bus up..."and declared myself a dissident and lone wolf. So off we set, my dad and I to the opening friendly of the new season, Celtic v Penarol from Uruguay. After the obligatory 15 minutes standing outside the pub, well dad really had to see this guy about none of MY business!

We arrived at Parkhead a little early and got into a good position at the Celtic End. I had one eye on the game and one eye on the right-hand corner of the terracing, known as the 'telly' corner with the cameras positioned above the Jungle. If a corner was awarded there was a fair chance you could end up on the television that night and you were made for life, and of course, that's where the boys would be... 10 minutes into the first-half I spied them. "Dad, can I go and see the boys, down there?" I suggested.

My dad was now in conversation with a guy and gave me strict instructions to return to him at half-time... I stood with Gowser and Martin as we jostled with the other wannabes for prime television exposure. Come half time I turned to look up for my dad and there was a sea of heads." I need to go and see ma da, be back shortly," I said as I barged my way through the budding TV stars. I was sure I knew where he was.

Returning to the corner boys I said, pitifully.,"A cannae find ma da" to which came the reply "he was doon here lookin fur ye" After I'd steadied myself I came up with a gem "It's okay. If I don't find him before final whistle I can come home on the bus" nerves getting the better of me, I'd forgot my oath earlier in the day. Gowser hadn't. Quick as a flash he hails a policeman, going round the track "This boy's lost his da!"

This boy! I'd been a neighbour and compadre since birth! This was clearly vengeance on my earlier slight on the supporters' bus. So the policeman motions for me to come on to the track. I had to, he was a policeman. I was escorted along the trackside by this towering bobby, who was rather unsure of the situation, and with calls from the stand of "let him go!" and "Is that the best you can do!" grabbed me very tightly by the cuff as if I was arrested.

We passed the Celtic dugout and - this picture will stay with me forever - Big Jock Stein looked right at me, shook his head and muttered something to the tracksuit beside him and shook his head in disgust. OH NO HE THINKS I AM A HOOLIGAN (at aged 13 I was 3foot 11inches and weighed in at 4 stones).

The usual announcement was probably made, I heard nothing from deep in the bowels of the stadium. Dad must have got pelters when he returned home....

Childless. Because he picked me up in the car (no post-match pint for him!) from Baird Street police station before I could finish the tea and cake I was given and I missed the end of Spartacus which was on the station's TV. My Father died March 10, 1980, and I hope when he met Big Jock he put the record straight.

JOHN DURKIN, Craigton, Glasgow

How would you like
to be Celtic boy?

IT was 1968, I was 10, standing outside Easter Road (visitors' end), and I was Celtic daft. In those days the *Celtic View* had a feature called 'Celtic Boy', which chose a boy at random from the crowd each week, then each month's lucky lads would be invited to Celtic Park for a tour and free seats in the stand for the boy and his parent/guardian. As my dad had died, my cousin James was elected to take me through to Glasgow.

My memories of meeting the Lions, Mr. Mochan, Mr. Stein and the tour of the trophy and dressing rooms will never fade. James, who was 10 years older than me, nearly fell off his seat when Big Jock said to him, "It's a great day for the laddies." James and I had a reunion for our 40th and 50th birthday as our families gave us VIP package tickets as presents. Harald Brattbakk scored four goals that day, and we emptied Fergus' wine cellar.

ANTHONY HARRIS, Prestonpans, East Lothian

MY story concerns the great Jock Stein and the fact that he often said the punter always comes first. Well, he proved it to me in the early '70s. I travelled that day with my uncle, Harry Dempsey and cousin, Iain Young to a home league match against Hibs. It was a good day and we had a fabulous time in the Jungle cheering the Bhoys on to an odd goal victory. When the game was finished we tramped back to where Harry had parked his car.

When we arrived he realised he had lost his car keys. When we thought about it we reckoned the keys had probably fallen out of his trouser pocket when Celtic scored the winner and we three jumped up and down in celebration. We therefore trekked back to Parkhead and approached the big front door entrance. As we walked in we noticed Jock Stein standing against the opposite wall deep in conversation with a guy who looked like a reporter and an old gentleman (Jimmy McGrory) approached us to see if he could help. We told him about our lost keys and he told us to hang on.

After a few minutes Jimmy came back from the office area with a very large door key. I think he was a bit hard of hearing then or he had misunderstood what we had said. I could see out of the side of my eye Jock Stein, although still talking, was watching every move. When he saw our heads shaking he excused himself to the reporter and walked across towards us.

"What's wrong lads, can I help you?". We told him about the lost keys and he said, "Do you remember where you were standing?". We said yes and he said,

"Come on then". We then proceeded to walk down the tunnel with Jock Stein talking to him about the game. What a feeling of elation for three guys who had supported Celtic all their days and now to be walking down the tunnel with the man who had recently brought the European Cup back to their beloved Parkhead, the first British manager to do so.

Jock went back up the tunnel and we ran across the park and there were the keys lying right where we had been standing. We came back up the tunnel and into the office area where Jock was back talking to the guy he had left to look after us. He shouted to us "did you get them lads", we said yes Jock and walked out the front door thanking our lucky stars that in inadvertently losing the keys we had met and spoke to the Great Man who proved he practiced what he preached. For a few years after this I used to cheat in my local when the standard trick football questions came up.

Mine was - what uncle and two nephews ran down the tunnel with Jock Stein in a game against Hibs in the early '70s - needless to say no one ever got the answer.

BOBBY DEMPSEY, Milton of Campsie, Glasgow

MY granddad played for the Irish league team many years ago. He was a right full-back. When he was playing against the Scottish League team. He came up against, in his eyes, the best Celtic player ever - it was Jimmy Johnstone.

My granddad was giving him a rough time. At this time Jock Stein was the manager. Then my granddad shouted to him: "Take him home before he gets hurt," and Jock Stein wasn't a happy man so he complained to the Irish FA and my granddad got banned for three weeks for unprofessional behaviour.

GARRY DUNNE (age 14), Dublin

The Glory Bhoys!

JOCK STEIN is as much a part of Celtic's present as its past. It was the first time in Celtic's by then 110-year history that any terracing or stand in the ground had been named in honour of one individual. Twenty years after Jock Stein's final departure from the club, his widow, Jean cut the ribbon to formally open the new building.

That warm afternoon, the Celtic fans spontaneously broke into 'Jock Stein, Jock Stein' a gentle, respectful chant of appreciation for the man who gave much of his life to the club. Their thankful gesture showed how the significance of Stein's time as manager remains firmly thought of in the heart and minds of all those with a Celtic connection. The West Stand was the final part in the construction of the new all-seated Celtic Park, which is entirely unrecognisable from the basic stand and terraces that Stein looked out on when he took control at the club in 1965.

Yet while the supporters' surroundings may have changed, the emotional links between their club's past and present are continually reinforced, most particularly by their awareness of Jock Stein's magnificent achievements. Stein could be hard on his players but his integrity was such that he could not be accused of any motivation other than attempting to get the best for Celtic Football Club. A glance at Celtic's exceptional league and cup winning record under Jock Stein shows the virtues of his methods. Tough, hardened footballers who played under him for years and years talk of the manager's aura and of his charisma. Jock Stein's time at Celtic Park is continually a fresh source of fascination.

ROSLYN ADAMS, St Paul's High School, Glasgow

That number seven

What about that number seven
Flying down the wing
Jinking round the opposition
Made us want to sing
Right before our very eyes
Flying feet that mesmerise
There really could be only one
Who else but Jinky Johnstone

What about that number seven
Preying round the box
Alert and always on the ball
He shakes off all the knocks
Heart of a lion, nerves of steel
Mark him closely, or away he'll peel
Heading goalward, what a shot
Henrik Larsson's got the lot

What about that number seven
Leaping from the bench
Yelling his instructions
(Sometimes sounds like French)
Jumping high when Celtic score
Who could ask for one thing more
Than how our manager makes us feel
The one, the only, Martin O'Neill

What about that number seven
Overlooking Celtic Park
Decked out in the best of linen
Place to party when we're in heaven
The place to dine, the place to be seen
Where we'll enjoy the best cuisine
And fill our glasses, raise a toast
To those that we admire most

VAL McCAFFERY

126

Chapter Ten

Some man, the Jinky

JUST as it was getting to the stage where things couldn't get much worse. McKenna sliced off the lid of his digit and bled all over the lunch. It was a tin of sardines. He had been trying to open them with a Swiss Army knife and a sandy boulder. The boulder kept disintegrating, causing his concentration to err, and off went his fingertip, taking with it the last chance of sustenance for the foreseeable future.

In time, the wound would recover, but there were more immediate concerns. It was stifling. We had no water and, now, we had no food to go with it. I felt like I was stuck in a lift. Taking a deep breath, I reflected on the situation.

We were sitting by a slip road on to a motorway, halfway to the middle of nowhere in the Basque heartland. We were supposed to be in Greece, but had stumbled across a one-way ticket to Madrid for £37, a price too good to be overlooked. That it was at the opposite end of Southern Europe to where we wished to be was of no consequence. We would simply work our way there. Looking at it with an optimistic eye, it was part of the adventure we had embarked upon.

Three days into this wonderful adventure, we were hungry, thirsty, bored, increasingly anxious and exasperated. The heat was intolerable. McKenna, more than once during the course of the day, had referred to his "peeling, boiling head." The tension had been rising since early in the afternoon and we were starting to get on each other's nerves. Here we were, under a baking sun, drowning in the misfortune of circumstance and acquaintance. It seemed only a matter of time before we were engulfed in a sudden eruption of fisticuffs.

"Knowing our luck the only car to stop will be the stock car psycho," said McKenna glumly. Ah, the stock car psycho! Our encounter with him, only a matter of hours earlier, seemed long ago. Then, things had looked so promising...

No sooner had we stuck out a thumb than a battered old car pulled up, throwing open a door. We mentioned the name of a town and the moustachioed driver nodded, gesturing for us to get in. We quickly realised that small talk was useless. The driver ignored all attempts at conversation. Yet, glad of our good fortune, McKenna and I relaxed and looked out of the window.

Suddenly, and without warning, we were interrupted from our meditative state and flung all over the place. The driver was executing a manoeuvre that would be illegal in most countries. He was crossing the central reservation at high speed, hanging off the sleeping wheel. For balance, his head was pressed against the side window. I was sprawled in the back, from where I could see a look of utter terror on McKenna's face.

There was a dream-like quality to the sequence of events, from the vegetation brushing the window as the driver fought to remain on the road, to the pressure of gravity pinning me to the chair. It reminded me of the first time I had gone on the Waltzer with a drink in me. The whole thing had taken me by such surprise that I found myself in a fit of laughter. Luckily, my fellow traveller had a much more sensible head on his shoulders. Immediately the car straightened up, McKenna launched a verbal assault on the driver, demanding that he stop forthwith and allow us to remove ourselves at our leisure. This urgent request seemed to fall on deaf ears, not to mention psychotic eyes. Our moustachioed friend turned his peepers in McKenna's direction, simultaneously curling his hirsute upper lip, and the physiognomic result terrified McKenna to such an extent he made a grab for the steering wheel.

As reward for this bold initiative, McKenna received from the picaroon's fist, a stunning blow to the head. This, coupled with the demented howling emanating from the driver, convinced me of the seriousness of the situation. I leaned forward and covered the kidnapper's eyes with my hands. With his foot still on the accelerator, he removed his hands from the steering wheel and grappled with mine. Ever alert, McKenna delivered a telling blow to the driver's testicles with a 1.5 litre plastic bottle of water, applied with rapid velocity and deadly accuracy.

Our sightless, winded friend was in no position to argue as, for the second time, McKenna took a grip of the wheel. This time, in conjunction with a sharp application of the brake, he managed to bring us to a halt at the side of the road. Grabbing the key from the ignition he hurled himself out of the passenger door into the dirt, where he was joined in an instant by the rucksacks and yours truly.

It was at this point that my now piebald friend, his eye coming up an intricate bluey shade of black, announced with some dismay: "The water! I lost it in the scramble."

Lacking options, we put on a brave face. There would surely be a town not too far away. Some hours later, with the sun a formidable presence above our melting heads, we stumbled across our present position, under a tree by the slip road.

"How hot?" asked McKenna, gasping.

"Nineties," I ventured.

"Wouldn't like to see it in the hundreds," he replied, with a weary shake of the head and an agitated eye. The essential requirements for short-term survival were beyond us.

After some hours, we were granted a glimmer of hope. A car stopped. By the time we had lugged our rucksacks into touching distance, the driver changed his mind and screeched off. McKenna and I walked back to our base below the tree in silence. Perhaps the driver had reconsidered when he saw the state of us in the mirror, or it could have been a joke all along. Whatever, the wheels had come off our sense-of-humour bogie and run into a stagnant pond.

Desperation was beginning to rear its head. Conversation was minimal. We were dehydrated, starving and suffocating in each other's company. Words could have only made it worse. It came to me that to look less filthy might prove to our advantage. As I rummaged in my rucksack for something clean, a light-bulb went on in my head. The Hoops! Of course!

I pulled the Celtic jersey over my head. "Don't tell me, you're working on a plan?" said McKenna sarcastically.

"They like their football here," I said. "You never know."

I stood up, shielding my eyes against the now low sun. A car drove past. It was nothing new. Cars had been driving past on a regular basis. This one pulled in about a hundred yards up the slip road and flashed his lights. McKenna and I watched without moving. The lights flashed again.

"It could be for real this time," I said.

"But then again..." countered McKenna.

The rear lights of the car came on, indicating a reversal. Slowly, McKenna got off the ground and we stood in silence watching the car coming towards us. The driver's demeanour was friendly.

"Hola!"

"Eh...Hola!"

"Johnston," he said.

"Por favor?"

"Johnston." He nodded at the Hoops.

This perplexed me. The year was 1991. For two years, the mention of the name Johnston had led to much confusion and anger. Everywhere you went, people wanted to know what you thought about the unfathomable volte-face. It was a terrible event, which had followed me to Spain.

"M...M... Mo Johnston?" I asked, hesitantly.

"No, no, no, no, no, no," tutted the driver. "Johnstone, Johnstone." As he said the name, he worked a squiggly line in the air with his finger. "Johnstone."

"Jimmy Johnstone!" I shouted.

"Jeemy Johnstone! Si! Si! Jeemy Johnstone, " replied the driver.

We shook hands and jumped in. The driver had a cooler with beers and a couple of sandwiches in it. He told us to help ourselves. He was a Real Madrid fan. They were the team he'd supported as a boy, and he still went to as many of their home games as he could. When he was younger, he went to every game. He'd watched the great players; Puskas, Gento, Del Sol, Canario, Santamaria ... He saw them winning European Cups by the handful. But, then he stunned me.

At the Bernabau in '67 for Alfredo di Stefano's testimonial, he watched the newly crowned Kings of Europe putting on a show. He said it was a great game, a fantastic occasion. That night he saw "Jeemy Johnstone" run riot. His performance was a work of art, a magical thing that he had never forgotten. Jimmy Johnstone, the number 7, was a football genius... And this from a guy who had seen it all! From that night on he had supported the Celtic. I was astonished. McKenna was agog.

"Jimmy Johnstone, well I never," he said.

Some way towards revitalisation, I took another beer, smiled and shook my head. Some man, the Jinky; not only a legend, a lifesaver too. From the edge of a nightmare, he had come flying in from the wing, dropped his shoulder and scored the hitchhiker's equivalent to a last-minute winner.

TONY CLERKSON, Chiswick, South London

A FEW years ago, when Paolo Di Canio was a Celt, me and a few pals were in a pub up at Dundee having a few refreshments before the game. We noticed some guys in the corner were filming us, with a camcorder. After much deliberating we decided to ask them what was going on? We soon realised the guys were Italian, so the penny dropped: "Are you here to see Paolo Di Canio?" I said.

"Oh, no," the guy replied. "I'm his brother!"

PAUL DALY, Renfrew

Chloe's dream

CHLOE WHITFIELD banged the mouse hard off the computer table. "Why me! Why me?" she shouted. She had been on the computer for hours but had had no success.

Chloe Whitfield lived in Surrey, England. For months she had been searching and searching for a football club that would coach girls and take them to tournaments and festivals but there seemed to be none in her area or even anywhere near her town.

"Chloe" shouted her mum, Sophie, from the kitchen "That's long enough on the computer for today."

"Okay" replied Chloe and dragged herself away from the computer.

"Tomorrow," she told herself "Tomorrow."

Chloe got changed and climbed into bed.

"Night mum." She called downstairs.

"Night Chloe." Replied Sophie.

The light bulb pinged on.

"Come on Chloe. Time to get up." Said Sophie cheerily.

"Whatever" mumbled Chloe. She hauled herself out of bed and pulled on her red and blue uniform for Woodhill Primary. She finished her breakfast, grabbed her bag and ran out the door to catch the bus.

"Cheerio mum!" she called back over her shoulder.

"Bye love!" replied Sophie.

She leapt off the bus and ran up the path to school. But she banged into her worst enemy Christine Thompson and her two weak followers Debbie Pierson and Julie Fisk.

"Where you off to in such a hurry Chloe?" questioned Christine.

"The class" replied Chloe firmly.

You could see by Christine's face that Chloe had angered her but Lucy Spear, Chloe's best friend, ran up behind Chloe. Christine and Julie walked away but Debbie had to have the last words;

"Just you wait till break," she said "Just you wait." And with that she hurried off after Christine and Julie.

"What was that all about?" asked Lucy.

"Don't ask." Replied Chloe.

"So any luck with the football?" questioned Lucy.

"Not yet. But I have a funny feeling that today is the day."

"You always have that feeling!" laughed Lucy as they lined up to go up to class.

"It doesn't matter how long it takes, one day I will get us a coach and a team." Said Chloe firmly.

In class their teacher, Mrs Key, gave them maths again! But at playtime Christine and her crew were going to try to get Chloe again.

"Not this time" Chloe thought to herself. At break as Christine, Debbie and Julie approached Chloe Christine went to say something, but Chloe just turned her back rudely and walked away humming.

"That's it!" roared Christine as she stormed after Chloe. But Maria didn't know that Chloe was heading for Mrs McAllister's office.

Christine grabbed Chloe as she spun around. But just as she was about to hit her Mrs McAllister burst out of her office, "CHRISTINE THOMPSON! GET INTO MY OFFICE NOW!" roared Mrs McAllister. "Don't worry Chloe I don't think they'll be bothering you again." With that she smiled then walked into her office and slammed the door behind her.

At the end of school Mrs Key held Chloe and Lucy back after the bell.

"I have good news for both of you." She implied. "My husband was talking to one of his work mates and he mentioned a trial for the Celtic junior girls."

Chloe's face lit up more and more as Mrs Key continued:

"He gave a date and a place and my husband has offered to take both of you in two weeks! So what do you say?" she said cheerfully.

"We say yes!" they chorused.

"Well that's that sorted. A letter will be sent home informing both of your parents."

"Thank you Mrs Key!" they said together and ran out of class. The moment they got out the door Chloe jumped up and punched the air with joy;

"What did I tell you! I knew today was the day!" she boasted "I just knew!"

"MUM! MUM!" blared Chloe as she burst into the house "MRS KEY GOT LUCY AND I INTO THE CELTIC JUNIORS TRIALS!!"

"Calm down Chloe! No need to be so loud!" laughed Sophie.

"When do you go?"

"I don't know yet Mum. Mrs Key is going to get the school to send home a letter!" said Chloe excitedly.

Through the next two weeks Chloe and Lucy couldn't sit still for one minute and every day after school Lucy went to Chloe's house and they practiced and practiced and practiced.

Finally their big day came. Chloe was up at 6.30 in the morning shouting,

"MUM! MUM! WAKE UP I HAVE TO GET READY FOR THE TRIALS!"

"What trials where are they when?" murmured a very tired and confused Sophie as she grabbed her clock "CHLOE! It's 6.30 in the morning! Mr Key won't be here until 3 o'clock! Go back to bed." Chloe ran down the stairs and made herself some breakfast. She plonked herself in front of the TV and watched The Saturday Show for half-an-hour then went and dragged Sophie out of bed then she went for a shower.

She put on her football kit then phoned Lucy to see when her mum was dropping her off.

"I'll be down at 2.30" said Lucy.

"Okay" replied Chloe "See you then." And she hung up.

"Mum" shouted Chloe as she bounced down the stairs, "Lucy's here."

"Good luck" shouted Lucy's mum as she drove away.

"I can't wait." Said Lucy as she jumped into Chloe's house cheerily.

"BEEP! BEEP!" It was the horn of Mr Key's land rover.

"He's here!" blared Chloe jumping around the living room like a mad woman.

"Jump in girls, we've got to get going!" urged Mr Key.

"Good Luck Love" said Sophie as she hugged Chloe.

"BYE" shouted Lucy and Chloe through the open window and Sophie signalled thumbs up. At the trials it seemed to be mostly boys but there was a few other girls there. A voice on the loud-speaker blared loudly:

"Could all the children come to the middle of the field for their instructions, numbers and rules."

"Good luck girls." Said Mr Key.

"Right." Said the instructor cheerily. He was tall, young, fit and he had black-gelled hair.

"I see there are a few girls here today so can I just reassure you that you have as much of a chance as the boys. Okay then. The rules, 1: One ball to each person, 2: No fighting and 3: No shouting. So it's pretty straightforward. Everybody take one ball each and start practicing your keepy-ups."

The trials seem to go for ages but Chloe and Lucy enjoyed every second of it and finally the time came when the final team would be picked. Chloe and Lucy prayed that numbers 307 and 308 would be read out; because that was the numbers they were given. The instructor waited for silence then started to speak "In the final team there will be 11 players and to make it clear some of the girls have got in. So let's get stuck in.

192-Brian McCray, 457-Michael Manning, 012-Michaela Scott, 177-Jordan Beal, 369-Sophie Cullis, 131-David Wright, 448-Kelly Lavelle, 456-Paul Gallagher, 134 Gordon Burkett, 308-Chloe Whitefield and…" he paused.

"Please be me, please be me, please be me." Whispered Lucy to herself.

"And 289-Jill McFadden. Could the numbers I just read out please make their way to the main hall across the road. To the rest of you I am sorry and thank you for coming." With that he headed off after the crowd of excited children heading for the main hall. Chloe shot Lucy a sympathetic look before she disappeared into the building with the rest of the crowd.

"Unlucky Lucy" said Mr Key sympathetically as he rushed up to her "Maybe next year."

"I'm happy for Chloe." She replied shakily but he could tell she was very disappointed. But through all the championships and tournaments Chloe played Lucy was always there cheering her on and screaming: "GO ON CHLOE! YOU CAN DO IT!"… Chloe's dream had finally come true.

LAURA McLEAN (age 11), St Helen's Primary. Bishopbriggs

The Jungle at night

We had the famous Lisbon Lions; we had a bear on the pitch called Yogi
We saw a penalty skied by Deans; we shouted Brogan's gonna get yi
We don't care what the animals say we were herded like coos
We ducked when gangs threw glass we smelled of cheap booze
We roared at Kenny's class we had a team to go to jail for
We felt safe in the Jungle throng
We felt warm snakes of piss, we sang the Soldier's Song
We cheered as Jinky took the pass
We knew it would be nine-in-a-row, we miss the atmosphere in the Jungle
We need a man a lion-like Stein
We were the atmosphere in the Jungle we had the best I've seen
We have the Jungle memories we never walked alone

JOE DOCHERTY, East Kilbride

Heroes and sinners

MY grandfather was a wonderful storyteller. I spent many a winter's evening sitting on the floor in front of a roaring coal fire as he looked down at me from his brown leather armchair. The red-yellow, flickering light from the flames lit up his long, wrinkled face in the darkened room. His one good eye glistened animatedly while the other stared straight ahead, lifeless and sinister. As well as being a wonderful storyteller, my grandfather was also a lifelong Celtic fan and the past, as far back as the 1920s and the days of "Shaw, McNair and Dodds", the first three names of a line-up which is indelibly stamped in my memory even to this day, forty years later.

When I was 11, I was playing football with my fellow street urchins one warm Sunday evening when I spotted my grandfather walking along the street with that familiar stoop and his hands clasped behind his back. He sported the usual battered old bunnet and worn-out hounds tooth jacket as he walked slowly and nonchalantly, seemingly without a care in the world. I called out his name and he stopped and, on recognising me, raised his arm to wave. He stood for some minutes watching the game, occasionally shouting words of encouragement.

"Good ball Thomas...Give it to Thomas...Great goal Thomas..."

At half-time I went over to speak to him.

"Are you going to our house granddad?"

"No son," he replied. "Just out for a walk and a bit of fresh air."

He pulled a white paper bag from his pocket and held it towards me.

"Have a mint Thomas."

"Oh thanks grandfather."

He always carried a supply of rock hard white mints.

"You looking forward to Hampden on Saturday then?" he said, after waiting for his dentures to negotiate the hard sweet.

"Aye granddad, I can't wait. My first cup final."

"I can still remember my first final."

He looked at his feet and shook his head as he spoke.

"Celtic and Rangers it was. I well remember not being able to sleep the night before, a bit like yourself Thomas."

"I'm glad it's Dunfermline not Rangers this time," I said. "Mum wouldn't let me go if it was Rangers."

"Aye it's a shame all this religious nonsense still goes on. I wish they could enjoy the rivalry without all that baggage. But mind you, the new manager Jock Stein's a Protestant and a good man at that. Maybe he'll make a big difference."

My friends were now preparing to resume the match.

"I better get moving," I told him.

"Aye, I'll away then Thomas," he said. "See you soon then."

"Aye, see you granddad. Take care."

I moved towards my friends but was stopped in my tracks.

"Just a wee minute Thomas," he called after me and I turned to face him once again.

"What is it granddad?"

"If anybody asks," he said. "If your gran asks like...well...you never saw me, right?"

I looked at him in silence.

"If gran says anything, don't let on you saw me, right?"

"Sure granddad, I won't say a word."

I didn't ask for an explanation but he offered me one anyway.

"It's just that, I'm supposed to be at six o'clock Mass. Couldn't be bothered going. She'll give me merry hell if she finds out."

"No problem granddad," I reassured him. "She'll not hear it from me."

"Good lad," he smiled warmly. "Go on then. Enjoy your game."

I felt a great surge of pride in the realisation that my grandfather, the great hero, had shared a secret with me and that my silence would protect him from a nagging, or worse. At the same time I wondered how it was that my grandfather, who had fought hand-to-hand combat with a German soldier for more than an hour; who had lost an eye under the piercing blow of a German bayonet; who had stood up to the Protestant gangs who stoned him and his family as they walked to Mass every Sunday morning in Edwardian Motherwell; who had stood shoulder to shoulder with his fellow workers and battled with the riot police during the General Strike - how could this great hero be walking the streets alone, rather than tell his wife, my grandmother, that he couldn't be bothered going to Mass?

Three years later, just days after my grandmother's funeral, my grandfather was telling me what a wonderful and strong woman she was. For the first time I asked him about that Sunday night and he told me he remembered it well.

"I bet you were wondering why I couldn't just tell her I wasn't going to the chapel."

I admitted that the thought had crossed my mind.

"When you get to our age Thomas, me and your grandmother I mean. When you get to our age, you start thinking about death and that. Not the actual dying. No, I mean the passing on, you know, what's waiting for you on the other side."

"Like Heaven and Hell?"

"Aye, that's right. It's just that, I haven't believed any of it since I was your age."

"You mean you don't believe in God?"

"Well, it's not as simple as that. It's just this going to Mass on a Sunday thing. I just don't think it's such a big deal if you decide to give it a miss now and again. But to listen to your grandmother, it was hellfire and eternal damnation for me if I so much as mentioned staying in the house when I should be at the chapel. The thing is Thomas, she believed in it all the way, and if I committed a mortal sin, as she saw it like, by missing Mass, she'd just worry herself sick that I'd drop down dead and go to Hell before I had the chance to go to confession or change my underpants. She even told me I'd spoil it for her cos she'd go to Heaven and couldn't enjoy it knowing I was burning away in the Bad Fire."

"So you don't believe in the Bad Fire either?"

"Maybe there is a Bad Fire, maybe not Thomas, but if there is, I can't believe that God would put somebody there just for missing Mass on a Sunday. Bank robbers and murderers aye, but not for missing Mass or telling the odd white lie or using bad language or stealing a loaf of bread or, or whatever. Surely the God grandmother and your mother worship every Sunday can't be that cruel."

To me, my grandfather was now a hero and a sinner.

In the summer of 65 my grandfather took me, my mother and grandmother to Glasgow to see *The Sound of Music*. I set off in trepidation as the whole idea of such an outing filled me with feelings of horror and embarrassment. I was 11-years-old and wanted to be playing football or kick-the-can or chap-door-run-away with my friends. My street credibility took a nosedive as I was dragged off on the big bus to watch a film about singing nuns in some far-off country full of hills and girls with flowery frocks and men in leather shorts.

The bus took an hour to trundle its way through Lanarkshire towards the big city. I spent the whole time with my nose against the window as I took in the sights and sounds of the countryside, then small towns, more countryside, until the towns got more frequent and bigger and the countryside got sparser. And before long we were rolling noisily through the East End of Glasgow. I knew we were in Glasgow when my grandfather excitedly pointed out the four gigantic, towering pylons which were the floodlights of Celtic football ground. For many years to come I would feel time and time again that familiar feeling of awe and breathless excitement as I saw the very same floodlights, shining like a beacon, growing nearer and nearer as our bus approached on match days.

The cinema was packed to capacity and the audience was peppered here and there with a collection of priests and nuns of all shapes and sizes, giving the auditorium the feel of the main stand at Celtic Park. Some months earlier, on a Saturday morning, I had queued outside the Rex Cinema in Motherwell, along with a few hundred excited youngsters, waiting to see *One Million Years BC*. I began to imagine hundreds of priests and nuns lining up outside the picture house on the first showing of *The Sound of Music*. This set me wondering whether the priests got in for free, like they did at Celtic matches.

My grandfather once told me how he and my uncle Tommy spent much time and effort designing two makeshift dog collars which they wore with suitably adjusted black shirts and jumpers. They managed to see six matches, free of charge, before my grandfather forgot himself and rose to his feet to berate a linesman with language that would make a coal miner blush. As a policeman came to eject him, uncle Tommy stopped him with a right hook which sent him sprawling across three rows of seats and about half a dozen spectators, at least two of whom were bona fide priests. Their scam was rumbled and, after a weekend in the cells and a Monday morning visit to the Sheriff Court and a ten shillings fine, they had to walk the 15 miles or so back to Motherwell.

They sang Irish rebel songs as they sauntered through the mining village of Viewpark, where they got into a fight with a trio of local Orangemen and were promptly arrested yet again. The Motherwell Celtic Supporters' Club organised a whip-round and a committee member was dispatched to bail them out and return them to the safety to their families. Safety? My grandfather suffered a headache for four days, courtesy of my grandmother's rolling pin.

The incessant babble, which filled the auditorium, subsided as the house lights were dimmed. Several rows behind me a mother berated her young daughter in hushed but audible tones.

"For heaven's sake Angela," she cried in exasperation. "Why wait till the film

135

starts before wanting a pee?"

I burst out laughing and all around me, a dozen grown-ups said, "Ssshhh!" in perfect harmony.

"Don't you tell my grandson to Ssshhh," my grandmother snapped back.

"But I'm bursting," pleaded Angela, who sounded like she was straining to hold back the torrent for a few seconds longer.

"Ssshhh!"

I glanced to my right in the direction of the Ssshhh. That was when I first noticed him. He was sitting just two seats from me, right next to my mother. He looked at me and smiled.

"Can I have your autograph please?" I asked him, almost breathless with excitement.

"Thomas," whispered my mum urgently. "The film's starting."

The man smiled and took a shiny pen from his pocket and asked his wife for a piece of paper. The lady tore a page from a notebook and handed it to her husband.

"What's your name wee man?"

"Thomas."

He scribbled for a few moments and handed me the piece of paper with a smile.

"There you go son," he said. "Enjoy the film."

My mother smiled back at him before moving her face towards mine.

"Who is that man Thomas?"

"Oh mum are you kidding?" I replied. "You're sitting right next to my hero Billy McNeill, captain of Celtic."

I don't remember much of the film. All I could do was hold the piece of paper in my hand and dream of one day playing for Celtic. I imagined that somehow the magic would rub off on me just by holding that piece of paper. I had to wait until the interval before I could read it…

'To Thomas…Best wishes…Billy McNeill.'

THOMAS McLAUGHLIN, Edinburgh

Chapter Eleven

The Old Firm

FOLLOW, follow, I will follow Celtic.... Or should it be Rangers? From a very early age and with no logical reasoning, I had become a staunch Celtic supporter. Perhaps being born of Irish parents, along with 11 other siblings, four of whom were born in Ireland, I became obsessed with the Celtic football team. As one of six boys, two who were mildly enthused with football while the other three showed no positive commitment to the sport, but it seems like I made up for them.

Apparently I was more of a rebel than any other family member, possibly being the only redhead in the family drew my ire to the Irish Catholic cause. I received my first Celtic jersey when I was about seven years old and wore it constantly when playing football at any location. I was very involved in collecting lots of memorabilia relating to Celtic and other teams in Scotland and England. This included players' cards, autographs, newspaper clippings, team photos, etc. I was very fortunate to be able to attend many games at this time and as a youngster I remember watching many great players, but of course if they played for Celtic, they were all great.

I feel that the skill level of today exceeds that of yesteryear but the entertainment and character of the past players will never be matched. I remember watching Charlie Tully, Willie Fernie, Bertie Peacock, Bobby Collins, Bobby Lennox, Bobby Evans, Pat Crerand, Jim Kennedy, Frank Haffey and Bertie Auld only to mention a few. These players were all great in their own right. My story concerns a Scottish Cup replay between Celtic and Rangers, back in 1955 or 1956. At that time I was about ten years old and a student at St. David's Primary School in Johnstone. In the original game the score obviously ended in a tie, so the replay was scheduled for the next Wednesday.

During the school session on the prior Tuesday, my teacher remarked that if anyone was absent the next day, he would understand that they would be at the football game supporting Celtic. This obviously was the signal for us to attend the game so I told my mother of my intentions. She gave me some money but did not believe that I was really going to the game on my own. My father had died in an accident a year or so earlier, so I had to go it alone.

All dressed up to support the "Bhoys", I commenced on my journey to Ibrox Park. Although I took the public bus and didn't really know where the park was located, there was no problem exiting the correct bus stop due to the number of other football fans on board. Upon leaving the bus I just followed the crowd to the turn-styles at the stadium and like many games before, I asked an adult for a lift over the gate. It did not dawn on me why so many were resistant in doing this good deed because I had done this many times before.

Apparently, dressed in my green, white and gold scarf and no other Celtic supporter in sight, I was attempting to gain entry at the Rangers end of the stadium. Even after being finally given a lift over the turn-style, I made my way up towards the terracing and attempted to move closer to the front and nearer the field to gain a good location to watch the game. As the park started to fill, I began to be on the receiving end of some verbal and physical abuse. I did not comprehend at that time why this was happening but with a little of my rebel instinct, I began to retaliate by punching and kicking back at those nasty Rangers fans.

Adhering to the advice of some choice words from those around me, I kept moving away from one spot only for another skirmish to start at the next area that I stopped. Must have been the red hair but there again the Celtic scarf might have come into play. The more this abuse continued, the more riled and angry I became, but even at 10-years-old I did believe an old adage.... outnumbered but not outfought... although I did have some idea of my limitations. I had respect for all adults, but when another boy got nasty, then I became very defensive.

After moving around the terrace by about seventy yards or so, an adult came over and whispered in my ear. He had taken notice of these incidents and heard many of the nasty threats. This man gave me some valuable advice. He told me to hide that green and white scarf and move to the Celtic End of the field. He was nice enough to escort me down to the pitch area where he called to a policeman and explained the situation. I was helped up to the track and the policeman walked me around to the Celtic End. I was very grateful for this man's gesture but of course I had plenty of bruises, dirty clothes and a cut lip to remind me of my little escapade.

I had been knocked down several times, kicked and punched, but like a true little trooper...there were no tears because I was probably more determined and maybe more rebellious than ever. One lesson I certainly learned from this experience was that I should know what end of a stadium to enter. I do not recall the final result that day but the game was certainly very memorable for me. My experience did not make me bitter or change anything. I was still "Celtic daft" and had many friends who were Rangers supporters, one notable at that time being a future Celtic player, namely John (Dixie) Deans. This also happened in an era of extreme hooliganism, and bottle throwing was not uncommon.

Thankfully those days are gone, at least for the best part. Later on in life I was about to marry a "bluenose", and still together after thirty-seven years...but I still haven't been able to convert her. What I find amusing is when we have my wife's family visit us in Michigan, USA, and two or three of them walk around my house wearing Rangers jerseys. They are really nice people. It is great if Celtic happen to be the prime team at that time and it feels real good. I still feed them though. I have another brother-in-law who is a staunch Rangers fan and of course we trade barbs throughout the season.

During the mid-70s, I stopped receiving the *Celtic View*, because there came a time when I could no longer relate to the players. The bond apparently had weakened. I also realised after I had left Scotland that even if Celtic lost a game, I would still awaken the next morn. The 80s were pretty bad for sports communications for me and all I could rely on were letters and phone calls from back home, plus the annual *Wee Red Book*. This did not rekindle the enthusiasm, but due to technology and the "Super Highway", the excitement returned via the Internet.

My wife still thinks that I am daft. She is still amazed that virtually every day

I log into the Internet BBC or ESPN and follow the Celtic and the football world's scores and stories. I particularly enjoy Jim Craig's comments on the Celtic website. My wife figured that after all this time; the memories and the excitement would fade. Not so. Even after all of these years. I am still coaching football (soccer) in the USA and still an avid Celtic fan. Of course I do not get to see the Celtic play very often but when I return for a visit, I always make sure that I get to attend a game or two. I do not have my Celtic strip I wore as a boy, but I have the current version that I wear often at my practices.

When an American asks about the Celtic jersey, I am only too glad to relay some stories about Glasgow Celtic. Old memories never die… they might fade a little, but are sure rekindled when one reads of the success of the team. My wife's suggestion that I am still living out my childhood is completely false. My story had ended here, but I now have to add another chapter due to a recent encounter. Living in Michigan, I recently travelled over to Windsor, Canada, to watch the Scottish Cup final.

I had taken an American soccer coach with me to experience an Old Firm final. I had called prior to game day to confirm the match time at the Scottish Club where the game is always televised. We arrived early at the club, only to be informed that the club management had changed. It was no longer the Scottish Club but now it was the Rangers Club and had changed operators several months earlier. An Englishman who was collecting the admission at the door informed me to consider going to another new club, which was relatively close by…the Celtic Club. I joked with him about the Celtic motto…. outnumbered, but not outfought…I just wanted to watch the game. He was a very pleasant young man.

I was not aware of the new location so I figured that I would just stay there considering I had paid the money and rather than driving around trying to find the new hall. There was no food available in the Rangers Club, so my friend and I were directed to a restaurant close by. As we walked along the street towards the eatery, suddenly a Ford truck pulled up right beside us. It had a custom license plate, "Bhoys", was displayed. I knew right then that he was a "Tim" The man inside the truck quickly informed us that we were at the wrong club and gave us directions to the "right" club. I did wonder how someone driving by could detect that I was a Celtic supporter…maybe the red hair… but then again, I was wearing a Celtic jacket and underneath and quite visible…the Celtic hoops as well as green training pants.

My friend and I discussed the switch for a couple of minutes and decided that we should make the change. Earlier in the morning, prior to leaving for the club, my wife had suggested that I do not dress up in this fashion, because, as she put it…"someone will hit you". I quickly over-ruled her because I felt the need to show support for the "Bhoys", anyway, who is going to tangle with me? We went back to the Rangers Club and informed the doorman of our decision. There was no problem getting our money back and the Englishman and an older Scot gave us more specific directions with honest courtesy. Scotsmen always make you feel good when they call you "son"…if they don't use "Jock".

Even if I had stayed there, I would probably have known more people in the Rangers Club than I did in the Celtic group. We finally got to the other club and watched the very disappointing game. I was a little embarrassed with Celtic's

139

performance; after all, I had really created this super team image to my friend. Wait until next year. The next day I was brooding a little, very common after any disappointing result, I was out working in the garden and looking at the flowers.

The orange lilies that my wife had planted were looking right at me. I started to wonder a little. Is the good Lord upstairs trying to tell me that maybe I should really be a Rangers supporter?

B. TURNER, Brownstone, Michigan

Oh what a season!

Oh Ibrox in the sun
Celtic three, the Rangers none
The Broomloan Stand's a sea of green
Oh what a season this has been

The first time in almost seven years
We went to Ibrox with no fears
Oh what a job O'Neill has done
The league and cups have all been one

The score was level at the break
But in the second the points we'd take
Lubo and Henrik were the Bhoys
In front of goal they showed such poise

The Rangers defence didn't have a clue
As Lubo scored not one but two
And just to end the perfect day
Henrik scored number fifty!

JOSEPH CURRIE, Clydebank

My first Old Firm game

"WE'RE gonnae win the league at Ibrox!" had been the chant for the last few weeks at Celtic games. Now the day had come. Celtic needed three points to clinch the League Championship. So, in reality, a victory was not quite enough as it was only two points for a win in 1981. A further point would still be needed.

On the morning of April 18, 1981, this 11-year-old boy awoke with an unbelievable tremor of excitement inside him. Today he was going to Ibrox for his first ever Old Firm game. I had travelled everywhere in Scotland in my short life to watch Celtic but my mum and dad would not allow me to go to an Old Firm game, as I was "too young to go." Now, at last, they had agreed to let me go, probably because alcohol was now banned from the football grounds, following the riot at the Scottish Cup Final in 1980.

Dad and I left our home in Cumbernauld, to meet my Uncle Davie at my gran and granddad Davis' house in Roystonhill. I got the usual kidology from gran and grandad about wearing a tin hat to these games and gran even offered me one of her small pots, as tin hats were not readily available. I laughed. I was not scared of the prospect of an Old Firm game, just excited and buzzing like a busy bee. I could not sit down, and just wanted to get to Ibrox.

To my surprise, Gran and Granddad came with us to Ibrox. This had never happened before. The adults went for the customary pint or two before the game. I had my usual can of Coke and a packet of crisps.

Sitting just inside the pub, listening to the endless debates about Celtic and savouring the electric atmosphere had me very excited. Soon the confidence, which was sky high, hit fever pitch and a few songs and party tunes were sung in anticipation of what was to come. I looked at my granddad. He looked just as excited and enthusiastic as I was. It had been a lot of years since he had been in the middle of an enthusiastic and confident Celtic support. I am sure, even now, that if he had been offered a ticket that day he would have taken it and left my gran in the pub.

We left the pub in plenty of time and walked the short distance down Edminston Drive, past the infamous Edminston Club. In 1981, Rangers were so bad that to fill the ground they gave Celtic the usual Broomloan Road end, half of the Main Stand, the old enclosure and a small part of the Govan Road stand. We were in the Main Stand.

When we got to the stadium, I said my goodbyes to my gran and granddad and approached the turnstiles with my dad and Uncle Davie. Me first. Arms out, my dad went to life me over, as was the custom in those good old days. Then it was bedlam.

"Officer, Officer," shouted the aged gentleman as if he was being murdered behind the mesh. Before we knew it, two stewards and at least half a dozen policemen had descended upon us. After a heated discussion and argument the stewards were adamant no lifting over. Only two tickets, so only two can be admitted. These guys were now my firm favourites for the "That's Life Jobsworth Cap" as seen on TV at that time.

We retreated and regrouped on the grass in the middle of Edminston Drive. My Dad had one last try at reasoning with a big Police Sergeant, explaining to him that the boy had been everywhere to watch Celtic and, that he really had to see this game as we were going to win the League today. "Try another turnstile and slip the guy a couple of quid," explained the helpful Sergeant.

My Dad tried this but to no avail. The stewards were now watching the turnstiles like hawks. "If you had come to me first then I would have," said one sympathetic turnstile operator, "but they are now watching here very closely."

Grandad was now explaining why he and my Gran had come with us. They were going to take me home if I did not get into the ground. Frankie wept. I so much wanted to see this game.

As I stood weeping in the middle of the road another casually dressed gentleman approached our little contingent. He seemed concerned about the young boy as he enquired about the reasons for my distress. My dad proceeded to explain about the circumstances surrounding our predicament.

He explained that he was a press photographer and that he was returning to his car to get some film for his camera. "I may be able to help when I return," he proclaimed before departing our company. Leaving our party, he went back to his car promising to return.

I was still crying, believing that all I was going to see of this game was the recorded highlights on *Sportscene* that night. We did not think the photographer would return, despite his promise.

Within 10 minutes and to our surprise that gentleman of the press returned. The press photographer explained that I was too young, at 11-years-old, to be taken into the ground via the press entrance. A short discussion followed and he agreed to take my Uncle Davie in through the press entrance.

The plan was risky and Dad and I were to wait five minutes before entering by the proper means. When the photographer and Uncle Davie went through the press entrance, a vigilant steward challenged them. "I thought only one of you went out. Why have two returned?" he asked. They explained that Davie was going to load the film into the camera and they were allowed to proceed.

Outside, we had a very anxious wait. My gran, granddad, dad and me cringed every time the press door opened. It felt like we had waited hours although it was less than ten minutes. By now, I had stopped crying and was again eager and keen to get to our seats.

At last, we ventured back to the gate manned by the cantankerous operator and gave him his tickets. Two tickets and two admitted. My dad and I went to our seats in the Main Stand. We stood savouring the atmosphere though my Dad was pre-occupied. Down in the enclosure waving up to us was Uncle Davie.

All I can remember about the game is that Celtic won 1-0 with a goal from Charlie Nicholas, but still needed one more point to clinch the title. Aberdeen had also won. Despite the constant chants of "We want Celtic", Billy McNeill refused to allow any title celebrations until it was mathematically impossible to be caught.

We were to learn later on that Uncle Davie had been down on the side of the park. Behind the goal with the photographers, he was enjoying himself. Then they went for a pie and a Bovril and afterwards the kind photographer left Uncle Davie saying, "I never met you." I for one will be forever grateful to this man with no name.

It emerged later that the league really was won at Ibrox in the season 1980-81. The following Tuesday, Rangers and Aberdeen fought out a 2-2 draw at Ibrox, which meant that Celtic were Champions without playing. The next night the real celebrations began at Tannadice as Celtic swept aside Dundee United 3-2 with true Champion class.

Unfortunately, for me, it was my brother John's turn to go to the game. He saw the team carry Danny McGrain on their shoulders at the official celebrations that night. I was content to watch the highlights on TV.

A few weeks later, dad was in Partick and had got lost. He stopped two policemen to ask for directions and one of them asked, "Do I know you from somewhere?" Being hopeless with faces, dad said, "No, I don't think so." "I know," said the policeman. "A few weeks ago at Ibrox you tried to lift your son over the turnstile. Did you eventually get him in?" "Yes," said dad. "And he enjoyed every minute of it." It was only the sergeant who had suggested bribing the other turnstile operator with a few quid. Small World?

FRANK DAVIS, Lancashire.

Do you remember where…?

They say they remember exactly where they where at the shooting of JFK
What they were doing to the very second
When the tragic news from the US beckoned.
In my life there's a moment ingrained
Which caused me undue emotional pain
For I recall precisely where
I was, when plunged into deep despair.
Into the shop I'd nipped for fags
And the headline screamed from the tabloid rag.
My heart stopped. My mouth fell open
"Surely" I thought, "you must be jokin'"
I forgot the fags and the fact I was late
As I read the words - surely a mistake?
I rushed into work looking for proof
(The paper I'd read not renowned for the truth)
But my fears were confirmed, no others to blame
I was in shock - he has no shame!
Can you remember where you where
The day *The Sun* screamed, 'Mo Signs For Gers'?

JULIE MACKAY, Glasgow

MANY years ago I believe I found myself in a unique situation regarding Celtic and our great rivals the Gers. I was a salesman in the transport industry and visited companies to sell our products. One day I was in a customer's office, only to be confronted by many Celtic photographs, and being a Celtic fan I commented on them, showing my delight (not to enhance a sale remember) and conversed about Celtic.

I further explained my brother-in-law played with Celtic in the 7-1 game (John Donnelly full-back) and was then offered a cup of tea and a seat. I then was given a strong enquiry for one of our products which turned to an order! As conversation continued I then advised them (father and sons) my cousin played with the Gers. Trying to explain this was hard but I did come out alive and with an order.

My cousin was Billy Stevenson who played halfback with the Gers at the same time and was transferred to Liverpool after the progress of the famous Jim Baxter. This came about by my mother being a convert to Catholicism when engaged to my father, whilst her sister remained non-Catholic and Billy qualified to play for the Rangers (a fine player).

By the time this was explained they were glad to give me an order and leave, to enable them to work it out. Not to confuse them more I did not tell them my Dad played with both Hibs AND Hearts long before I came along! (True) check the records if required using surname.

LEONARD LANGTON, Broxburn, West Lothian

Brigton Bhoy against bigotry

AS I child I was raised in Bernard Street, no more than a long upfield punt from Celtic Park. Like most kids in those streets, football was the only recreation we knew. We played before, during and after school, a lack of traffic in those days made it a lot safer than it would be nowadays. The goals were the gap between the tenement building and the lamppost on the edge of the pavement, diagonally opposite each other and about 40 yards apart.

As our 'pitch' took in the front of the Kick-Off Bar in Marquis Street we had to contend with the adults at closing-time displaying their 'skills' to the roars of encouragement from their more inebriated pals on the sidelines.

Going to Celtic Park wasn't an obvious option for me given my father's persuasion, so it was more the entrepreneur in my mate John that led me on the path to Paradise than any burning desire to see the Hoops in action.

I was invited to join my mates on their latest sure fire money-making scheme which involved collecting empty 'screwtaps' discarded on the terraces at Celtic Park, returning them to the Bottle Store on London Road at the corner of Montgomery Street and spending the spoils on a Hot-pea special and a Coke in the café next door.

So it was, on the last day of August 1957 and just two weeks after my 10th birthday that I embarked on what was to be the start of a lifelong love affair with my local team. Armed with a potato sack rescued from the local Templeton's grocery shop, we joined the throng on London Road and traipsed up to the stadium.

We had two options with regard to gaining entry to the park: approach an adult and ask to be lifted over the turnstile (common practise in those pre-all-seater stadia days); if the first failed, wait until the final 20 minutes of the game when the big green doors at the corners of the park were opened to allow fans inside to exit. But most often those without the readies got the chance to see the last minutes of the game.

I was in awe of my mates ease in gaining entry to the park, and being a little shy I found it hard plucking up the courage to ask a complete stranger for a favour, but with time getting short I managed to utter those oft to be used pleas: 'Gonnae gies a lift, mister!' and as if by magic I was propelled through the turnstile and into a whole new world.

This was the day my life was to become a rollercoaster ride. Once inside the park there was next to no chance of me finding my mates as they went about their business in collecting the empties needed for the treat after the game. I gave up trying to fight my way through the mass of people and found myself drawn to events on the pitch.

I quickly gathered that Celtic were playing Hibs in a League Cup clash, and as the game progressed I became aware of a slightly balding figure playing in the Hoops and I was mesmerised. This guy was doing things with the ball that bordered on the impossible. I couldn't take my eyes away; I was hooked. Before the game had finished he had laid on two goals and I had become a slave to the skills of Charles Patrick Tully.

That was the day I chose to follow Celtic and friends and family who support a certain other team in Glasgow have vilified me ever since. Schoolmates and workmates who accuse me of 'jumping the dyke', whatever that means, will never know the pleasure of truly great and skilful players, like Tully and his ilk who have worn the Hoops and graced the game irrespective or race, creed or colour.

Today, I'm a supporter of 45 years (standing and sitting), a season ticket holder, a shareholder, and a husband and father to season ticket holders, and all because one fateful day in 1957 I had the privilege to see Charles Patrick Tully play football as it should be played.

HUGH MORROW, Glasgow

Six weeks in '71

IN the aftermath of an Old Firm cup final defeat, it is pleasant to reflect on past glories – especially upon battle honours gained against our greatest rivals.

A stroll down the sun-dappled memory lane of great Celtic victories over Rangers reveals many epic triumphs. Rarely, though, have Celtic exerted such dominance over the 'Gers as they did between the 4-0 cup final drubbing of April 1969, and the equally one-sided 3-1 League win (also at Hampden, due to reconstruction at Celtic Park) in September 1972.

This "broad, sunlit upland" of Celtic supremacy ironically coincided with a period of transition during Jock Stein's reign, in which the Lisbon Lions were gradually being replaced by the Quality Street Kids – the remarkable crop of talented youngsters who were making Celtic's reserve side almost a legend in it's own right; McGrain, Hay, Connolly, Quinn, Davidson, Macari, and...Dalglish! These lads were scoring goals at a phenomenal rate, including some spectacular totals against their Ibrox counterparts, and were so good that Jock Stein even proposed them for admission to the old Second Division, on the understanding that they would not accept promotion should they gain it. Stein's bold plan would have given the Celtic Colts tougher match practice than they would encounter in their own reserve league, but the Scottish League mandarins refused permission – probably on the grounds that the young Celts would embarrass their opponents week in, week out.

The zenith of Celtic's Old Firm success during this period of hegemony came in six glorious weeks in the late summer of 1971. Celtic and Rangers had been drawn together in the same League Cup section – at that time, the season always started with groups of four teams playing each other home and away in sections, with the winner advancing to the knock-out quarter-final stage. There never seemed to be any seeding plan, and often the season would explode into life with the likes of Celtic, Rangers, Aberdeen and Dundee United all grouped together. It certainly made for a spicy entrée! In 1971-72 season, Celtic and Rangers were joined by Morton and Ayr United, and both Old Firm games would be played at Ibrox due to construction of the new main stand at Celtic Park.

August 14, 1971 was a warm Glasgow summer day; from the top of the Broomloan Road terracing at the Celtic End of Ibrox Park, the sun-bathed Campsie Hills could be seen beyond the cranes of the Govan shipyards. Meanwhile, on the pitch, the sun-tanned heroes of the Old Firm took to the field for the first tribal battle of the new season in front of 72,000 spectators. Celtic fielded young Kenny Dalglish at centre-forward in place of more experienced contenders like Hood and Wallace – the 20-year old had scored freely in the pre-season Dryburgh Cup tournament. Celtic's line-up was: Williams; Craig, Hay; Murdoch, McNeill, Connolly; Johnstone, Lennox, Dalglish, Callaghan, Hughes. The first half was goal-less, with Celtic comfortably holding Rangers and looking increasingly likely to score themselves with Bobby Murdoch in complete control of midfield. Midway through the second half, Hughes' shot cannoned off McCloy's post straight to the in-rushing Johnstone, who shot Celtic into the lead. Three minutes later, the game was over: Hughes, rampaging into the Rangers box, was hauled down by keeper McCloy – a clear penalty. To everyone's surprise, debutante Dalglish stepped forward, and even paused to tie up his bootlace before slotting the ball to McCloy's left while the giant keeper obligingly lurched to his right! As the disconsolate Rangers fans streamed out of the ground, Hughes came close to adding to the misery by crashing a shot off the crossbar. It didn't matter. Celtic were easy winners.

The warm weather continued throughout August, as Glaswegians learned to adjust to the new decimal currency which had been introduced in February. A pint of lager, which had cost 2/3d, was now 12 'New Pence', which was equal to 2/6d in old money. It wasn't only events on the football field that left fans saying, "We wuz robbed"! Diana Ross topped the charts with *I'm Still Waiting*, but Celtic fans couldn't wait for the next Old Firm game. Before it arrived though, Rangers were handed a shock League Cup lifeline as Celtic slumped to defeat at home to "cannon fodder" Morton. It was one of those nights when Celtic just could not score. Dalglish missed a penalty, and Morton's 15-year old debutante, Charlie Brown, laid on a perfect pass for Osborne to slide the only goal past Evan Williams with only 15 minutes left. So, it was all down to the rematch at Ibrox on 28th August.

Again, the sun shone brightly and soon the visiting supporters in the 74,000 crowd were basking in the warmth of a superlative display from the Hoops. Celtic had replaced Jim Craig with Danny McGrain, after the first match, then replaced Danny with Jim Brogan for the second Ibrox clash. Macari took over from Hughes in attack. Murdoch and Hay again dominated midfield, and big Tommy Callaghan, so often the target of the fans' criticism because of his ungainly style, stretched the Rangers defence to breaking point with his searing runs up the left wing. Amazingly, Rangers survived intact till half-time.

The deadlock was well and truly broken three minutes into the second half – Murdoch split the 'Gers defence wide open with a perfect through ball, lofted over the running Dalglish's shoulder, and the youngster had time to steady himself before lashing the ball high past McCloy. Celtic continued to impose themselves, and Tommy Callaghan capped a brilliant performance with a rasping drive from 18 yards following a Lennox cross from the left. The Rangers support were half way home when Bobby Lennox ended their interest in the cup, cracking home a right-foot drive with eight minutes left. A comfortable 4-1 home win over Ayr ensured there would be no more reprieves for the Ibrox men.

And so the long hot summer trundled lazily, and pleasurably, on for Jock Stein's new Celtic; the League campaign started with a bang, as Clyde were swamped 9-1 at Celtic Park – the visitors' late consolation was scored by the young Dom Sullivan. And so to the first Old Firm league meeting of the season on Saturday, September 11 – the third Old Firm game in six weeks, and all at Rangers' south-side red-brick fortress. This time, the attendance dipped to 69,000 – perhaps over 3,000 Rangers fans had seen enough already! Celtic were unchanged, and for the record, the Rangers line up was: McCloy; Jardine, Mathieson; Greig, Jackson, MacDonald; McLean, Penman, Stein, Conn, Johnston. This was the third permutation Rangers had tried – Henderson, McKinnon and Derek Johnstone had all featured in the earlier games. At last, we had a goal in the first half, and again, it went to Celtic. Murdoch's perfectly flighted free kick from the right was expertly dummied by Lennox to wrong-foot the home defence, and Macari bulleted home his free header from six yards. This strike prompted desperate retaliation from Rangers; they roared back, and equalised with a penalty, harshly awarded when Jim Brogan's arm was struck at point-blank range by a driven cross.

Willie Johnston converted the award, and Colin Stein battered Rangers ahead on the stroke of half time. Celtic hit back after the break, and Kenny Dalglish coolly shot home through a ruck of players to claim his third Old Firm goal in three games. 2-2! Rangers screamed blue murder when the referee denied them a goal mid-way through the second half, despite the fact that Colin Stein's boot nearly took Evan Williams' head off as the pair both went for a high bouncing through ball. Just when it seemed that we would have to settle for a draw, Macari lobbed the ball high into the Rangers box in the last minute, and wee Jimmy Johnstone, the smallest man on the park, incredibly out-jumped big Peter McCloy, the "Girvan Lighthouse" to nod home Celtic's winner! Pandemonium! Rangers' season had got off to the worst of all possible starts, and really their challenge was stillborn.

Just to complete a perfect Old Firm record for the season, Celtic won the New Year game at Parkhead by 2-1. It looked as though a draw would have to do when Colin Stein cancelled out Jinky's first half goal with a late equaliser, but Jim Brogan ran through a static Rangers defence to head home another last-minute winner for the Celts! Happy days! Celtic eventually won the league by 10 points from Aberdeen, with Rangers six points further back, and completed the double with the record Scottish Cup final score of 6-1 over Hibs. The only disappointments of the season were losing to Inter Milan on penalties at Parkhead in the European Cup semi-final, and the comical 4-1 loss to dear old Partick Thistle in the League Cup final – after all that epic work against Rangers.

To give a modern perspective on Celtic's performance in 1971-72, they amassed 60 league points from 34 games; if they had played 38 games, won the other four, and been awarded three points for a win instead of two, they would have racked up exactly 100 points! They also scored 96 goals, and would certainly have broken the ton barrier with four more games to do so. Consider, too, that Hibs, Hearts, Aberdeen and Dundee all put in credible challenges for the championship, and Rangers won the Cup Winners' Cup, you'll get an idea of just how good Celtic were 30 years ago. It's exciting to see another crop of talented youngsters bubbling through to the surface again; if the Healys, Maloneys and Lynchs can emulate their Quality Street forerunners, then we can surely look forward to a wonderful future.

TONY GRIFFIN, Ellon, Aberdeenshire

The glory and the dream

The passion of the game
The roaring of the stands
Enthusiastic faces
But beyond the smiles, is hatred.
They wait to rage
Cause others pain and grief
A divided nation
A shattered dream.

From glory to ashes
By one sectarian shout
The game is forgotten
A battle breaks out.
The honest fans watch in vain
As broken glass and stones take flight
They know it is better not to get involved
And walk away quickly.

In the end comes death
The flash of steel
A single stab
Blood staining a football top
The question asked is why such a small group
Causes so much trouble
Over a single cause
Have we lost the glory and the dream?
PAUL O'KANE, St Luke's High School, Barrhead

A NUMBER of years ago, in fact quite a few years ago, I was with my brother, who was the Administrator of Holy Family Parish in Belfast at the time, in Duncairn Gardens when we met a group of Celtic supporters heading for the Old Firm match. A number of these supporters were old Altar Boys and they stopped to have a chat with my brother who in his youth was no mean player in both disciplines viz.; Gaelic & Soccer.

Anyway, as we were chatting a large group of Linfield/Rangers supporters emerged from the Tigers Bay area onto Duncairn Gardens and upon seeing both the green & white scarves and the black suit complete with the Roman Collar commenced shouting "Remember 1690" etc.

It was quite intimidating up until one of the lads we were chatting to quipped: "Don't worry about them Father; sure wasn't that the last time they bate (beat) us!"

What could the two of us do but laugh and smile and that was enough to stop the slogans etc, being shouted at us. Whether those shouting actually heard what was said is open to conjecture but the shouting stopped anyway.

BRENDAN ARMSTRONG

148

WHERE ever and whenever Celtic Fhans get together, a good time is bound to follow. And so it was in 2000, when 1,700 Fhans gathered in Las Vegas for the North American Supporters' Convention. Wasn't it a party! The music, singing and craic were brilliant and never stopped for the whole week.

One afternoon the bar was rockin' as usual when suddenly an eerie silence enveloped the revellers. All eyes were looking in one direction. I, being nosy had a look too. Some poor misguided chap was walking through the casino wearing...a Rangers jersey! Apparently he was American and had no clue about football, never mind the Old Firm thing and was wearing it just as a fashion statement...a gift some relative had brought back from Scotland.

I'll never forget the bewildered look on his face when he was suddenly surrounded by 30 to 40 good-natured Fhans, all singing "No 'Gers in Vegas, There's no 'Gers in Vegas!!"

There was absolutely no animosity, just good fun, but the lad was advised in the friendliest of ways to go to his room immediately and change his attire, something he didn't hesitate to do, practically running for the elevator!

KIERAN S. KERR, Kitchener, Ontario, Canada

Green shirt, brown trousers

BORN of Irish parents in Birmingham, I was ultimately destined to support two of the greatest football clubs in the world - Aston Villa and Glasgow Celtic. Geography would dictate that Villa would be my first team, but there was always a special place in my heart for "The Celts", dating back to watching my dad go wild as Celtic gave Inter Milan a footballing lesson when they became the first "British" club to win the European Cup.

My 35 years following football have seen me travel all over England Scotland and the continent watching Villa and Celtic. On the whole I have enjoyed watching the teams I love most. However some games leave long lasting memories for the wrong reasons.

Season 1987/88 proved memorable. Villa were storming through the 2nd Division soon to be promoted to their rightful place in the higher echelons of the football league. Celtic were having another good year in the Premier League. One Saturday we were to play Reading while the Sunday saw Celtic take on their arch rivals Rangers at Ibrox. With tickets impossible to come by, I contented myself with a trip to Elm Park to see Villa dispatch Reading 2-0.

I arrived back in Birmingham to find that one of my mates had called from Glasgow saying that he had got me a ticket. I couldn't contact him to confirm my acceptance but left a message that I would be up the following morning. Like a young child on Christmas Eve I spent the night tossing and turning in excitement and trepidation at venturing in to blue territory. I recalled memories of previous Glasgow derbies, the atmosphere and the intensity of the pure hatred unmatched anywhere in football. I also remember when Rangers played Villa in 1975 in a "friendly" at Villa Park. With Villa leading 2-0 the game had to be abandoned as the Rangers "supporters" capped a couple of days of drunkenness and gratuitous violence by invading the pitch to exchange pennants and scarves with the Villa fans.

Leaving Birmingham at 04.30 I arrived in Glasgow at 9.00 and found my mate. His first words were "sorry, I didn't know you were coming, I sold your ticket last night." I was about to administer a size 10 Dr Marten in to the groin of my ex-mate when he redeemed himself by telling me that he had a spare ticket – but that there was a slight problem. The "slight problem" would have made an ideal present for any Catholic member of EXIT as the ticket was for the Rangers End. He said that seeing as I was bedecked in green and white the stewards would let me in with the Celtic fans. Having travelled all that way I wanted to believe him, but deep in my heart I knew there was as much chance of getting in to the Celtic End as Ian Paisley being chosen as the next Pope.

After a hearty breakfast, fit for a condemned man, we headed off towards Ibrox. Approaching the ground I felt a great stirring in my heart as I heard the strains of "Hail! Hail the Celts are here" echoing around the ground. I prayed that I would be let in with the Celtic fans, but my prayers were not to be answered that day.

As I tried to enter through the turnstile a steward and policeman asked to check my ticket. I explained my predicament but the two smug officials smiled and said "Sorry son you can't get in here with this ticket." I sought their advice "Take off you scarf and badges, zip up your jacket, shut up and you'll be okay." They obviously thought I wouldn't be so daft – but I am, so I did. The smiles soon came off their faces as I headed for the Rangers End. Getting in was no problem but I felt a bit out of place, as I was the only person not wearing any red white and blue. As kick off approached I found myself getting more edgy, well to be perfectly honest, terrified. I've been to Millwall, West Ham, Chelsea and Leeds, but any worries in the company of the aforementioned fans pales into insignificance compared to being surrounded by thousands of drunken, rabid Rangers fans literally screaming for Catholic blood.

The teams came on to the pitch and the ground erupted as both sets of fans sang their traditional anthems, reaffirming their respective heritages. Singing songs is considered an integral part of the game and if you don't sing you are thought to be a part-time supporter or even disloyal. I was getting a few odd looks from the Blue Meanies beside me, as I was the only one not singing. The game started at its usual breakneck speed and only calmed down after a couple of bookings. The Celtic playing their usual fast and flowing football took the lead through a Paul McStay shot from outside the area. Every Celtic fan in the ground went delirious, except one. While inwardly feeling elated I tried to give the impression of feeling as sick as a lighthouse cat. Rangers fans around me were none too pleased as sectarian screams rang in my ears. Half time came with Celtic still leading 1-0. I was bursting to go to the toilet, but there was no way I was going to risk life and limb in a crowded toilet in case some one twigged my accent.

The second half began as frantic as the first and 20 minutes of Rangers pressure told when they netted a scrappy equaliser. The other mob went wild, I didn't. As I hadn't jumped with the rest of the crowd I was sent flying down the aisle beside me. As I scrambled around on the floor I felt a hand on my jacket collar dragging me up. "This is it," I thought. I felt my heart sink. Fortunately the voice accompanying the hand meant me no harm, "Are you all right big fella?" he said "Aye" I replied in a totally unconvincing attempt at a Glaswegian accent.

The Rangers fans went wild; the noise around me was deafening, as was the noise in my underpants.

My heart was pounding, I just wanted the game to end, I was quite happy with a 1-1 draw. Encouraged by the equaliser Ranger went in search of the winner. With 5 minutes to go Celtic hit Rangers on the break and forced a corner from which Joe Miller rose above the statuesque Rangers defence to score majestically. I almost jumped for joy, but in a microsecond realised that instant death would have resulted. I restricted myself to a microscopic smug smirk and a millimetric raising of an eyebrow. Celtic went on to win but I did not breathe a sigh of relief until I was well away from the Rangers fans and back in the safer surroundings of the Bhoys in Green.

I will never forget this match, more for the fear I felt than the football played. I doubt I would do the same again should the opportunity arise. However, I would recommend to any football supporter of whatever persuasion to go to a Celtic v Rangers match just to experience what I believe is the greatest local derby in the world,

LAWRENCE DONAGHY, Solihull, Birmingham

AFTER I left school I had a job as a booking clerk with British Railways. When I was at Possil Station we used to run football special trains to Parkhead and Hampden Park. One Saturday afternoon after the last train had departed for Hampden, and I had done the accounts and banked the cash etc. at around 2.45pm, I jumped on my scooter and went to see the cup final knowing that I would be back at the station in time for the returning trains.

I arrived at the ground around 3.15pm and dashed in and up the stairs into the stadium. I WAS IN THE RANGERS END. Celtic won 7-1 and I could not show any emotion, gripping my hands together to prevent them shooting up in the air after each goal or I would probably have been lynched.

Needless to say I did not join in the singing of either set of supporters. I just stood there hoping that no one recognised me. I left earlier than planned.

WILL McDONALD, Pocklington, York

I KNOW someone who won't eat Penguin biscuits if the wrapper is green, and he's 45. It's a true story

JOE, St Aiden's School, Glasgow

Chapter Twelve

The Celtic family
(what Celtic means to us)

Glasgow Celtic, Glasgow Celtic, Hoops of Green and White
That warm feeling you get inside, from matchday's dawning light
The memories from years gone by
Like Inter in the final tie
Love Street on that final day
The friends we make when far away
Through thick and thin, we proudly stand
The best supporters in the land
We've shared those times of ups and downs
We've had our share of laughs and frowns
But, for all that we've been through
There is one thing that still holds true
Glasgow Celtic, Glasgow Celtic, Hoops of Green and White
We'll stand beside you, one and all, till Heaven's shining light.
LUCIAN BURLINGAME, Springboig, Glasgow

The right start in life

WE all feel that we are Celtic through and through. 'Born to it', we say, 'born to it.' We all regard being Celtic supporters as being part of one big family. I was brought up in times of success and enjoyed the stories told about the great Glasgow Celtic. I'm now looking forward to the day when I can tell my two sons they shared that Celtic feeling a bit earlier than most of us. Both of my sons had a family-style introduction to Celtic that I'll never forget and they'll never remember.

Neither Paddy (three) nor Jamie (one) have attended a game at Celtic Park yet. They have, however, been present at some of the more noteworthy events of the last few years.

How did this come about? As we all know, more and more women are now attending football matches. My sister and I have been regulars since 1989/90 (Not the most auspicious time to start, but we've all got to start somewhere; in our darker moments, we did wonder if it was our very presence that was causing the lean streak). However, pregnant women are not yet a common sight at football games. The gap in the turnstiles is, in my experience, the final deciding factor - that and the excitement.

So, gentle reader, imagine the situation. After the dreadful experience of most of the 1990s it is now May 1998. You are three months pregnant, you have day-long morning sickness, a doctor's recommendation to keep stress to the

THE BOSS Martin O'Neill has brought great success to Celtic

GOAL MACHINE Swedish striker Henrik Larsson celebrates yet another goal

EURO STRUGGLE Chris Sutton in battling form against Juventus

GENIUS Jimmy 'Jinky' Johnstone is one of the greatest ever Celts

LEGEND Jimmy McGrory was a phenomenal striker for Celtic

HAIL! HAIL! CAESAR Billy McNeill with the European Cup in 1967

THE GREATEST Jock Stein guided Celtic to unparalled success home and abroad

STAN'S THE MAN Petrov celebrates a goal in the 6-2 Old Firm victory

GIFTED Lubo Moravcik was an exciting and entertaining talent for Celtic

THE BEST FANS IN THE WORLD Celtic supporters acclaim their heroes

LISBON LIONS the triumphant Celts show off the European Cup at Celtic Park

PARADISE Celtic Park is a magnificent stadium envied all over the world

163

WONDERFUL SIGHT the pre-match Celtic Huddle is an inspiration to the team and the players alike

minimum and it starts to become clear that we might just win the league, therefore stopping our rivals' 10-in-a-row bid.

No pressure here then.

So you think, "Well, if we beat Dunfermline on the second last day of the season, I can go along on the last day against St Johnstone, have a relaxing game and enjoy the day." Makes you wonder if I'd been paying attention up till now.

History tells us that we found ourselves at the last day of the season needing a win to clinch the Championship. Not a completely stress-free event you might say. So did I go? Of course I went. Firmly welded to my seat, scared to jump up and down, eyes averted from the pitch, I tried my best to remain calm. I muttered relaxation mantras while rocking back and forth in that sort of loony kind of way that usually means you get a seat to yourself of the bus. At 1-0 up, I finished neatly plaiting the tassels of my scarf (an interesting displacement therapy I hit upon with about two minutes gone) and then locked myself in the toilets. Funnily enough, I was the only one there. Eventually, hearing a roar to signal 2-0 let me know it was safe to come out. Championees!

How does a 36-year-old pregnant career woman celebrate winning the league? By invading the pitch with everyone else of course and digging up my own piece of turf. And we've got the pictures to prove it. So baby No.1 certainly shared the experience.

The following season I continued to attend games until I was seven months pregnant (turnstiles defeating the bump). When the designated arrival date approached, I told my partner he wasn't going to the home match the day afterwards, so he gave his ticket away. Baby was born on November 20, 1998. Sound almost familiar? Try 5-1 on November 21, 1998...! Okay, so we both missed a fantastic event but our own event overshadowed it. Yes, we suddenly had perspective. And a beautiful baby Bhoy.

However, perspective is irrelevant when your team's fortunes suddenly go haywire again. After the ignominy of season 1999/2000, our only hope of success was the League Cup. And I was three months pregnant again. I had to go, of course, feeling a bit more blasé this time. I'd been there, seen it, done it and had the baby to prove it. But I was still as sick as a dog.

Luckily we won. And I began to wonder if I had to be in the process of reproducing for the team to win. A terrifying thought. We have developed a lot of superstitions over the years, and are now quite adept at interpreting a whole host of seemingly unrelated occurrences in terms of Celtic's fortunes. Green and white straws, killing squirrels on the day of the cup final, foxes (dead or alive), Empire biscuits, blue toothbrushes and never, NEVER asking the time during the game etc. It's quite a long list. But having babies?

Fast forward now to August 27, 2000. I was seven months pregnant and eyeing the turnstiles uneasily. I decided to try one last game before retiring as gracefully as you can when you start to waddle in that curious way. Good choice, as it turned out. Rangers games are usually nerve-wracking. But seriously, can you imagine what it was like staying in my seat during that 6-2 thrashing? Tentatively rolling to your feet about a minute after everyone else has hit the roof? Can you imagine what it's like wondering if yours might be the first baby born in Celtic Park? Thinking about those tannoy calls you've heard saying 'Seamus Murphy, go to the Rottenrow now' and wondering if you will be the first female going there directly from the game. Thankfully, this game was fairly stress-free. The only deranged excitement was the big worry factor this time. My best recollection is the laughter at 3-0. Anyway, despite some interesting kicking, beautiful baby Bhoy No.2 managed to stay calmer than me and stayed put until October.

Now their dad and I scramble for babysitters or take it turnabout for going to the game. The elder of the two doesn't bat an eyelid when he hears that his mum and auntie are away to the game and dad's watching them. Soon we'll have to investigate family season tickets and weep at the cost of children's football strips.

One day I'll sit the Bhoys down and tell them these stories and they'll look at their oul' ma in disbelief. And embarrassment probably. And then they will eventually realise that I may have been daft, but it was worth it. I hope that they'll understand their introduction to the Celtic family was a grand thing and that they will tell these stories with pride to their families.

One thing though. I've still got loads of superstitions but the team are going to have to win all by themselves from now on - my family is complete!

NOREEN McCARRON, Burnside

My Celtic

Can anyone say, that there isn't a day,
When Celtic is not on your mind;
Each game that they play, from league start until May.
When they score, they're seldom behind.

Lubo and Sutton, are right on the button,
And Larsson will soon find the net;
Tradition is there, as he flies through the air,
And some goals, we will never forget.

It's the Paradise fan, both woman and man,
And the children will shout, "have no fear";
Cause the Bhoys are all ready, staunch, and real steady,
For a win, three points, and a cheer.

Famous names will go down, in old Glasgow town,
For a team that are pleasing the crowd;
Celtic has pride, they are the best side,
And that what makes us proud.

So for a team with this history, it isn't a mystery,
That Parkhead, got the best of the deal;
That by making a move, that the team would improve,
With the signing of Martin O'Neill

ARTHUR McGUIGAN, Illinois

WHEN I was around eight years of age and living at 7 Parson Street, Townhead, Glasgow, I received from my cousin Sheila a thing of beauty – a tartan-covered autograph book with sepia-coloured pages in it.

On the inside of the hard-backed front cover she had written *"By Hook or By Crook I'll be the last in this book"* then signed her name and as a youngster, and before I could separate a laugh from humour, I was a bit confused and not too chuffed as this book was for Celtic players only.

At that age I could not go on my own to collect them and although my dad, Frank, took me to Parkhead, he claimed 'regularly' which my mum Josie refuted, we could not wait for the players to come out because we had a supporters' bus to catch. One day when I returned from the wee 'Mungo School' my mum told me that she had given my book to a neighbour, Mrs Ryan, who knew Bertie Peacock and said that Bertie would take the book to Parkhead and get me all of the team's autographs.

I was shocked as I could not believe that my mum could actually give my book to a person whom I considered to be ancient and a bit strange and for a couple of weeks, so the story goes, I was more 'greetin' faced than usual'. Lies of course!

Lo and behold I did receive my book back from Mrs Ryan, who became an overnight 'wow' figure because the book was crammed full of prized signatures and although I can still feel the tingle it gave me, I cannot describe it adequately. On the very first page and right across it, a certain Mr Tully had signed 'Sir Charles Patrick Tully' with a host of other Celtic greats like Bertie himself, though they all seemed to take second place to the knighted one.

Well, they do say that Irish nights are better than any others and Sir Charles was the proof of the pudding! A couple of years later Mrs Ryan again took my book for Bertie to get it updated but, horror of horrors, the book never came back as it had gotten lost.

Over the coming years between getting lifted over or waiting till the gates opened for the last 20 minutes, I thought it was understandable that a wee book could get lost in such a huge place but as I became used to the reality of the 'Celtic family' I began to think it a bit remiss that someone could lose such an important thing. Now, at 57 years of age and although I still miss that book, especially when the View looks back to the old school, I realise that not only was it the signatures that were so important but it was tangible part of human beings who genuinely felt like family.

The present days are great for the team but oh my, some of the old ones weren't so bad either.

FRANK McCLOSKEY, Glasgow

I AM a 36-year-old Englishman from South London, now living in Cyprus. Since the age of seven I have supported Queens Park Rangers with a passion. A season ticket holder for the 12 years leading up to emigration, I spent hours travelling up and down the country watching my beloved team.

Like most fans, I have a second team who you always want to win, so it's usually a team your own is not likely to ever play and mine is Glasgow Celtic. It came about by a complete accident. For my ninth birthday my parents bought me the new QPR home shirt. It was my pride and joy and I wore it everywhere.

One day my mum had put it in the wash and to our horrors it came out with green and white hoops instead of blue.

Mum said don't worry, we'll take it back and change it but for some reason they would not. My friends all made fun of me, I wanted my QPR shirt, not this.

So I was stuck with a shirt I didn't want, of a team I'd never heard of. It sat in my drawer for ages, but I was curious to learn of this team Glasgow Celtic, so I looked through my football books and learned facts like they were the first Scottish team to win the European Cup and had won the Scottish League Cup 6-1 against Hibs.

This amazed me that a team could win a cup final 6-1. It never happened in England. So I thought, sod it, I'll wear the shirt as Celtic were a bloody good team. I never met anyone who supported Celtic so I loved the fact that I was the only one in my town.

Due to my love of QPR, I never followed the Bhoys passionately, my weekend was only complete if QPR, Celtic and my pub team all won. Two out of three was not good. For the 1995 cup final against Airdrie, I checked out of hospital three days early because the hospital didn't have SKY TV.

To this day I have never seen them play. I got locked out of the Paul Davis Testimonial at Arsenal and you can imagine how I felt when I heard QPR were playing Celtic in a pre-season friendly at Loftus Road. All those years and when it finally happened I'm overseas. I couldn't believe my luck.

Everyone here knows who I support, there's a Celtic flag alongside a QPR flag on the roof of my house. They don't understand me. One day I'll have the blue and white hoops on and the next green and white one.

DEAN WARDE, Limassol, Cyprus

The Glasgow Celtic

Wull ye allow me tae steer wurds intae yer ear
about a team called the Glasgow Celic
Don't know how we met but in mha bein
we'r set an ahm sure it wiz sumthin angelic
It mite huv been inbred or perhaps sumthin sed
tae tell ye the truth ah don't even ker
Coz nay mattur how ah feel funny or unreal
ah jist know we'v allwayz been a per

In fifty sevin man that wis hivin az ah sent past Hampden in a bus
"Wits the score" ahz ah herd the roar
an the corporashon conductor made a fus
A man in a van shouteed "It's Scen Wan" an mha wee chist started tae swell
Oh the joy in such a young boy Celic's hsitory ah could start tae tell

A few years prior mha conshins nearly went
oan fire at five ah saw mha furst game
Mha Da's two mates took me through Ibrox gates
ah jist knew it wiznay hame

168

Sumthin deep inside az thick az a coo'z hide
wiz the feelin this place wiznay fur me
At the end o the game ah wiznay the same coz ah wiz a bhoy destined tae be free

Oan the nite sent tae Parkeed ah went
an saw Charlie Tully run the wing
At the jungle ah stood in an excitd mood
in fact it's wer ah learnt tae sing
Becauz ah wiz wee the geme ah coulnday
see bit ah thot "ah wit the heck"
So pleezed tae be among the songs that wrr sung
even wae hot Bovril doon mha neck

Ah lerned much aboot Bruthir Walfrid and such
an how the team started an thrived
How Jonny Thomson wiz brave as he tried tae save
when he ran oot his goal an dived
Cups wur collected by playurs selected
Coronashon and Empire to menshon bit a few
Wan thing ah no as in mha life ah go
the suporters ur faithful through an through

Well years went past as time disnay last an mha luv grew fur this famus team
Ah hardly missed a game getting aff
the Brigton train an ah bragged aw thit ah'd seen
Up the Lundon Road wae praise tae unload
oor wee groop's walk wiz knock an fast

Nimble oan oor feet coz 3 o'clock we hidtae meet an a life time frendship tae last
Then a new scene under the ey o Jock Stein
wiz birthed brick solid an no hollow
Hoo cood hiv telt wit wiz goin tae be felt by the
jenerashons that wur tae follow
Young playerz wur ammeled a lions pride
they resemled destined tae go far afeeld
Win looz or draw the Celts hud it aw an
a hart fur wan anuther wiz ther sheeld

Skill wiz the factor an harminy the reactor wae
enthusism borderin oan the raw
Everythin came az wan between player an fan
so aw that wiz needed wiz a baw
History wull reveal the exploits an zeal of performances
thit went waethoot a hitch
The Cubs did grow tae dae nine in a row cementid at Lisbon oan a big sunny pitch

Ah became contented wae the results cemented yitopia wiz at hand
Nay matter wit we saw even wae a saggin jaw

169

ahm sure ah alwayz herd a band
Aye we went through dreams fae wonderfull seenes and all wiz totally fullfilled
But az a Tim fae deep doon within ah jist luved oor critics bein stilled

McCarry McStay an Dalgleesh fitba wiz still released withoot any tipe o muddle
Then Mogga walked in cauzin a din wen he produced the wan an only huddle
Ah could go on an on like an old gramafone bit you know all the family's past
All ah kin say iz ah like the hero's of the day an ahm jist glad wer ah'v been cast

Ther wiz 'The Celts fur Change' ah found it a dod strange bit things wurked oot OK
Sum wer glad an sum wer sad bit in the end every wan goat ther say
We'v had oor ups an no jist wae winning cups bit becauz tae gether we ur az wan
An we'v hud oor doons like bust bloons az sumtimes things didnay go tae plan

Wee Fergus came wae a vision oan the insane or so sumbudy sade
Liftin the mast the wee man moved fast wae a new stadia custum made
It houses the lads Bhoys Ghirls and dad's and any creed ye'd like tae menshon
Completin the chance he went back tae Frans an tae him we staun tae attenshon

All managers up to O'Neel fur the club they'd feel wae support honest an true
The treble wiz wun wae skill an much fun an then ther wiz the wee score of 6-2
In Europe we'v moved wae pedigree approved we ur back we we shood be
Effurt an will wae a hunner per sent skill hiv patience yoo jist wait an see

Henrik up frunt wae Sutton getting the brunt an the fans givin it laldy
Lambert an Lennon sweep Douglas a goal tae keep an then ther iz Bobo Balde
Mjallby wae Joos look efter the reer hoose
wae wings patroled bae Agathe an Petta
The rest o the team fill in like a dream man things sure ur getting betir

Noo ahm older an a wee bit bolder like before ah kin pass oan mha luv fur the club
Walfrid made the move tae put Celtic in the groove an unity wiz tae be the hub
Nae matter if ye ur black or wite or fly a tangerine kite in this fold ther iz a place
Fur we'r the groop in the green an wite hoop
an we want tae put a smile oan yer face

Well that's mha tale telt wae feelins felt
an Celic hiv been good ah kin honestyl say
So az ah draw tae a close an no wantin tae impose your hapiness is what ah pray
Ah wid defend and also recomand it's tae Paradise ye shoold get up an go
It's a wie o life jist like the wife only mer joy tends tae flow

Ah find it hard tae stoap like oan a slippy rope in this wee ode ah canny hide·
The luv of the green an the effectshons
ah'v seen so ahl defend it wae aw mha pride
Harmany an perace gives the release in a team wae roots thit ur Keltic
They ur the best as far east is tae west an they ur called The Glasgow Celtic

PATRICK CLARK, Glasgow

170

My Celtic memories

BORN the youngest of seven children.

Hoops hand-me-downs until replica kits came in a box.

Envious that they all witnessed '67.

Other European Cups won on Subbuteo pitch though, on the bedroom carpet at home in Girvan...Paul McStay hat-trick in the final against Juventus the best.

1977, nine-years-old and the bug bites in front of the telly. Lynch penalty against Rangers. Dad pats my head as I've fallen asleep, as he and uncle Vinny argue over Johnstone's hand ball.

Up the coast to Ayr for my first ever game. Johnny Doyle was sent off and we lost 2-1. I'm convinced it was my fault. My brothers assured me that it was.

Many more travel sick trips to follow.

My first visit to Parkhead with my brother-in-law Alistair. He argues with the barman in the Horseshoe Bar for not letting me in. I was about 11 and had no intention of anything stronger than a Creamola Foam. We left Parkhead to 'beat the traffic' as Celtic scored their equalizer against St Mirren

My second visit was to pay homage to Danny McGrain in his testimonial against Man United - my other team.

Dad positions my sister Fiona down the front and warns: "Now, don't move from here, if you need me I'll be standing half way up." Oh, Yeah! Really easy to find among 20,000 plus in the Rangers End? A story my mum should never hear.

First trip to Hampden and we win the cup against Dundee United. Provan free-kick was world class and socks at the ankles his trademark (I copied it even on the coldest Saturday mornings). Frank McGarvey header and it's all over.

I'm there as we win the Championship 3-0 against St Mirren and panic in case the crowd scoops me up over the wall and on to the pitch at the end. I'm praying my dad doesn't see me on Scotsport and think I'm a hooligan.

Games are won and lost and our first ever video recorder (a Panasonic silver top-loader) is Celtic daft.

European dreams as we lead Real 2-0 going to the Bernabeu. My physics teacher Mr McCann lets the class discuss tactics rather than trig.

European heaven as Sporting Lisbon visit, 2-0 up from the first leg, and I'm there in the Jungle saying Hail Marys with my brother Paul and sister Fiona.

Goals from McAdam, Burns and McClair before half time followed by two in the second half. We were unbelievable and the all-lime green strip was awesome.

As we return home the car runs out of petrol on the A77 at Kilmarnock. Paul drives quietly after being rescued by dad and my brother John in the yellow British Rail van, having travelled from Girvan and back again.

Celtic v Morton. Fiona, Paul and I have splashed out on stand tickets. PENALTY! Nicholas gets his 30th goal of the season and the Daily Record Champagne (No socks and slip-on shoes his trademark, dancing to Simple Minds and U2. I copied it at many a school disco).

It's Centenary Year and cup final day. My nephew Peter is being christened. Well-planned to end in time for the game at my sister's student flat in Kelvinbridge.

Middle of the Kingston Bridge and another petrol disaster. The police helicopter above is asking lots of questions about a broken down Metro above the Clyde on the day Thatcher's in town.

Games are won and lost and the video recorder is still Celtic daft (A Granada own brand front-loader, now in trendy black).

Trophies pass us by, yet I hold out hope in the face of Rangers' celebrations.

I'm delighted as Paul McStay lifts the Scottish Cup. My dad and all his sons sit watching in my brother John's house. Dad's complaining that it wasn't five against such lowly opposition. Who cares!

I'm delighted for Tommy Burns on winning the cup. On reading a story of my aunt Rose's death from cancer he invited her two sons (one only nine-years-old) to visit Celtic Park for lunch with the squad. A fantastic gesture and the mark of a true Celt!

A strong confidence returns when Martin O'Neill is paraded outside Paradise. I continuously drive past the park hoping for a glimpse.

My dream day arrives when, through my work, I am invited to be a sponsor's guest at the game against Aberdeen at Christmas and I invite Gerard, John and Paul to thank them for my Celtic upbringing. The day of our lives as we sit in the Directors' Box and witness a 6-0 demolition.

The first of the Treble is secured against Kilmarnock and I'm there. Larsson is the King of Kings.

The league is captured against St Mirren and I'm there. Tommy Johnson is the king of miss-hits.

On to the Scottish Cup and Gerard treats me to not only a ticket but also a full day out in the Kerrydale Suite as thanks for the Aberdeen game.

There was never any doubt we would win as a fellow passenger on the bus back to Parkhead, sitting beside 'the' Stevie Chalmers, proclaims it was all down to fate: "Did you know Stevie, in '67 I was 14 and foot and mouth was rife. Now my boy is 14 and foot and mouth is rife, this was meant to be."

Times are good and my daughter Anna has seen her first game at the age of three.

Her favourite player? Larsson? Sutton? Lennon? No way, there's only one Hoopy The Huddle Hound!

The video is still Celtic daft (Only now it is a DVD).

CHRISTOPHER MacNEILL, Rutherglen

I have many great Celtic experiences to recall, each with its own 'magic' sprinkled throughout and every single one is special to me and intrinsic to my sense of identity. It appears an impossible task attempting to capture a single moment to demonstrate what is meant by the term Celtic; a term that I first learnt of as a 4-year-old while playing with my big brother's green and white hooped Subbuteo figures. It seems nonsensical to talk of a magic existing even then, but to my amazement (even today as a 30-year-old), magic is the only word to accurately describe how I felt about those wee men in Celtic colours, a magic I somehow sensed then, sitting on the high-rise landing playing Subbuteo.

I attended my first Celtic game as a 5-year-old in 1977, along with my two elder brothers, dad and uncle Jim. The venue was Firhill and the game was to be one of the most important, defining moments of my entire life; an epiphany, a moment that will live with me forever, even if I live to be 150. I remember the parking of my uncle's car and the short walk to the park. Once inside I can remember the passing round of beer cans, the slight whiff of sweat, the sway of the crowd and the sight of hundreds of faces sharing a common passion, Celtic. I remember feeling so secure and contented even though for a 5-year-old, this atmosphere was potentially overwhelming and frightening. But I was with my dad and big brothers and of course uncle Jim - they wouldn't let any harm come to me! And, I had my first glimpse of what I have come to refer to as those magic men - The Celts.

Tommy Burns took a corner kick 10 yards from where we were standing. Even then I was in awe, his bright red hair, his adult and athletic frame, his green and white hoops; they combined in their entirety to form my first real Celtic memory. And I dearly wish Tommy (who became my hero) could know this fact as I know he would be as proud as I am of it. My first ever game, like everyone's is special, and has truly left its mark, but what about the others? What about my first ever Rangers game? A game I told my dad that I was going to be accompanied by my friend and his dad. In fact, I lied. There was no friend's dad, it was just me and Stephen Sharp, and we didn't have tickets. (I have never told my dad this truth, and still feel ashamed to have lied to him)

We lived in Arbroath by this time and my dad would never have allowed me to attend (even though I was 16) without a responsible adult present. But off we went and arriving at the ground, we soon found ourselves among throngs of Celtic fans desperately searching for a ticket.

About to give up hope, at Janefield Street, we noticed a steward allowing two men in by a side door. The naive and by this time desperate 16-year-olds knocked on the door, feeling a little apprehensive about what we were about to say. A steward opened the iron door and after a nervous outburst of "we huvvnie got any tickets mister but we've come all the way from Arbroath…" he interrupted, "ah get in then boys, quick before you get seen…. I shouldn't, but only this once!" And we were in…in the Jungle for our first Rangers game. We nearly fainted celebrating the fact that we were there, the anticipation almost as great as the outcome. Billy Stark scored within 10 minutes from the edge of the box and we went wild. I had never experienced anything like it, and that feeling, like Firhill on October 8, 1977 has buried itself securely in a corner of my heart forever. Perhaps the most satisfying Celtic moments are when we act as Celtic missionaries, introducing a new brother or sister to the family.

Was it the time I took 35 Canadian students to Celtic Park on a Wednesday evening against Motherwell. Or was it the time I drove a minibus full of students to Norwich for a meaningless testimonial, and along with 8,000 Celtic fans, had to be asked to leave by the tannoy announcer 20 minutes after the final whistle? Was it one of the games where I've introduced a girlfriend or university friend to the Bhoys? (Probably around 10 people in total) Maybe my favourite moment has been as a guest of supporters' club? Was it the day I had a 'jungle-esk' experience in the Prince of Wales pub in Hammersmith, as a guest of the Shepards Bush CSC, standing, swaying, hugging strangers as we beat Rangers 2-0?

Getting up at 4am for a 2-hour drive to watch the unfurling of the league flag

173

in the Croatian Centre in the Italian district of Vancouver was something else. Once inside, I could almost have been sitting in Baird's, or my family home, with the warm Scottish greeting I received. That's the thing that makes Celtic magic. It's difficult to describe or to quantify, and it is unique. For us, it really was, and still is, more than a game. But not in a negative or embarrassing pseudo-religious way. It's about being with your family and friends, being with people who share your desires, goals, passions, fears, disappointments, being surrounded by people who understand and empathise with you.

They know where we have come from, they know who we are and they know where we are going, win, lose or draw. My dad always described the Celts as his surrogate dad (his father having given his life for freedom in October 1944, days after the birth of his son, a son he would never see). If Celtic acted as a source of comfort, a sanctuary of safety, a place where a fatherless child could seek solace, in effect act as a surrogate dad to my dad, then who was I to let the family down, by failing to recognise my rightful surrogate granddad? And what about the numerous other magnificent memories? - My first cup final in 88, or McClair's 20-yarder against Dundee one rainy Tuesday evening with my dad? What about the time me and my 2 best pals (as pools agents) get invited to Celtic Park for high tea with Liam Brady and co, to hear the plans for Cambuslang, and took part in a debate about whether Celtic Park should be sold to facilitate private hospitalising?

What about the Raith final when we thought we just could not get any lower? In a funny way, I am glad I experienced that, as I now understand the hardships endured by my dad's generation in the 50's and early 60's. Was it the day in '95 when the Maestro finally captained us to a trophy, and I hosted my first Celtic party in my new flat, and my dad pretended to need the loo, just to catch me exiting the toilet, in order to tell me he loved me? (My first recollection of my dad saying this to me as a man) Or what about the time I travelled to a game on the bus from Arbroath, all alone and draped in my hoops, scarf and tricolour, finding myself sitting next to an elderly lady of around 60 years old all the way to Perth? We spoke about many things which would surprise and amaze, when imagining a conversation between a 16-year-old boy and 60-year-old woman.

That lady made me proud to be a Celt, and made my parents proud also. She told me that I was 'a credit to your family and your team' and as she met her nephew (a Dundee United supporter) at Perth, she enthusiastically waved me goodbye and good luck. The memories are rich and vivid, weaving tales of magic throughout.

Or the time I sat in the Dundee United end with my dad, pretended to be home supporters, having to disguise the laughter as dad 'went too far' and clapped and cheered nearly every time United strung a few passes together. The common thread running throughout each and every special or 'magic' moment is one of relationships with family or friends - growing up, from boy to man, becoming a boyfriend or husband, moving onto fatherhood, passing on Celtic and her traditions from granddad to grandson.

The 'magic' that is Celtic you see, is not magic at all, it is really quite simple and straightforward, once stripped bare and deconstructed, it is an extended family in every sense. This is why, for me, my favourite Celtic moment is not standing bewildered and dazed, on the ' turf unsure of what emotion to feel, as we stopped 10 in a row, nor is it the moment we thrashed Rangers 6-2.

No, the greatest Celtic moment for me is, strangely enough a game we lost 4-2 to Rangers. Why did this game provide my personal favourite Celtic moment? Nothing complicated or difficult to comprehend. Simply, this was the first (and last) time that I stood at Celtic Park with all the most important people in my life (who shared a love with Celtic) present - my dad, 2 big brothers, my 2 best pals and one of their dads too. We were all there together and at 3pm that day, singing the Celtic song and hugging my family, I experienced my greatest ever singular moment as a Celtic fan.

A moment I would pay a million dollars to experience again. We had dreams and songs to sing, we didn't care if we won lost or drew, and we would not be moved by the Hearts, Hibs or the Rangers. We were faithful through and through, and from the first time to the last I had experienced Celtic, I would not be walking alone. I belonged! And THAT is the real 'magic' of 'the Celtic'!

JOHN KELLY, Hailsham

I GREW up listening to music which was totally old-fashioned, and my dad supporting Hearts, my brother supporting Rangers, and my mother not really having a clue about football. So I thought that I could be different by supporting Celtic Football Club.

My dad was always going on about how good Hearts and Rangers were but nowadays he has not tried to make me turn against Celtic, but he and my brother have started to support Celtic more and go on about how well they play in their games. They even know more about Celtic than they do about the teams they support.

CRAIG RENWICK (age 14), Dumfries

Threads of gold and white on green

Emerald green with sparse gold braiding
Torn by the tug of frantic fingers
Winding cotton cog minutes
Till final whistles
And victorious warwhoops
Signalled the outpouring of joy.
More vivid than the pulp of a thousand other histories
The pages of time written in beer stains and sweat marks
The ink of experience and proof of being
Woven together in its sight, smell and every touch

My father's scarf was a family heirloom
A testament to authenticate the glory days of old
In arid seasons and times of chagrin

175

Its vibrant colours and the touch
Of its texture brought comfort
Urging us to recall our team were once
'Champions of Europe' and 'Treble Winner'
The first to do 'Nine-In-A-Row'
A rub o' the green an we'll be Champs again next year, son.

For years it hung over
The coat rail of my cupboard
Oft times slipping to fall
Between building blocks and Subbuteo goals
The rudiments of learning gathered on the shelf below.
The outstretched white lines running parallel its measure
Mapped an ideal escape route
For toy cars to travel.
The bite marks of clenched teeth
On close-run cup finals
Perfect potholes to avoid
On rainy day seasons spent indoors.

Ah'm stuck on tap ay ma Da's sojers
An wir aw shoutin an
Screamin an
Singing 'Grand Old Team'
An ah'm feelin sick
Cos ah've stuffed ma macaroon
Bar doon ma gub too quickly
But ah'm no gonnae be
Cos ma Da hid tae plead way ma maw
Oan his knew tae let me come
An ah hid grabbed the macaroon
Afore oor Chris could see it
An left him wi a Snowbaw
An a manky Bovril tae drink
When oan goes thi troops and flash forards
An ah still cannae see
But the ol' man dis a stoorie

An thurs a great big ROAR! fae thi Jungle
Like thousands ay Lions git oot Calderpark zoo
An all ah knows is we'll be signin' 'Off Tae Dublin'
Aw thi way home
Til ma Maw tells is tae
Git tae sleep fur school in the mornin'!
An ah take a last bite o thi scarf
Like ma Da did when he wiz a boy
An watched the Lions thit won the BIG CUP in Europe
An dream ah'l see the Bear dae thi same

176

When not working the back shift
I would send him to sleep
With childhood stories
Of exaggerated characters
From provincial folklore.
If he timed it correctly
He'd leave the scarf as a car track
In the hope I would spy it
Tiptoeing a path
Across his toy-ridden floor.

It was then you were at your finest, Da.
Scarf draped proudly round
Yer bold neck and shoulders
Or flung high towards my ceiling
Of thunder strikes and wonder goals.
When, arms gesticulating phrase
Vowel and consonant
You spoke of your heroes of old
My bedroom became a green
And white flurry of scarves and flags
Screaming out Championees!
As Caesar and Murdoch
Brought back silver and gold
'Finest team in the world'

We're playin Alexandra in thi School Boys' Cup Final
An am no sure we'll beat em cos they hammered us twice before
Bet the Bear wouldnae be scared ma Da says
An ah kiss ma poster an pray thit the Bear keeps me right
But ah worry cos boys dinnae kiss other boys unless they score
An the Bear disnae look like he liked it.
Ah wantae be the Bear an scare all the Zandas away fae oor goals
An roar up the an score thi winner
So ah polish ma boots an say a prayer tae Saint Martin
Tae help us bring home thi cup like Jinky an Lennox.

Ah've sprayed oan ma Ralgex and shined ma legs up wi Flora margarine
So ah looks like a right Pro when a git oan thi park
Bit there's still somethin' missin an a realise
Ah've no got ma scarf
Ah try no tae cry cos the Bear wouldnae cry if he left his lucky scarf
Bit ma stomach feels like when Mrs Finnon gave us THE BELT
Fur swappin fitba stickers wi Steven McCall in the library.
An then it happens an ah've got water oan ma cheeks
An defeat in ma ears an some boy must've winded me
When a went tae header thi baw

177

Coz ah'm bawlin and greetin
Bit ah've no scarf to cry in tae an hide.

Ill health and family raising meant the scarf lay dormant most Saturdays
While McStay, Grant and Bonner made us proud to wear the hoops.
As the familiar trumpets signaled the waiting was over
Arthur Montford introduced weekend highlights
On STV's Scotsport and on special occasions
The live transmission of an Old Firm cup final.

Leaning on wooden chair backs for crush barriers
Pulses racing and scarves round necks
We were swayed to the throb
Of green and white terracing
Urging our team on to bring back the gold.

Ah'm wearin ma good scarf mi ma new CHAMPIONEES! pin badge
In pride o place next tae ma Da's '67 Cup Winners
An a badge of Johnny Thomson
More agile than a cat, son, and twice as quick.
Ah've saved two penalties an if ah score ah've beat McCall
An won thi Burnfoot Scottish Cup against the Rannoch Road Rangers.
Ah've kissed thi baw an put it oan its spot
An ah've bited ma scarf tae highlight thi tension.

Now ah'm Jinky Johnstone an Dixie Deans
Bobby Lennox an King Kenny
George McCluskey and Charlie Nicholas
An The Bear all wrapped up in one
An ah'm rarin tae score in tae McCall's McCloy
In goal fur thi 'Gers.

McCloy grins wi confidence
An the windae watchin Lears next door
Ready themsels tae grab an burst
Ma primrose bound banana blooter.
But ah've been watching Champagne Charlie
An ah know how tae send McCloy thi rang way
So ah grin back a ah stare tae the right
Bit hit it tae the left
An ah shut ma eyes fur hunners o' hours
Before ah hear the wooden crack
Uf baw struck Council fences
An ah know it's there
An ah've burst the back o thi net!

McCloy's on his knees
The crowd go wild (An so do thi Lears!)

An am runnin doon thi road
Wi ma scarf rippin thi wind
McCall no far behin me
Singin 'Feed The Bear'
Tae thi refrain o thi Lears
Goin mental at his Mammy.

The gold has returned now
Though The Bear has stopped playing
Glory days have been reinstated
By a new 'King of Kings'
Paradise itself has been restored
And is fitting of a new millennium:
Long gone are the days
Of crush barriers and the Jungle's roar;
The Lions and Jock Stein
Have new stands of their own.
Where the sweet vendor stood
Our stadium is all seated;
McDonald's have replaced
The macaroon bars and tablet
We fought over as boys.
Even the ten bob car watchers
Somehow seem to have vanished;
The songs of Rebellion
Silenced by season books and club laws.

But in change there still lies Tradition:
Glen Daly and The Huddle
A marriage between old and new.
Our cherished crest
Still a four-leafed clover
Green and white hoops
Still cross over our players' breasts
As they did Charlie Tully's and Willie Maley's
And all others etched in memory and folklore.

Though tattered and torn
My father's scarf sits not out of place
As we 'Stand Up for the Champions' of 2002.
Outstretched high above my shoulders
Taut and frayed by the clasping of hands
It intertwines both visions of present and past:
The hallowed days of the sixties;
The childhood memories of '81;
The Treble winners of last season;
How we romped home fine one.
But most of all I raise it

179

In a final chorus of triumph
It serves to remind as we sing 'Walk on'
Why as Celts, we will never walk alone.

PAUL SLUDDEN, Burnfoot, Airdrie

What Celtic means to me

WHEREVER I travel, people ask which part of Scotland are you from and what team do you support. I have a 50/50 chance of getting it right... Isn't it hard to try and explain just what Celtic means to a Celtic-minded family – isn't it hard to stop looking at Celtic issues through green tinted glasses – and isn't it difficult to not get upset when someone criticises our Celtic family?

I was brought up in the Celtic tradition, and to understand that we are not just a football team – but a family – a way of life. The importance of our Irish roots and our charitable background are instilled since birth – we believe in each other and we believe that in sticking together we can achieve the impossible. Just like any other family in your street or mine.

We laugh together, and we cry together. We win together and we lose together. Remember the day we beat Rangers 5-1 in 1998? My big brother and I walked through the turnstile and I turned to him and said, "please don't let us get beat," and he said, "just go in and sing like hell." What a day that turned out to be. I could have been physically sick with nerves. Without bad times, we would have no good times.

I will bring my children up to understand the importance of honesty, faith and forgiveness. I will bring them up to appreciate the joys of giving to those less fortunate. And I will bring them up to respect others regardless of their sex, race or religion. But most of all, I bring my children up to be a part of the best family in world...Glasgow Celtic.

ADELE WADE, Bannockburn CSC

In a green and white world, there's a green and white street
Where green and white kids have green and white feet
There are green and white dogs, and green and white cats
Where green and white kids live in green and white flats
The green and white people have green and white eyes
And the green and white kids eat green and white pies
There are green and white husbands, and green and white wives
With green and white kids and green and white lives.

JOANNE RUSSELL, Alexandria, Dunbartonshir

Chapter Thirteen

Farewell to Lubo

To a place they call "The Paradise", where Earth and Heaven meet,
Came a little Czech magician, with his magic in his feet.
Some looked askance and wondered, when we got him for a song;
But what sublimely-gifted play has proved the doubters wrong.
The deadly pass, the lethal strike, the vision, flair and fight,
A pocket titan, undeterred by age or lack of height.

The rapturous legions loved on sight and thundered their acclaim
Of a player certain of his place in Celtic`s Hall of Fame.
But now, although the Championship`s unstoppably on track,
The joy is tinged with sadness for Lubo won't be back.
Around the slopes of Celtic Park we'll miss that special thrill
As "Lubo, Lubo" fills the air, in homage at his skill.

Our fathers told of Gallagher, of Tully`s matchless way;
But we can tell our children that we saw Moravcik play.
Farewell, farewell, Wee Lubomir, your star is diamond bright.
They ever will remember you who love the green and white.
                                          LOUIS ROBB, Edinburgh

Moravcik is the man

Who can win the game for us, with dash, panache, élan?
The answer is quite simple, for Moravcik is the MAN.
On a muddy day down Tannadice way, when victory is the plan,
When a touch of genius is required, then Moravcik is the MAN.

Lubomir Moravcik, drink twelve pints, pronounce it if you can,
In any language, drunk or sober, Moravcik is the MAN.
The little maestro's God-gifted talent, cheers us every wan,
The facts are there for all to see, that Moravcik is the MAN.

Against Rangers, what better stage, wee Lubo is in the van,
Nutmegs, headers, right foot, left, still Moravcik is the MAN.
They can keep their Dutchmen, and big Tore And,
None of them can lace his boots, 'cos, Moravcik is the MAN

Henrik, Paul, team mates all, from Sutton, through to Stan,
All agree, especially me, that Moravcik is the MAN
One regret, we all must share, about Lubomir the MAN,
Can we not turn the clock back? And make you Twenty WAN
                                FRANK McCLURE, Buckhaven, Fife

On Saturday 2nd February, we were driving home from Falkirk after doing some shopping, when we decided to go up to Airth Castle Hotel for a little drink. As we walked up the path, we see this rather large bus, with blacked out windows and "Celtic Football Club" written on the front window!

Therefore, we definitely havd to go inside! There we were sitting in the bar and who was sitting with their back towards mine, none other than John Robertson, yes John Robertson! Me and my mum decided to go and stand outside and watch the players go on the bus – as you do. As every player walked by she would say "Good Luck" and everyone answered her with a thank-you! We were standing there smiling as we waited for the next player to appear (and me putting on my lip-gloss!) It was LUBO.

I was shouting to my mum "he's coming!" There he was chewing his gum, smiling, walking down the path! I had been waiting for this moment for ages to see my hero and I just froze! To think he was just a footstep in front from me. All I could manage was a smile, a blunt one at that! Next I saw this wee Bhoy walking down the path blushing; yes Shaun Maloney!

He was smaller than I was. I couldn't believe it! You could tell he wasn't used to getting this attention, even if there was only about 5 people standing there! Here he came with a smile and hair that could light up a room! Neil Lennon! He was lovely! He stopped, had a wee chat and laugh and away he went! A wee gem!

We saw this tall, well-dressed man running. and I mean running, out the hotel and down the path, probably hoping we weren't there to annoy him! He still had time, even if it was while he was running, to sign a few autographs and say a "hello!" which was much appreciated! Again I can't say how much we appreciated that, even if it is just a smile! It can change everything!

TONI LYNCH, Falkirk

The day Lubo cured my Parkinson's

MY name is Michael Righetti, a proud season ticket holder and shareholder for several years now, and I was diagnosed with Parkinson's Disease 11 years ago. Fortunately, my illness doesn't restrict me from attending Paradise every other week to cheer on the Bhoys. So let me tell you my story …. The game: Celtic 5 Rangers 1.

I attended the game with my brother in law, Marco, and by half-time Celtic were leading Rangers 1-0, thanks to a superb strike by Lubo. As the teams left the park, it was at this point that I began to feel unwell with the symptoms of my illness taking over. ie. muscle spasms and rigidity of my whole body. To cut a long story short, I was wheeled into the first aid room, complete with tartan blanket thrown over me, and lifted on to a 'bed'.

After taking my medication, I now had to just lie and wait for it to kick in while Marco explained to a somewhat bemused looking 'first aider' that I had Parkinson's. As I lay on the bed barely able to move, I realised that a lot of the first aid people were talking about me and appeared to be wondering what they were supposed to do with me. Then it happened.

The huge cheer that went up could only mean one thing …. Celtic were 2-0 up! Well, even if a cure for PD is never found, I'd swear I came closest to experiencing it at that moment. With blanket thrown aside, I was off that bed and running out the door before you could say Hail, Hail.

  To this day, I will never forget the look on all the faces of everyone in that first aid room. One minute I'm lying there totally unable to move, the next I'm off and running out the door cheering as I thanked them all. Call it an adrenaline rush when I heard the roar, call it what you like ... but I got to the top of the steps just in time to see Henrik chip Niemi to make it 3-0. Fate, ... or what?

  After confirmation that it was Lubo (again) who scored the second, I couldn't settle down and enjoy the rest of the match .... for singing and dancing! And the rest is history ..... Or was it a masterstroke pulled by Doctor Jo?

MICHAEL RIGHETTI, Clarkston, Glasgow

There's only one Lubo

Lubo, a great Celtic player
Lubo, with his original trickery and funky hair
Lubo, a great ambassador to the game
Lubo, week in, week out, the crowd chanted his name.

Lubo, he punished Rangers with his flair
Lubo, oh, how their defence just could not bear
Lubo, Jozef Venglos brought him here
Lubo, I think he deserves a great big cheer.

Lubo, he dazzled us with skill
Lubo, oh, how he gave my spine a chill
Lubo, he's leaving us for Japan
Lubo, he'll achieve success because he's the man.

MARTIN DUNWOODIE, St Luke's High School, Barrhead

Chapter Fourteen

Visiting Paradise

MY story is one of generosity by Celtic Football Club. My husband's family come from Glasgow and they moved to Bexley in Kent before he was born. He still had family in Glasgow and for many years spent his 6 weeks school holiday in Glasgow. His family supported Celtic and when he was old enough he went along to see them play. I, however, was born and bred in England and spent my childhood going to see Charlton and West Ham.

When we married he told me that one day we would go to Celtic Park and I would see how proper football was played. The years went by and due to having children and no money we never got to see Celtic live, occasionally on TV we would see them. When Sky started to broadcast live games he was in his element and I got to see them play, albeit via TV. And I must admit they were good. In 1998, my husband was diagnosed has having cancer of the throat. We were devastated.

My daughter knew that he wanted more than anything to take me to Parkhead before he was too ill. She wrote to Celtic explaining the circumstances and she waited. She did not tell anybody .A few weeks later she phoned me and told me that she had received tickets from Celtic to see them play Dundee United at home. I was gobsmacked. My husband was right in the middle of his radiotherapy and we did not think we could go, but the doctors thought it would be good for him. So my father-in-law paid for the train tickets and my children paid for the B&B and of we went.

I have never been to Scotland before and it was great. We had a great day we went to the shop before the game where I phoned my son (Celtic fan). He was gutted. Before the game we went into the bar upstairs where my husband was amazed to see Danny McGrain - his hero (autographs). The match was great. Celtic won and afterwards we saw all the players leaving, though he has not forgiven me yet for not getting Henrik Larsson's photo. The day went by in a haze and before we knew it we were back on the train to London.

This break to see his beloved Celtic helped my husband to get through this bad time. He is now in remission and as soon as we can save enough we are coming back! Thank you Celtic you made a very sick man very happy and allowed him to forget reality for a small time.

ELAINE WILLIS, Dartford, Kent

Different class, on and off the park

DINING at Celtic Park with my parents, sisters, nephews and nieces gave some of us a great opportunity to possibly get our replica shirts signed if we saw any of the players. Our first opportunity came with Henrik Larsson. Henrik was quiet and pleasant, duly signed our shirt and we went back to our table. Next up was Jonathan Gould who splendidly helped a young boy celebrate his birthday. Jonathan exchanged a few pleasantries with us and also signed my jersey. I was a little disappointed later to notice that his 'signature' looked more like that of Craig Burley's.

The real highlight of our evening, though, was that Tommy Gemmell, a Lisbon Lion and the only British man to score in two separate European Cup finals, was seated at the next table to us. With slight trepidation we approached big Tam. We wanted to get his signature, but were also mindful of interrupting his lunch and his company.

We needn't have worried. 'Big Tam' welcomed us with open arms and took the time to ask us our names, where we came from and genuinely take an interest in us, and all with a wonderful smile and great sense of humour. In addition, Tam didn't just sign his name, but signed a personalised message then added his signature.

My conclusion from meeting 'Big Tam' was that I now knew he was different class, both on and off the park! Corollary: At our table afterwards, my six-year old nephew asked, "Who was that man?" When we explained that 'Big Tam' was a Celtic legend and European Cup winner, my nephew replied "Him? He's never a footballer, he's too fat!" (Sorry Tam! However, while no longer in his prime, I know that this would not offend 'Big Tam's' sense of humour).

JIM MOONEY, Hook, Hampshire

My tour of Celtic Park

THREE years ago my grandpa and aunt came from Ireland, to stay for a couple of days. My dad decided to get us a tour of Celtic Park, so he asked Tommy Boyd to arrange it for him. Two days later my dad, grandpa, cousin and I set off for Celtic Park. When we arrived we met up with Tommy Boyd and started the tour, but we kept getting interrupted by fans looking for autographs from the players.

My cousin and I got pictures with all of the team, and we got to hold the Coca-Cola Cup and the European Cup. We also got to sit on Billy Connolly's seat and stand on the park. I got to go through the tunnel as well and after the tour we went to the Celtic Shop, where I bought a Celtic T-shirt which I still have.

I really enjoyed my tour of Celtic Park and my dad got us some tickets for the Dunfermline v Celtic game. So we went all the way to Dunfermline for the game which I also enjoyed a lot.

KIERAN O'BOYLE (age 11), St Bridget's Primary School, Baillieston

Birthday Bhoy story

ON my last birthday I had the most superb present. My Mum and Dad had secretly booked a tour of Parkhead. They said we were going to Glasgow so I could spend my birthday Monday. We turned down some back streets and suddenly I had my first glimpse of Parkhead.

First thing we did was we went to the Celtic Superstore and I bought a "Golden Bhoy" t-shirt. I also bought the latest *Celtic View*. When I went outside there was a gang of people crowding a person, when I got closer I recognised it was Neil Lennon and I got his signature on my *Celtic View*. I also had Chris Sutton's, Rab Douglas' and loads more, my Mum had a photo with Tom Boyd the club captain. I also saw this big man and I didn't know who he was. Now I know that he's Bobo Balde, one of Celtic's top defenders.

At last we went on the tour. We went into the trophy room and I had a photo with all the cups even the European Cup. We sat in the heated seats. We also sat in the pressroom. We visited the Jock Stein Stand. We sat in the away dug-out because we come from Wales. We did lots of other things as well. This was a day to remember.

SEAN TAYLOR, (age 9), South Wales

A grand day out

I SAT anxiously in the school hall as the winners of the competition names were called out "Julie Patoin', Christopher Rice". I couldn't believe it, I had won! Lots of feelings were flashing through my head, I felt over the moon, overjoyed and amazed because this was no ordinary competition, the prize was a trip to CELTIC PARK!

I had many sleepless nights and the days slowly progressed to the actual day. Finally the day arrived and I had butterflies in my stomach. I couldn't even eat my breakfast. We had to be at the Police Station for 10 o'clock, as this was the meeting place. As I walked up to the police station I thought about what might happen during the day. I thought I would see the stadium and that I would be at it.

We were travelling by bus and we arrived early so we went to the Celtic Shop. I bought a Celtic lollipop and a copy of the Celtic View and after five minutes or so we went in. We were then greeted by our tour guide. This was the first time I had been to Celtic Park so had no idea on the size of the stadium, it was huge! The tour guide took us to the Directors' Box and the dugouts where I could imagine the tension felt by the manager watching a closely fought match. We then visited the trophy room, I was glad I did not have to clean all those cups! I had such a good time and I met Stilian Petrov and Bobo Balde, who both signed my t-shirt. Can you imagine how I felt? I won't let my mum wash it now!

My visit to Celtic Park was so exciting; I took so many pictures that I had used two rolls of film in my camera. I sent copies to my uncle Jim in Australia, he phoned to say how much he liked them and he has pinned them on the wall of his office. He pays extra just to be able to see Celtic on television on the other side of the world.

I gave my Celtic lollipop to a friend who lives in Holland and supports Ajax: it was the week after Celtic had played them and won. I hope it made them feel a bit better.

By the way my great uncle, Johnny Price played for Celtic.

CHRISTOPHER RICE, Holy Family Primary, Kirkintilloch

The Jock Stein Stand

Grass green and cloud white scarves
Knotted plumply
Are variegated leaves of merino wool.
Grey Glasgow winds sting tarmac paths
Casting a chill kiss.
My wife and I clasp gloved hands,
Walking together as close shadows.
Traipsing the stairs of the Jock Stein Stand,
Our mouths curl like lemon wedges
Tasting syrup anticipation.

Sprinkler watered lawns and fresh paint smells
Radiate with tempered zeal.
Through the concrete fissure a vista unfolding.
The green pitch of paradise,
Neat and regular, as baize on a billiard table.

Swelling tides of emerald and opal shaded supporters
Singing sounds of a stormy symphonic sea.
Sharing a drink of steaming Bovril
Sipped from a tartan vacuum flask.
We talk of players running out to glory
Larsson, Sutton, Nicholas, Lennox and McGrory;
Chapters in the Celtic story.
The centre circle.
Hush!
The referee's whistle.

DAMIEN DONNELLY, Louth

Paradise

I WOULD like to tell you about my favourite place and try to explain to you why it is so special to me. This place is a football stadium, in fact it is one of the biggest and best stadia in Britain, but that is not why I love going there. The place is magical to me. It is like a green island full of splendour out on its own, so different from the depravation of its surroundings. This magnificent football stadium is situated in the East End of Glasgow.

The stadium towers above all the buildings around it, as it is an immense structure and a magnificent piece of architecture. Parkhead is the name of this football stadium and all the supporters who frequent it affectionately know it as Paradise. Through the turnstile you go and enter into a vast green and white heaven full to capacity time and time again with 60,000 supporters full of passion for their heroes.

You cannot help but be affected by the compelling atmosphere that surrounds you, overwhelmed by the sheer magnificence of your surroundings and with a heart full of hope and anticipation willing your team to win is a great feeling.

Cheering on your favourite players, trying to encourage them, letting them know you are behind them even when they are getting beat. You experience a rollercoaster of emotions - from happiness when you are winning, to devastation when you are losing.

Most games put you through all these emotions and many more, but there is nothing to beat the feeling of joy and pride you feel as you leave the stadium after your team have won a game. I love to play football myself and I enjoy watching the players displaying their skills on the pitch. I can only hope that one day I might have some of these skills. I watch and learn and then I try to copy them when I am next playing or training. I think football is the best form of entertainment and I am very lucky to have a season ticket that allows me to go to Paradise and see my heroes play every home game.

This is the highlight of my Saturdays and I get excited when my uncle comes to pick me up to go. You can also go to Parkhead when there is no football match being played to have a look around the stadium and a tour of the trophy room and the boardroom. This is a brilliant day out; seeing all the trophies from the past and recent times. There is a tour guide who explains the history of Celtic to you. I thoroughly enjoyed this day out and I found it very interesting, it made me even prouder to be a Celtic fan. Being near the dressing room where the players prepare for a match was just unbelievable to me, and being allowed to sit in the dugout and walk around the perimeter of the pitch was magical and like a dream come true. So many times I had watched from the stand and wished that I could be down there on the pitch where the action was.

Nothing can beat the feeling of being in Paradise surrounded by another 60,000 Celtic fans when your team is winning - it is like being at a great big party. You feel like part of a great big family and they are all very happy, laughing and singing songs. It is just magical and I enjoy it very much and that is why Paradise is my favourite place.

RYAN BURNS (age 13), Bishopbriggs

Celtic Park (Paradise)

WHEN I was in primary six I made my first ever trip to Celtic Park. Celtic Park is nicknamed by many Celtic fans across Scotland, Ireland and the rest of the globe as Paradise. Celtic Park is situated in the East End of Glasgow. For many Celtic fans it is a fortress. The Celtic team was founded for the poor in the East End of Glasgow and for that reason Celtic Park was built. This stadium is indeed my favourite place and fondest childhood memory.

When I first visited Paradise it was in the developing stages of what would be one of the largest club stadia in Britain. Celtic Park was soon to and now does hold just over 60,000 Celtic fans for almost every home match.

The seats are green with a few white seats spelling out that magical word Celtic. When I got off the coach outside Celtic Park I was surrounded in a sea of green and white. It was on that day I had my very first experience of the green and white hoops of the mighty Glasgow Celtic. As I walked deeper into the crowd I felt as if I was being swallowed up by the sea of green and white.

When I first entered the stadium I was struck down by the noise and the atmosphere around the stadium, which was electrifying. It made the hairs on the back of my neck stick up and if I hadn't got gel on I think it might have made the hairs on my head stand up as well.

Over the years, Celtic Park has been the home of many great players and has always been renowned for its atmosphere. Legends such as Paul McStay, Willie Maley, John McPhail, Bobby Lennox and without a doubt the best legend ever to wear the green and white hoops of Celtic was Jock Stein. He brought European Cup glory to Paradise and added to the roar.

The greatest roar at Celtic Park on that dull Saturday afternoon was when the players broke away from their traditional huddle before the match kicked off. At that moment my eyes filled with tears and I knew that moment would stay with me forever. When you are at Celtic Park it is like a fairy tale. You are within a stone's throw away from some of your greatest heroes and idols. When you are standing on the terraces you are like the extra player. Many teams would say that about Celtic. The reason why they have such an outstanding record at Celtic Park is because of the 60,000 fans who are singing for their team inside the magnificent stadium.

THOMAS STANLEY (age 15), Belfast

Celtic Park

You can see Glasgow,
You can see the grassy pitch,
You can see people,
Eating chocolate bits.
You can feel plastic seats,
You can feel cold concrete,
You can feel vibrations,
As people stamp their feet.

You can smell hotdogs,
You can smell Bovril,
You can smell pork pies,
Everyone's had their fill.
You can hear cheers and chants,
You can hear songs,
You can hear hissing,
When the referee wrongs.

A busy day at Celtic Park,
That's what my dad says.
I really hope we go again.
It's one of my favourite days.

GARY CAMPBELL (age 10), Lossiemouth, Moray

189

Chapter Fifteen

The scarf

THIS a 1950's story and if you were around then and poor (and that was just about everybody!) and lived in a Lanarkshire mining village then phrases like (1) "Do you know how long father's got to work the pit to earn enough for that?" (2.) "Waste not, want not", etc will be very familiar to you. I'm not saying this kind of story could only happen then, but it definitely has a 50's ring to it.

Anyway, to our story…

My father bought me my first Celtic scarf in 1957. Not one of those 'cheaper' woollen ones but a rather more 'upmarket' smooth cottony affair probably acrylic! (The reader can, if they like, revisit familiar phrase number 1 from the first paragraph here)

Then: - "What d'you mean you lost it?!" roared my mother looking as if she was about to go into orbit. (Familiar phrase number 1 again perhaps?)

"Well, I didn't, er, exactly lose it", I pleaded.

"Look my lad, this better be good. Sit down and tell me exactly what happened", she commanded.

"Well Ma, we went to the game… and… well… seven-one. I mean Ma seven-one! Well I just sort of got carried away, overcome".

"Overcome? You'll be well overcome when you father gets back from the pit and you get the back of his hand. What happened?"

"I threw my scarf onto the pitch, and one of the players picked it up," I replied. "And wore it" I added, trying to soften the blow by trying to inculcate an element of vicarious pride. She was not for softening.

I went to bed that night wondering what had become of my scarf. What had apparently happened was that it got caught up in the player's kit in the dressing room arrived at Celtic Park but a cleaner threw out a whole load of stuff and my scarf ended up in a rubbish dump.

Near this dump a couple were walking their dog when it suddenly took off to chase a rabbit.

"I told you we shouldn't have taken him out without a lead. We'll need to find a rope or string". They spotted the abandoned scarf and used it for this purpose. When they got back home: -

"Put that scarf into the pile were putting out for the Ragman** tomorrow". (The reader can refer to familiar phrase number 2 from paragraph 1 if they like at this point)

**For young readers or those not familiar with this practise let me explain. The Ragman – or Rag-and-bone-man, a Central belt version of Steptoe, would go round the streets blowing his bugle to "drum up" trade. You would give him clothes you no longer wanted and he'd give you a balloon or some other such desirable trifle. Very astute: - Give clothes, get balloon. Derivative market traders we were not!)

Anyway, the scarf was on its way in the Ragman's lorry to be recycled.

190

However, his helper, a waif who was a dead ringer for Jimmy Johnstone (maybe it was wee Jinky!) rescued it after work and wore it proudly to the evening kick-about in the park. The convention was that jackets and other sundry items of clothing were placed judiciously on the ground to form the goals. As was the custom, play continued well into the dark and the scarf could not be found so Jinky ran home to get his Mother's statutory scolding for being so late.

During the night a strong gusty galeforce wind got up and carried litter, paper and the scarf for miles and the scarf would have been carried even further but it got snagged up in the branch of a tree, the one in my garden.

"Ma, Ma! my scarf's come back! I knew it would".

I rushed out into the garden to retrieve it but it wasn't there. I did this every morning for over a week, but no sign of it. It must just have all have been a dream. What a fool I felt. I had dreamt the whole thing, and worse, believed it.

"Don't worry" consoled my mother; "we'll get you another scarf… sometime".

The next day… "Answer that door," shouted my mother.

I opened the door and there stood a smiling Charlie Tully. Charlie Tully! Was this another dream?

"I think this belongs to you wee fella" he said, proffering a scarf, my scarf!

I grabbed it and shouted, "Ma! Maaaaaa! I told you I hadn't exactly lost it!"

"Come in Mr Tully," said my mother, "it was very nice of you to take the trouble to return the lad's scarf. But how did you know it was his?"

Charlie, having a quiet chuckle to himself, indicated a part of the scarf that wouldn't be noticed when folded in the usual way where my mother had written in small but clear letters, in indelible ink, my name and address. And that particular practise, of marking everything with indelible ink, like rocking and rolling, listening to Como, Calvert and Cole, and standing in The Jungle, was another familiar feature of our visit of our Lanarkshire world in the 50's!

DAVID BREMNER, Elgin, Morayshire

I saw the Celts

OUCH! I cried, as Miss Marshall, our English teacher, squeezed my left ear between the thumb and forefinger of her right hand, with her left she reached over and lifted my English writing book. She marched me up to the front of the class, ear in hand, and read aloud what I had written. "I SAW THE CELTS"

It was Monday morning back in nineteen seventy-three, I was twelve-years old. We lived in the port town of Larne in the North of Ireland, where the ferries cross to Stranraer in Scotland, the shortest sea crossing between Ireland and the British mainland.

Miss Marshall stood me in the front of her desk, facing the class. She held up the open book, where I had written 'I SAW THE CELTS' in big block capital letters, for all to see. Standing behind she informed the class, "Danny Maguire will spend the remaining fifteen minutes telling 2.b why he used a full page of his good English writing book, to say he saw the Celts".

Rubbing my ear I turned and said, "It's coz, me and my mate Packie Nugent'…

"Tell the class" she bawled, interrupting me! And remember you have fifteen minutes."

I straightened up, faced the class, took a deep breath and began.

"It all started about a month ago when me and my mate Packie, who's in 2a, were in the dressing room after football training. We play in the town league under 12's. Our manager is Jim Hamill, and he was asking the under 14's manager did he want tickets to go to the Scottish Cup Final between Celtic and Dundee United, coz he was organising a coach. I looked at Packie, and Packie looked at me, because we always, always wanted to see Celtic playing.

"Because," Miss Marshall said behind me, "Not coz, the word is bee...cause".

"Ok Miss," I said and carried on...

"Jim said the tickets were £6.00, altogether. £2.00 for the match tickets, £1.50 for the coach, £1.00 for the boat, and 50p for the coach driver. When I said, 'that was only a fiver'. Jim said, 'There is a free cash draw on the coach that cost a pound.' When I asked Jim could we go, he said that as long as we had the money, and our parents agreed, he would keep an eye on us. But the next day when I met Packie, the two of us were mad as bulls, coz... I mean because, neither of us were allowed to go. My Ma said, 'No way would she let her twelve-year-old son go gallivanting round Scotland,' and Packie's said more or less the same. Both of us knew that this was our only chance to see the Celts. So we came up with a plan.

"Getting the money was easy, we both have paper rounds, I minded my sister's pig of a son a few times, and ran errands for the neighbours. Packie was lucky; he had £3.00 in the post office, so he didn't have to work as hard as me. Jim said the boat was leaving at 8am. And we would be back in Larne by 9pm the day of the trip. We told our parents that the under 12's were playing in a football tournament in Belfast on that date, to explain why we were missing for a whole day. I felt a bit guilty because our Ma made us up lunches, and my Ma gave me a pound for chips the morning we left."

I looked around and asked Miss Marshall, "should I go on to the bit about the boat?" She said "Yes, but I shouldn't call my nephew a pig." I said OK. I turned to face the class again, and continued.

"The ship was called Stena Nordica, and when we got on I says to Packie 'Jesus, Packie. Did you ever see as many Celtic supporters in all your life?'"

"Leave our Lord out of it Danny," said Miss Marshall, interrupting again.

"OK Miss" I said, and went on.

"There must have been two hundred Celtic supporters on the boat, they had come from all over the place, Donegal, Derry, Belfast and though it was only eight o'clock in the morning they were all singing Celtic songs... 'Hail Hail' and 'It's a grand old team' but the one I like the best was a song about 'wee Jimmy Johnstone', because wee Jimmy is easily my favourite player. When we pulled away from the harbour, Packie, and me went up to the breakfast bar. We had sausages, bacon and egg, white pudding, black pudding, fried tomato, fried bread and beans, for £1.80 each. The ice cream bar was open, so we clubbed the rest of our money together and bought a chocolate sundae between us, then we went up to the deck to be sick.

"I said 'I thought it was the fried tomatoes that done it'. But Packie said he heard you should never eat on an empty stomach. When we felt a bit better we fed the lunches our Mas gave us to the seagulls, then back down to the boys in the bar. When Jimmy saw us he told us not to eat on the boat, as it was too expensive, and that we would be stopping at a café outside Stranraer, where a full breakfast cost only 50p.' Packie went back up to the deck to get sick again.

"The coach trip to Glasgow took forever; we stopped for breakfast, then stopped at a pub. Twice after they stopped at the side of the road for a pee..."

'Yes, yes Danny, we get the picture,' Miss Marshall said. "Now carry on." All the class giggled.

"It was two o'clock, and we were just coming into Glasgow, Jim stood up at the front of the coach, and announced he was starting the free draw, that we had paid for. Everyone got five yellow tickets for the first prize of £20.00, and five green tickets for the second prize of £10.00. My green tickets were from No's six to ten. I separated No-7 from the rest and said to Packie, 'look Packie green for Celtic and No-7 for Jimmy Johnstone, I bet you I'm going to win'.

"I know you won't believe it, but you can ask Packie Nugent if it's true. Green ticket No-7 was called out and I won the second prize of £10.00. When we stepped off the coach at Hampden Park, Jim warned us 'To stay beside him at all times, because if we got lost he'd kick our arses'. Then he clipped Packie round the ear for saying 'If you can't find us, how will you find our arses?'"

I could hear Miss Marshall snigger behind me.

"As we went to the turnstile we could hear the noise of the crowd, they were chanting, 'CELTIC! CELTIC!' I could smell hot-dogs, and though I was hungry again I was far too excited to eat. Jim pushed us through the turnstile and handed in our tickets. Packie said he was going to keep his eyes closed 'til he got to the top of the steps but Jim told him 'not to be bloody stupid, that he'd trip and break his neck'."

Miss Marshall said, "Language, Danny." I said, "OK Miss," and continued.

"There was loads of steps to climb, the noise of the crowd was getting louder, and louder; my heart was beating like a machine gun. When we got to the top it was like a dream, there must have been eight thousand Celtic fans around the stadium. The noise was deafening. We took our place high up on the terrace behind the goal. From where we stood, all the way round both sides of the ground, Celtic flags and scarves were waving. Behind the goal at the other end we could see the dark orange, of the Dundee United supporters. All of a sudden the noise got even louder, Jim said 'there they come lads' and pointed to the side of the pitch, the teams were coming out. First big Billy McNeill, the man who lifted the European Cup for Celtic in 1967, then the yellow shirt of the goalie. I think Davy Hay was next, he was followed by a few more Celts, then like a rabbit jumping out of fire, wee Jimmy came flying out and kicked the ball he was carrying towards the goal at our end'.

At this point I stopped, I felt a lump in my throat. I turned to Miss Marshall and said, "Miss I don't care if the class laugh at me, but when Jimmy Johnstone ran into the penalty box after the ball, I started to cry." Miss Marshall looked at me, and said, "I don't think they will."

And she was right, I looked at all the faces in the room in front of me, not one person was laughing.

"Celtic scored after twenty minutes, Packie and me went mental even though it was at the opposite end, and we couldn't see how, or even, who scored it. We grabbed on to each other and jumped up and down, shouting 'CELTIC! CELTIC!' the whole stadium was a sea of green and white. Just four minutes later, we scored again. From then on the crowd sung every Celtic song that was ever written, and I'd say no one sung as loud as Packie Nugent and me.

"When the players came on for the second half, Jim pointed to the sideline near the dugout, and asked, 'Lads do you know who that is?' There in a long black coat talking to Billy McNeill, was Jock Stein, the greatest manager in the world. Later on we saw a banner that read, 'IF GOD WANTS TO QUIT, BIG JOCK WILL TAKE OVER!' Celtic were on the attack most of the second half, and in the eighty-ninth minute Hood scored for Celtic, making it 3-0, a few seconds later the whistle blew. Celtic had won the Scottish Cup'

"After the game I bought a scarf each, for Packie and me out of my winnings, we ate hot dogs and chips before we boarded the coach, then set off for Stranraer. Nearly everybody, including Packie, slept on the coach. I sat looking out of the window at the Scottish countryside, thinking about the game; it all felt like a dream, I was the happiest kid in the world.

"We waved goodbye to Scotland as the boat sailed out to Stranraer, then went down to join the rest of the supporters in the bar, all the way over we sang Celtic songs and waved our scarves. Packie and me went up to the deck to watch the boat dock as we came into Larne harbour.

"It was then my heart stopped; I could see my Da waiting on the quayside. I said to Packie, 'We've had it Packie' but Packie wasn't listening, he had spotted his Da as well. Getting off the boat I walked slowly down the gangway, and over to where my Da was standing, my whole body was shaking. I looked up at him and just said, 'Sorry Da', I was expecting a belt round the ear. But imagine how surprised I was when he asked 'Did you enjoy the game?' I stuttered an answer, 'Yea...yes'.

"As we walked to the car my Da told me Jim had told him a few days earlier that we had paid our money, and that he would keep an eye on us. But if I ever pulled a stroke like that again, I wouldn't get off so lightly."

Just then the bell rang signalling the end of class. As I made my way back to my desk, Miss Marshall told the class, "Danny Maguire will write one hundred times in his best handwriting, 'I saw the Celts' and produce it first thing in the morning."

Everyone laughed when I replied, "No problem at al,l Miss'."

ALAN McGORRIAN, Co. Clare, Ireland

1,2,3,4,5, everybody's outside so come on let's ride
To the Parkhead stadium around the corner
The Bhoys are all here and it's time to do what we wanna.
A little bit of PETTA on the wing, and some AGATHE he's a fast wee 'hing,.
A little bit of HARTSON there up front,
A little bit of DOUGLAS for a great big punt.
A little bit of LAMBERT running back, A little bit of MJALLBY he doesn't hack.
A little bit of LARSSON banging them in,
A big bit of BOBO he'll have you for his dins
A little bit of the MARTIN O'NEILL ... man!

MARY FRANCES BLAIR (age 12), Motherwell

The best day of my life

I DIDN'T know I'd never see them again. What would I have done? Everything would be so different. I am Craig Maverick and I am 13-years-old. Two months ago my parents were killed in a car crash. I ask myself every day, why am I left to face the world alone?

The social workers moved me into this hellhole they call a children's home. Nobody understands me, nobody even knows me.

The only thing I have is a dream, a dream that one day I'll be the star player for Celtic Football Club, the best team in the world. I'll score the winning goal for Celtic and hear 60,000 fans screaming my name. For now, I suppose life in this dump is all there is. Nothing more and nothing less.

There are other boys here in this place as well. Some of them hang around in small groups, quietly sneaking around day after day. I try to avoid them, as mean as it seems. The other boys, they're worse

When I first arrived here, everything seemed to have been blocked out my head and that's why I didn't realise. However, the longer I've been here, as the days go by, I seem to notice more and more how different the gang are. They always get more treats than others, more sweets than others and, worst of all, they're a lot bigger than others. I've heard some of the other guys whispering stories about them.

There was a big search when a boy reported something missing. A couple of days later, the boy was in hospital with a broken wrist. Another boy, he won a big competition to visit France or something along those lines. The week before he was due to leave he was injured so badly he had to stay in hospital for a week.

So you might say these boys could have suffered from careless accidents, but I wouldn't be at all surprised if this gang were to blame.

I was completely dreading my birthday. It was my first birthday without mum and dad. I miss them more than I can say, but I've got to concentrate on other things – or so the social workers keep telling me. I think my birthday party was the first time I really felt at ease in the home.

Some of the guys I'd never talked to before got me presents. They all knew I was a massive Celtic supporter so they got me a big Celtic cake. It was the best time I'd had since the accident but it wasn't to last.

Somebody had warned me before that the gang of lads didn't like Celtic. In fact, they hated them. I still kept my posters and everything I had, because they were the only things I had to make me feel at ease. However, that day I was too glad to even notice the gang. That's why it happened.

I was taking my gifts upstairs, shutting the door behind me. I turned round to see the gang on the other side of the corridor. As I took a step forward, they took a step forward. They were almost mimicking me, apart from the fact there were more of them, lots more.

I was panicking. I could feel the presents slipping because my hands were so sweaty. The pounding of my heart getting faster and faster was all I could hear. They were heading straight for me. I was alone, nobody could help me now.

The leader of the gang knocked the presents out of my hands. I was too petrified to even care. Then another boy shoved me against the wall.

"Betcha you're loving all this attention, ya wee Celtic wannabe!"

I felt each kick going inside me, each blow landing on my terrified face. That was the last thing I remember.

I woke up to the smell of disinfectant, with voices chatting away. I dreaded opening my eyes to face the world again. Somehow, I felt the need to see where I was and that's when the biggest blow came.

I'd seen those distinctive eyes so many times before, but only on my bedroom walls. There he was, the one, the only Henrik Larsson. My hero and there he was, staring straight into my eyes.

"Hi, I thought you'd never come round." These were his first words. He stayed with me in the hospital for a couple of hours. At first, I didn't know, what to say, but we talked about everything – football, Glasgow, the home and, of course, Celtic. The time flew by and before I knew it, it was night-time. That night, before I fell asleep, I thought, maybe this was the best day of my life.

A couple of months on and things are looking great. The gang have all been split up and sent to different homes. Everyone seems to be so much friendlier with them gone, even the adults. I've made some new friends here as well. We get on really well, even though they don't support Celtic.

There are a lot of things that have happened, like the accident and the beating I got, but I've got to look to the future now. You never know, you might just see me score that winning goal for Celtic one day.

TERESA WONG, St Luke's High School, Barrhead

TIM sat down at his desk. The teacher was handing out a piece of paper to everyone. He looked at the paper. It said Celtic Writing Competition at the top. Tim loved Celtic. His favourite player was Henrik Larsson. Tim had met him and he had never been to a Celtic match because his dad supports Rangers and his grandpa is too old to take him. No one else likes football in his family that much. He read the paper. He could win the chance to go and see Celtic and meet them! Then he realised, he was no good at writing stories.

Tim went home that night and told his mum and dad about the competition. They said, "You can go if you are with a friend and there is an adult with you", said Tim's dad.

"Ben's dad can take us, he loves Celtic".

"Well you can enter the competition then as long as you are with an adult", said Tim's mum.

"Thanks mum, thanks dad".

"Don't get your hopes up, remember that you still have to win the competition first".

"I know".

The next day Tim entered the competition. He had written his story out the previous night with the help of his dad and his mum. He gave it to the teacher then he asked Ben if he had handed his in. "Yep!" said Ben.

"I can only go if an adult takes me, there are three winners so if you and I win can I go with you and your dad?" said Tim.

"Sure, but I will need to ask my dad first", said Ben

"Okay".

Tim got out of bed. It had been two weeks since he and Ben had entered the competition. Today they were supposed to find out which three people won. Tim got up and into his school uniform. His dad drove him to school but when he got out of the car, there was no sign of Ben. The bell rang and he went into his classroom, still no sign of Ben. The teacher did the register and just as she was about to read out the winners of the competition. Ben walked in. "Sorry I'm late miss" said Ben.

"Have a seat Ben, we were just about to read out the winners of the competition" said the teacher.

"Okay miss" he said.

"Okay children the winners are Ben, Tim and Joseph".

Everyone clapped and Tim had a big smile on his face. He looked over at Ben, he didn't look very happy at all.

Tim saw Ben at break-time. "What's up with you, aren't you happy that you won the competition?" said Tim.

"Of course I am but there is a problem. My dad isn't well and he can't take us to the match, the doctor said that he has to rest".

"That's terrible, is he okay?" said Tim.

"He should be, I am sorry we can't go".

"It's okay," said Tim.

Tim felt really bad. He wasn't going to the match and Ben's dad was unwell. Instead two of the runners up got to go and they brought Tim and Ben back the players' autographs, so it wasn't that bad.

LYNNE McCORMICK, (age 13), St Luke's High, Barrhead

Excited fans, the game's about to begin,
I have a feeling we are going to win,
The Celtic team stand strong in their huddle,
The opposition walk about in a muddle,

Kick-off is taken, and the fans gasp and stare,
As the ball darts about from player to player,

Big Bobo stands solid at the back,
When the ball comes near he hits it with a whack!

Up to midfield, the Bulgarian Petrov,
He shows the courage the Celts are made of,

Through to Larsson, number seven,
When he scores, the crowd's in heaven,

The fans are singing a familiar tune,
"What a goal!" they're over the moon,
From the stands comes an almighty noise,
Another great victory for the Bhoys!

LYNDSAY WALKER (age 13), Jordanhill School, Glasgow

Gerry's Treble

YOUNG Gerry woke with the sun warming his face through the large hole in his bedroom curtain. He jumped out of bed with a spring in his step murmuring to himself "Saturday! Football Day!"

Gerry played centre forward for his local under 14's team 'Norten Boys Guild'. They played in the Glasgow and District under 14's league. Gerry was the top scorer in the team and was being watched every week by senior scouts, keen on getting him to put pen to paper.

Gerry was an only son, his mother died giving birth to Gerry. His dad, Dominic, was a huge build of a man, whereas Gerry in comparison was very slightly built, more like the build of his late mother Bernadette. Gerry's build was to stand him in good stead for later years.

Gerry's dad worked as a Drayman with the local brewery and through the nature of his work was extremely fond of a tipple.

As Gerry grew up he was more or less left to his own devices. His main ambition in fact was to become a professional footballer. In stark contrast his dad Dominic had no interest in football, he was more of a betting man (horses and dogs). His dad had never saw Gerry playing football. His only recollection of Gerry's football was when he got his report card with the comments from his class teacher 'Gerry will need to realise that there is more to life than just playing football'.

Gerry was playing for the Under 11's school team at the age of seven he was that good. Gerry's spare time was spent on the hills above his village of Norten. With his heavy boots he would run up and down the purple heather clad hills. This was a great stamina builder and would play a great part in his later football career.

Gerry was always pleading with his dad to come and watch him play, but 'Big Dom' as he was known in the pub, was more interested in his tipple and his flutter on the horses and dogs. To be fair to 'Big Dom', Gerry never wanted for anything to do with his football. He just had to ask and it was there – boots, new tops, anything that was ever needed.

Gerry hurried downstairs where his dad had his breakfast of cornflakes and toast waiting on the table. "Good morning dad" Gerry said excitedly. "Are you coming to the game today? We're playing in the 'George Russell' Cup Final!" "I'm sorry son, I can't make it" Dominic answered. "I've got to meet one of my mates from the brewery." Gerry was visibly disappointed that his dad wouldn't be there to see him in his first cup final.

The cup final was to take place at Firhill, the home ground of Partick Thistle, their opponents were Rangers Boys Club, joint leaders with Gerry's team in the Glasgow and District Under 14's league. What a potential thriller of a game this was going to be.

The Norten team bus arrived at the main door of Firhill a full hour and fifteen minutes before kicking off time. The team filed off the bus one by one, resplendent in their green blazers, grey flannels and club ties and each carrying their club bags with the club crest emblazoned on the side. The club was well known for being the best-dressed team on and off the park. This was due to the hard work and discipline of their team manager, Jack MacKay, a school teacher at the local St. Patrick's High school. The Norten team also held a record of never having a player booked or sent off throughout the season. A record of which the boys and their manager were very proud.

Norten Boys Club were famous for their all-out attacking style of play with two tricky and lightening fast wingers and Gerry a deadly finisher at centre forward, whereas, Rangers Boys Club were a more defensive team hitting on the break and hoping to score. They were a big team, with few of them under six feet in height. Gerry's direct opponent on the day was Findlay Menzies, a six foot, three inch – twelve stone, 14 year old, already a schoolboy signing for Glasgow Rangers. Both Gerry and Menzies were reckoned to be the two best prospects in their league. A ding-dong battle looked to be on the cards.

As kick off time approached the boys began to become excited as they could hear the noise of the crowd assembling in the stands. There were nigh on 600 spectators in the ground by the time kick off happened. A roar went up as the teams emerged side by side from the players tunnel. Norten immaculate in the green and white hoops of the famous Glasgow Celtic, their adopted team colours. Ranger Boys Club in Glasgow Rangers royal blue, who sponsored the boys club.

Gerry scanned the crowd to see if perhaps his dad had come along to watch the game, but was unable to pick him out. The game kicked off to a hectic pace with end-to-end thrills and spills. Half time arrived with the two teams still locked in battle and a score line of nil–nil. The second half kicked off at the same hectic pace. Rangers Boys Club broke away up the park when their centre forward went down in the penalty box, as though he was mortally wounded, the referee immediately awarded a penalty kick, from which the centre forward amazingly recovered to slot home the spot kick to put 'the wee gers' one up. Norten unleashed an onslaught on the Rangers goal for a full thirty minutes and were rewarded with a magnificent goal from centre forward Gerry. It was game on now. Gerry's stamina which he had acquired through his hours of running through the heather in his big heavy boots was paying off for him. He was running the big centre half of Rangers Boys Club ragged. With one minute to go, it looked as is the tie would go to extra time when Gerry was upended by Menzies 35 yards from Ranger's goal, when he was clean through with only the keeper to beat.

Menzies was immediately red-carded for the foul, as he was last man. Gerry recovered after treatment with the 'magic sponge' and volunteered to take the all important free kick. The Rangers wall lined up, their whole team back inside their own 18 yard line. Gerry placed the ball and back pedalled ten yards, never once talking his eye off the ball, a tip given to him by Jack, his team manager (who himself had played senior football for numerous Scottish Second Division teams and held a wealth of experience).

Gerry began his run up to the ball and hit a ferocious left drive which swerved around the Rangers defensive wall and the only time their keeper saw the ball was when it exploded in the net behind him. Gerry immediately ran to the crowd with arms outstretched in acclaim of his wonder goal. His eye caught a familiar face in the crowd, it was his dad 'Big Dom', he had come to watch him play!

Big Dom had gone down the local pub as was his Saturday habit where he met his pals from the brewery. It turned out they were all avid Partick Thistle supporters and they talked Dominic out they were all avid Patrick Thistle supporters and they talked Dom into going along to the final. When they found out the young centre and man of the match was Big Dom's son, it was celebrations all round. Dominic muscled his way to the podium just in time to see Gerry being presented with the cup and his man of the match award.

His heart was bursting with pride, but the day was not finished, as Gerry and the team arrived in the dressing room with the cup, his dad came into the dressing room accompanied by an elderly man in a cloth cap. The duo called Gerry and Jack, the team manager aside. The elderly gent was the chief scout for 'Glasgow Celtic', Gerry's boyhood idols. The scout asked him if he would like to sign on an 'S' form.

Form for Celtic? Gerry took 2 seconds to give his answer. What a day! What a treble! Winning the cup, signing for his boyhood idols and best of all, his dad coming to watch him play, which was to be repeated week after week as his dad gave up his horses and dogs to watch his son carve a niche for himself as a professional footballer with 'The Famous Glasgow Celtic'.

PETER ROWAN, Alexandria

Celtic are white
The clover is green
The Celtic View
Is my fave magazine.

Celtic are white
The clover is green
Our Henrik Larsson's
A goal machine.

Celtic are white
The clover is green
Martin O'Neill
Has a wonderful team.

Celtic are white
The clover is green
All over the world
The Celtic have been.

Celtic are white
The clover is green
I like Balde
Because he is mean.

Celtic are white
The clover is green
I hope to play for Celtic Football Club
by the time I'm seventeen!

JORDAN LOVIE (age 10), Peterhead

Chapter Sixteen

Martin O'Neill

Words for this man are not hard to find,
Determined, hardworking, brilliant and kind.
But putting to words the work that he's done,
like the indelible 'TREBLE' that was second to none.
He came to our club and took up the task,
within a few weeks we knew he was class.
He reformed the team, in terms of their spirit,
and the new-found spirit that went along with it.
They brought this to games both home and away,
in the goals that they scored, in the way that they play.
As the winter went by, and the summer drew near,
we had a hold of the league with our point score so clear,
but a chance at the 'TREBLE', no one had guessed,
and with O'Neill at the helm we would give it our best.
It came to the day, the party was booked,
and there wasn't a thing O'Neill overlooked.
We did it with courage, leadership and pride.
We worked as a team, we stood side by side.
When the whistle was blew, the party began,
in the eyes of the fans, it was thanks to this man.
So I leave you with thanks, to express how I feel,
no matter the journey, 'WE'LL MARCH WITH O'NEILL.'

GARY LAFFERTY, Viewpark, Uddingston

An engagement with Mr O'Neill (a true story)

WE had decided upon the engagement ring that Saturday morning in the Argyle Arcade in Glasgow. I knew of the arcade as I had lived in the Dear Green Place for six years, having emigrated from my hometown of Dublin in 1989.

In terms of Celtic, they were to be miserable and lean years, except maybe for an occasional St Patrick's uplifting, that is! Then to add irony, the Bhoys won the Scottish Cup in 1995 on the very weekend I moved back to Dublin.

But being Irish, surely I had to have some luck in life... It just so happened that Celtic were unfurling the league flag at Parkhead against St Johnstone that Saturday, so the weekend visit to 'Glesga' served more than one purpose.

And so I got the opportunity to bring the dear lady to see my other beloved! We had met the previous March, in Dublin. She was touring the pubs after a Texas concert and I was just touring the pubs trying to avoid the French rugby supporters. When I bumped into her, I had to pass comment on her flamboyant red hair, a typical 'Maureen O'Hara' image, but was I to be her 'Quiet Man'? Time would inevitably tell. She was from Armagh in the North of Ireland, only a hundred miles away.

So e-mail addresses were exchanged and modern communication technology was to determine our futures and bring us closer together. At that stage, my Scottish mate Tam (a Rangers fan) and myself both had red-haired girlfriends, so we decided to stick a tenner on Red Marauder to win the Grand National. It only romped home at 33/1, the same day as the Bhoys won their first Championship under Martin O'Neill's shrewd management. So the proceeds of that flutter helped to send us on a leisurely break to the Costa Brava. We had got on so well that I decided I wanted to spend more time with this lady. So we discussed getting engaged and eventually becoming man and wife.

When I felt that I had a fair chance of acceptance, I set about planning how to 'pop' that question. It didn't take long to pick a venue – good old 'Embra', a handy place to pop over to see the Bhoys, especially on the occasion of an Old Firm game. So that was the date sorted too. Now all I had to do was make arrangements, and the small matter of wrestling my mate's Celtic season book off him, so that my potential wife could attend the game with me.

Booking the hotel and flights was easy, a posh five-star hotel and budget airline seats. Convincing my fellow season ticket holder, Noel, to part with his ticket was a bit more difficult. I tried every trick in the book, but no way on this green earth would he even contemplate such a sacrilege. In desperation I hinted about the special occasion involved, when his attitude suddenly changed – "ah sure why didn't ya tell me" – he replied.

So I had to refund his already-paid flight cost, and then promise to give him my ticket for the next Old Firm game. Having got over that obstacle, the stage was set for the big occasion. Edinburgh was in full swing that day.

The 'All-Blacks' were in town with a promise to give Scotland an education in rugby (as they tend to give most other nations). We arrived in the hotel, a rather posh one too and we soon knew by the frequency of the knocks on the door from the various attendants – bar stocker, shoe polisher etc!

So we ventured out to acquire some vocal lubrication, as there were no spare tickets for the rugby. A pub-crawl later, I suddenly remembered that I had not booked anywhere for dinner. In panic, we rushed back to the hotel and pleaded with the concierge to assist us with a venue. Due to the rugby, everywhere was booked solid. Of course he recommended the nice posh restaurant in the hotel, and after a few seconds deliberation, we decided it would suffice. So it was time to get suited up, time to rehearse the question, but surely it would be nice and quiet downstairs.

The restaurant transpired to be really nice and we were shown to a waiting area where we had an appetiser and perused the fine menu. Suddenly the good lady thumped me in panic, " there's only one man in Scotland wears those glasses" she commented as a man rushed past us

"Guess who" she asked. I looked at her in disbelief, surely thinking that I was the subject of a good old wind-up. Our waiter then arrived and sensed our excitement and curiosity with a smile. "It's him alright," he said. I explained about our special occasion and asked for some advice on matters of etiquette.

He whispered that he would send the headwaiter over discretely to have a wee word with me. We were shown to our table and then my mind was on the serious matter to hand. Alcohol had only slightly numbed our nerves. Then I looked around and noted that Mr Martin O'Neill was sitting at the adjacent table with his family. Talk about pressure! The good lady went to powder her nose and the head waiter came over immediately, shook my hand, wished me well in advance of my quest, and then reassured that refusal rates at this particular table were negligible.

In my mind I envisaged other diners watching, thinking " That man must be somebody if the manager is shaking his hand and not Mr O'Neill's!" I had been advised well. After the main course and before the dessert was the time to pounce. A nod to the waiters and the champagne came down, and the table was then moved out. I went down on one nervous knee and popped the question. Nervous deafness meant I had to ask again. Assured eventually of an acceptance, a kiss was then exchanged to rapturous applause from the other diners. I turned around and Mr O'Neill was applauding me, shook my hand and exchanged a witty view about married life!

The high of the occasion had me nearly in tears, as we tucked into a beautiful dessert which had 'Congratulations' written on the plate with chocolate sauce. Later as he was leaving the restaurant, I made a feeble attempt to wish him and the team good luck for the game the following day. Dumbstruck would be an understatement.

As my fiancée was from the North of Ireland, (and much braver than me) she chatted away to him. For once, I was the 'Quiet Man'. My excuse, of course was that I realised the pressure he was under and didn't wish to disturb him.

It was with a heavy post-engagement hangover that we ran for the Glasgow train that Sunday morning. Celtic won the match as I shared my story and good fortune with fellow supporters. We have since won the league, but nevertheless, that was a season with some very special memories that we will never ever forget. We had also made some special new friends in Scotland. So now we are planning the wedding. Believe it or not, the only suitable date available was Friday 13th September, but with our luck, that certainly will not be a problem.

I have even considered sending the Bhoys' boss an invite, and I have secretly reserved a place, for you never know who might show up on the big day!

KEVIN McGURK, Palmerston, Dublin

The man they call O'Neill

A saviour came to Paradise one sunny day in June.
Dear Lord, we prayed, please let him be the one to lift our gloom.
And, as he went about his task with passion and with zeal,
We knew our prayers were answered by the man they call O'Neill.

The weeks and months went swiftly by and we started to believe.
That the Bhoys would be the Champions – A goal we did achieve!
Each time we beat the Bhoys in blue, the feeling was surreal.
And who had worked that miracle? The man they call O'Neill.

Now Celtic are the Champions – we're back on top once more.
And, from a sea of green and white, you'll hear a mighty roar.
As we acclaim our heroes and the man who gave them steel.
One day we'll carve his name with pride, the man they call O'Neill.
MARGARET PORTER, Glasgow

The Bhoys' Prayer

Our Martin Who art at Celtic
Hallowed be thy name
When thy will is done thy game is won
At Parkhead as at away games
Forgive us our bad passes and give us more wins against Rangers
For thine is the Larsson, the Lambert and the Lubo.
O'Neill.
SHERRY DOCHERTY, St Hilaire de Riez, France

Martin O'Neill oh Martin O'Neill,
I've often been to Parkhead for a meal,
Hoping to meet your fantastic team,
But all I got was vanilla ice-cream.

Martin O'Neill oh Martin O'Neill,
When my mummy sees you it makes her squeal,
In sheer delight it must be said,
She even wears the Hoops in bed.

Martin O'Neill oh Martin O'Neill
The fans all think that you're the real deal,
You led the Bhoys to the top of the league,
We all knew that you would succeed.

Martin O'Neill oh Martin O'Neill,
I wish I knew how it must feel,
To be a winner in green, white and gold
And for your Bhoys to score a goal.
KIERAN McHALE (age 7), Duntocher, Glasgow

Chapter Seventeen

Paul Lambert- Player of the Year

P is for the passes he makes
A is for the accuracy of his shots
U is for the ultimate player he is
L is for those long, raking passes.

L is for the leader he is
A is for the ambition he has
M is for the master of Celtic
B is for the best player in Scotland
E is for his European medal
R is for the respected player
T is for the top guy.

GERRARD HUGHES, St Luke's High School, Barrhead

Johan Mjallby

At the right of a three-man defence he'll go
One side Joos in the middle Bobo
Super Swede, strong as an ox
Big as Goliath, but cunning as a fox.

Fantastically gifted player
But he should not be a mayor
Playing for his beloved Sweden
You'd never see him beaten.

Sent off in the recent Old Firm game
John Hartson the same
A great player we cry
We hope we don't have to say bye
For a while anyway.

CHRISTOPHER McDAID, Holyrood Secondary, Glasgow

There's only one Johnny Hartson
There's only one Johnny Hartson
He may have no hair
But we don't care
Walkin' in a Johnny Hartson land.

JONATHON CONEY (age 13), Coalisland, Ireland

Jinky or Kenny?

WHO is the greatest Celtic player of all time? Many people argue about the legends that have worn the Hoops. In my family two names crop up all the time, Johnstone or Dalglish. My dad is adamant that this title belongs to King Kenny (as my dad calls him) but my grandfather is equally adamant that it's Jinky.

Jimmy Johnstone was born on September 30, 1944 in Viewpark, Lanarkshire and joined Celtic in October 1961. In a career spanning 14 years, he was among the team that brought the European Cup to Britain for the first time. With his amazing dribbling, 'Jinky' was appreciated around the world by both fans and opponents. His hero and pal George Best described Jimmy as "a genius who could walk into any team in the world". He was an important part of Jock Stein's team that swept all before them, winning countless Championships and cups. He made his debut for Celtic in 1963 and played his last game 12 years later in 1975. The only disappointing statistic of Jinky's career was the amount of Scottish appearances he made. In total he only played for Scotland 23 times which was a major disappointment for my grandfather and people of his generation.

Born in Glasgow in 1951, Kenny Dalglish is regarded as one of the greatest British players of all time. Dalglish joined Celtic in August 1967 and was one of the many classy youngsters ready to step into the shoes of the Lisbon Lions. He could play as either a midfield player or a striker and he made his league debut at Celtic Park in a 7-1 win over Raith Rovers in October 1969. A splendid career with Celtic ended in 1977 with Dalglish as Celtic captain as Celtic won the League and Cup Double. He was transferred to Liverpool for a record fee of £440,000 where he continued his remarkable career. Unlike Jimmy Johnstone, Dalglish holds the record for the most appearances for Scotland having been capped 102 times. It seems to me that both of these players have the credentials to be "the greatest Celtic player of all time". My dad and my grandfather just beg to differ. One thing I know they do agree on, is the fact that it has been to Celtic's great benefit that Jimmy Johnstone and Kenny Dalglish have both pulled on the Hoops and let's face it could any of us disagree?

LAUREN HART, Glasgow

My favourite goal

ALAN THOMPSON scored the goal I have chosen to write about. It was scored during the game against Dunfermline. Celtic were 4-0 up and on the attack. Stilian Petrov was running with the ball at his feet trying for the fifth goal of the match. A Dunfermline defender tackled Petrov about 30 yards out, and down he went. Henrik Larsson stepped up to take the free kick. He placed the ball carefully. The wall of defenders retreated a few more yards. Would it be a goal?

The tension was building. He raced up to the ball and launched it into the air, trying to curve it over the wall. His plan did not succeed. However it was Celtic's lucky day! The ball rebounded to the feet of Alan Thompson, who volleyed a shot into the top left-hand corner of the net. What a magnificent goal!

BARRY McGINLEY (age 10), Corpus Christi Primary School

My favourite Celtic player

MY chosen player is Stilian Petrov as he is my idol and I respect his amazing skill. He has brilliant speed and is forever directing inch-perfect shots that almost always beat the keeper. He has excellent commitment to his team and is a very talented individual. He is a team player and he displays good sportsmanship. Stilian is always completely focused on the game and he deserves nothing but praise no matter what the critics say.

He leads by example and has a positive impact on his peers, which enables him to be an outstanding role model. He has recently held a Charity Dinner party to raise a remarkable amount of money for someone less fortunate than himself. I think Stilian is an asset to the team and Celtic are extremely lucky to have his services.

RYAN LIGHTBODY (age 10), Corpus Christi Primary School

Battling Balde

Bobo Balde
A skilful player
Defending the goal
On the ground and in the air.

Bobo Balde
He's tall and strong
With him in your team
You can't go wrong.

Bobo Balde
A focused cool guy
Who dribbles and tackles
And jumps sky high.

Bobo Balde
A footballer's dream
Proud to wear the Hoops
He's a credit to the team.

LAUREN McCARRON (age 10), Corpus Christi Primary School

Valgaeren

I THINK it was in January when my family took me to Edinburgh. We were walking through the streets looking for somewhere to have our dinner when my dad saw a pub. We went into this pub and sat down. My dad went to get the drinks with my mum. My sister and I sat down. Nicola was staring at the people behind us. I said "Nicola stop staring, it's rude!" What did she do? She opened her eyes even wider.

The minute dad came and sat down she started saying "Isn't that... isn't that ...? And my mum got angry and said "Isn't that who?" My dad said, "Oh, it's Valgaeren from Celtic." For a moment I paused, then I said, "Oh my gosh!" My dad told us to ask for his autograph but Nicola and I were too shy to ask so my dad did it instead. Nicola told my dad not to ask because Valgaeren was eating his dinner but he did it anyway.

I'll never forget that night as long as I live because I had always wanted to meet a Celtic player and finally I did.

LISA FEENEY (age 10), St Bernadette's Primary School, Tullibody

The ghost

When I was young I saw a ghost. It could have been a dream, I saw a man I did not know. All dressed in shamrock green. He just stood before me. He stared out my window. He cleared his throat and turned to me. Then he softly spoke. He said I am John Thompson. Then he said how do you do. I said my name I wasn't scared I think I've heard of you.

He told me of his accident. He called it that himself. He told me of the crowd that day. How he was playing well. I asked if it was worth it. His young life for a save. For a football's not a bullet. A goalmouth not a grave. He said if I had to do it once again. Or even ten times more.

I'd never change a thing that day. Because I never let him score. I asked him what it felt like to wear the green and white. He told me to imagine an eagle in mid-flight. He said picture an ocean. At dawn's first kiss of light. Or the joy of Christmas morning. Then triple it five times.

I asked just one more question. Before he said goodbye. He said, of course, I live in heaven. They call it Paradise!

MICHAEL McNEIL, St Catherine's, Ontario

John Thomson's sad death

BY 1931 Celtic had a great young keeper named John Thomson who was the best in the country at the time. Although he was still in his early 20s he had already won four caps for his country Scotland. Shortly after the half-time break during the Old Firm match fixture on September 5, 1931 at Ibrox John Thomson made a brave clearance at the feet of Rangers centre forward Sam English, but was kicked in the face and suffered a serious head injury. Sadly he died later in the Victoria Infirmary. Nobody blamed Sam English for what he did.

CHRISTOPHER GORDON (age 12), Glasgow

Chapter Eighteen

Plastered in Porto

WHEN this tie was drawn I thought, nice, a couple of days in the sun and watch the Celts in their quest for a European away victory. If only things were that simple. My friends and I set off very early Tuesday morning on a four-hour drive to Bristol where we would get our flight to Faro in the Algarve. We had no plans, only a flight and a much-coveted match ticket and we were going to play it by ear. Off we went with our scarves on and our Hoops firmly in place. We arrived in Bristol right on time - about 9 o'clock - and, flying at ten, everything went to plan.

Whilst we were having a drink at the airport we spotted a guy with a Celtic top on working in a bar so we had a good chat about our chances. The flight was smooth - about two and a half hours long - so we had enough time to knock back a couple of drinks. And when we arrived at Faro we saw Celts scattered all around the airport and had a few conversations, mainly about finding somewhere to stay and how to get to Porto. Being completely unorganised we had to act fast.

We managed to find out that quite a lot of Celts were staying at Albufeira in the heart of the Algarve, so we got a taxi and off we popped. Finding suitable accommodation for the night, we set off for a night on the town. Away we went, the three of us with the Celtic tops on, and you could imagine our shock when one of the first bars we visited, the bloke who owned it served us wearing a Rangers shirt. He was actually a good bloke and we enjoyed a good football conversation and put the world to rights.

After a few beers we came across a bar called the Kilt and Kelt, a nice Scottish bar with many Celts drinking in the bar, and we got lucky when we saw a sign behind the bar that said 'Coaches to Porto' and promptly put our names down. Looking around the bar there were autographed jerseys framed up on the wall, including a Jackie McNamara top and even a signed Ally McCoist shirt. The bus was setting off at about ten o'clock the following morning, so just enough time for a beautiful Scottish breakfast to get rid of the hangover of the night before. And what a night that was. I would tell you about it but, to be honest, it is still a blur.

The weather was just like home - raining cats and dogs - but it didn't matter as we were on the bus for about eight hours. It was during this journey to the ground that we were to enjoy the highlight of our trip. About an hour away from Porto we pulled into a motorway service station and as we all started to get back on the bus, word spread around that Jorge Cadete was in the car park. You can imagine our shock, surprise, pleasure, call it what you like. The singing started, "There's only one Jorge Cadete" and then he came on to the bus, signing tops and letting Celts take pictures, still doing his goal celebration - the finger spinning around in a circle. Absolutely brilliant!

He was summarising for Portuguese television. The guy loved it, joining in singing and dancing... Unbelievable, just unbelievable. When we managed to prise our way away from the great man we set off to the ground still talking about our meeting.

On arrival in Porto we were met with what can only be described as an army of police officers, and in all my days of watching the great game I have never been marched to the ground with police with batons, riot shields, shotguns, tear gas and even machine guns.

They certainly wasn't going to get any trouble off me for sure. And the Celts, to their credit, were outstanding, making these guys have an easy night and even sharing a laugh and a joke with the police.

The number of fans travelling to watch the match was incredible there must have been about 8-10,000 fans, only half with tickets, but that was not a problem with everybody getting into the ground with no trouble. We found out the reason for the stormtroopers. It was a couple of years earlier when Manchester United came to town - 15,000 of them - and proceeded to wreak havoc. And in the words of a guy who witnessed it, he said it was the nearest thing to civil war he had ever seen.

When we got to the ground we found a rundown, open ground with fences and barbed wire. When we finally took our seats, the Celts were in fine voice with the songs ringing around the ground. It took just 90 seconds or so to stun both the team and the fans alike. A cross diagonal ball to Capucho, who ran us ragged all night, was swung into the box and Balde timed his jump too soon; Clayton made it 1-0 with an early header.

That left our defenders looking at one another trying to work out just who was marking who. When we finally sorted out some sort of sanity we thought, let's go in at 1-0 and then Mr O'Neill can wave his magic wand. Right on cue, and with the referee poised to blow for half-time, thy made it 2-0. What a disaster. Surely the game had gone now. We went in at half-time in shock. It is bad enough playing a team full of quality but when you are also playing lady luck you know its not going to be your night.

In the second-half they completely battered us and, but for the woodwork, we could have been staring at a 6-0 defeat. With about half an hour to go they scored the goal of the game and what a build-up; neat little passes and then an exquisite back heel right into the path of Clayton who just smashed the ball in off the crossbar. End of story. That left us 30 minutes of damage limitation.

Only another 8 hours on the coach back to look forward to, which is not recommended after a 3-0 gubbing. But still the Bhoys were light-hearted, singing and joking all the way. And what a good sight after the match to see both sets of fans swapping scarves and even police with Celtic scarves on, shaking supporters hands. A nice touch indeed.

We finally reached the Algarve about five in the morning pitch black and with nowhere to stay we were wandering round looking for somewhere to rest our weary heads.

We managed to get a breakfast and washed and changed at the airport then set off on our painstaking journey home. About eight hours later we got home and I have been asleep ever since. A great time was had by all except for the harsh lesson in football by Porto.

ANTHONY WILLIAMS, Burnley

449 miles for Celtic

"SARAH, we're going to Europe."

"Yeah, Dad, I know. That's what usually happens when you win the league." Even after more than two months of celebrating a smile still crossed my face when I said those words.

"No Sarah, we're going to Europe." I couldn't believe it, the furthest I had ever travelled to see Celtic was the icy no-man's land known as Pittodrie and I had always longed to travel abroad to see a game like all the people in my Dad's stories of the good old days. As it turned out, however, I was not yet guaranteed such a trip as my Dad, known more for his love of luxury than his adventurous travelling nature, had constructed a brief list of conditions: "I'll go to France, Spain or Italy. If pushed I might do Germany but I'd rather not. Russia's out. In fact all of Eastern Europe is out. So's anywhere North of Germany. And no third world countries."

"Dad, it's a European competition, there aren't any third world countries involved."

"Portugal, Sarah, Portugal."

Anyway, as luck would have it we were drawn with Ajax (Holland had been given the official stamp of approval) and we began to plan our trip. Luxury-lover Dad started to talk about the three of us - him, myself and my brother, Jamie - flying out ourselves the day before, taking some time to see the sights, then spending the night in a nice hotel before making our own way to the game the next day. This ridiculous plan was, obviously, instantly discarded by Jamie and I, and Dad was reluctantly forced to book three places on the one-day trip run by a well-known Celtic-supporting travel agency.

This involved my Dad and I leaving our house in Edinburgh at 3am to pick up Jamie in Glasgow at 4am to get to the airport at 5am to make the 6am flight: clearly a much better plan. Well, when we finally arrived at Glasgow airport there were two loud gasps. The first, one of total exasperation from my Dad, who, by the way, is also not famed for his airport patience, as he stared, horrified, at the winding queues of Celtic fans waiting to check- in. The second was from me, despite my reputation for being completely unable to even crack a smile until at least noon.

On this day I had been in a somewhat crazed state of excitement from the moment I woke up, as I stared, mesmerised, at the winding queues of Celtic fans waiting to see their Bhoys march once again to European glory, or something like that. And it was hard not to laugh at the lone Rangers fan trying to push, unnoticed, through the green and white masses. After waiting in the check-in queue for so long that our eyes began to close even as we stood and Dad's incessant complaining of "clearly incompetent staff" became no more than a distant, muffled drone, we were finally able to go through to the departures area.

There are few sights as wonderful as a WH Smith's where the only magazine to be found is the *Celtic View* and the book recounting the previous season is on special offer! And there are few sights so typically Scottish as a group of football fans propped up against the bar in full 'replica-strip' regalia at six in the morning! Wherever you are, no matter who you are with, or how big a crowd you are in, there are always some characters who stick out. In this case it was a short, round man who could be no more than 5ft tall with a green afro wig and a long, flowing Irish tricolour cloak.

Or as we named him from an awe-struck distance, "the crazy man." He certainly was a 'character', although, in truth I think much of his character that day came courtesy of the airport bar. Anyway, typically 'the crazy man' was in the seat in front of us on the plane, from where he took charge of the singing for the entire flight. Jamie laughed and I grinned, my dream of a trip to see Celtic was taking shape. Dad still couldn't believe there were no upgrades. So we finally reached Amsterdam.

Well, to be exact, we finally reached Rotterdam Airport from where a coach drove us to the Amsterdam ArenA. It is useful to know that the Amsterdam ArenA is nowhere near the centre of Amsterdam and that the match was due to kick off in about nine hours.

However, a train station was soon found and we set off towards the city centre. Do not be fooled into thinking that this was a physically comfortable journey. It sounds like the start of a bad joke: how many Celtic fans can you get into a Dutch train carriage? But the sight of the amazing stadium had reminded us all of the night ahead and comfort was forgotten as every song we knew was belted out. I say 'we' but really, in order to try and get even more people into the carriage, Dad and Jamie had shoved me into the smallest, furthest corner with a Dutch man and his bicycle. But, once I had extracted the handlebar from my side, the atmosphere around me seemed electric.

This is not an article in a travel brochure advertising Amsterdam and nor could it be because our experience of the city was far from that of a normal tourist. I couldn't tell you what the Dam Square looks like because the only time I have been there it was filled with hundreds of Celtic fans in full voice and all the buildings were shrouded with massive banners and flags. Even when we wandered away from the busy town centre and found a quiet bar down a side street we were greeted with shouts of "hail hail!"

And, as we settled down at a table outside the bar, a frantic Chick Young and his camera crew sprinted past chasing a taxi - not exactly a typically Dutch sight! We did do some sightseeing in Amsterdam, including going to a traditional 'coffee shop', although we did not stay long as Dad, apparently oblivious of the state of those around us, could not comprehend why they did not sell alcohol - "Well, what do they sell?"

Anyway, after a few hours in Amsterdam and a near death experience involving an irate cyclist I began to tire of sitting in street cafés trying to pass the time and I was ecstatic when we finally started on our way back to the ArenA. Inside the stadium the atmosphere was even better than I had anticipated and I was amazed to see that all of the 8,000 seats allocated to Celtic fans had been filled. Somewhat inevitably, out of eight thousand supporters Dad ended up sitting next to one man who was clearly high on drugs, and not the ones you would expect in Amsterdam, as he was far from mellow!

However, he seemed happy enough and was forgotten about the moment of kick-off. He was quickly remembered though when Bobby Petta casually lofted the ball into the net for the first time that evening as his celebration consisted of leaping onto my unsuspecting Dad's back! This was laughed off but, as Didier Agathe began sprinting up the right wing twelve minutes later, Dad began to get that sinking feeling. Sure enough, as we delightedly watched the ball rolling gently into the far corner, the man pounced once again.

This time, however, his sheer joy was such that he managed to strain Dad's back, resulting in Dad spending the rest of the match grimacing in pain whenever he moved and praying that it would finish 2-0.

Well, that is until Shota Arveladze fired the ball past Rab Douglas, when he began to think that another goal would be worth the pain! However, when Chris Sutton headed an Agathe cross under the bar Dad was ready and, as his neighbour came flying through the air once again, he pushed him away with all his strength, which was considerable as the man ended up lying on the ground in the row behind us!

"Just as well I didn't aim the other way" laughed Dad, half out of relief as he peered forward from his seat in the front row of the top tier. Luckily for Dad further wrestling was avoided as the match ended 3-1 to Celtic. My dream of a trip to see Celtic had been realised and it was even better than I had imagined. So we started on the long, overnight journey home, and even though the plane was delayed and the coach driver decided to fill the extra time by taking us on a two-hour, moonlit trip of Dutch motorways, we couldn't wipe the smile off Dad's face!

SARAH FAULDS, Edinburgh

Three carry-outs and a wedding cake

BRIAN CLOUGH'S Nottingham Forest, still then a European force, were the opposition for my first away European trip. The game was played on a frozen night by the River Trent in December 1983. I was a whippet-like 19-year-old, with a thick head of hair, eager & expectant, on that now distant (and absolutely Baltic) UEFA Cup evening for Davie Hay's Bhoys.

Travelling on the East Kilbride No.1 Supporters' Bus, we arrived in time to enjoy the 'invasion' of the city to the full. Plenty of community singing on the bus (and I don't mean Kajagoogoo or Wham!) and all your mates with you, ready to take on the might of the English First Division.

As usual, the English press had written us off as no-hopers. We managed a 0-0 draw, and deserved better, with the 'Maestro' shooting just over the bar from around the penalty spot late on – that and our (considerably sizeable) three-person carry-out getting nicked from behind our parked bus wheels sticking in the memory.

That old fox Clough trumped us at a packed Celtic Park in the return leg, and we were out. Drat, and double drat. Nearly 20 years later, and I've completed my 21st away European trip, with our visit to Valencia. This time we came by Air France, not the EKCSC. Nowadays the whippet is now more like an old heavy arthritic Labrador, and the hair isn't thick anymore (somewhat of an understatement!) but the feelings are the same.

Nottingham to Valencia via Ghent, Vienna, Old Trafford, Cologne, Berne, Paris,

Hamburg, Innsbruck, Liverpool, Dublin, Zurich, Lyon, Luxembourg, Helsinki, Bordeaux, Amsterdam, Turin, and Porto.

Thousands of laughs and hundreds of characters later, the thrill of the Friday European draw is the same. Who will we get? Are tickets a problem? Bus or plane? How much time off work? When best to tell the wife? And then there were the adventures, of course....

In October '84 in Ghent, we found a wee pub in the town on the night before the game. Four us, all about 19 or 20 years old (and skint) had enjoyed three or four rounds and hadn't yet paid a single Belgian Franc. Naturally, we were a bit worried about running up a hefty bill.

We tried to pay a few times, but the owner kept smiling, shaking his head and muttering 'gratis' – it turned out it was his birthday, and once a year he had a free bevy night for all his customers! Yes, ya dancer! Ever lasting shame on you, Joe McH. This guy refused to go the bar, even when it was free all night. Tight? Make up your own mind!

Then there was the five-foot tall bare-chested 'Ready Brek' man from Leeds, who arrived in Cologne in '92 with his luggage - a battered sports hold-all containing a Celtic scarf and a brown piece of cardboard box paper with 'Dover' written on it – and NOTHING else!

He slept on the floor of the city's Corkonian Bar, and the kindly landlord gave him a free pub T-shirt – the sight of 'Ready Brek's' bare sunburnt midriff wasn't helping pub snack sales, after all. We saw him, Lazarus –like at the match, in full voice for the pre-match Walk On.

This from a guy who could hardly stand up, never mind walk, in the three days before the game. En route to Dublin for the St Patrick's Athletic game in '98, a Finnegan's Wake Supporters' bus full of ravenous fans stopped at a country village bakery.

Every sausage roll, sandwich & pie had been scoffed by the time the portly bus convenor reached the counter...viewing the empty shelves, he asked, in a state of malnourished exasperation, "Is THAT for sale?" "Yes", replied the bemused counter girl, and the Marlon Brando look-alike promptly munched his way through.... an entire four-tier wedding cake (whole).

Mmmmm. Marvellous ... Plastic Bride & Groom were spared...but only just. Two final items from our Champions League odyssey. Being stopped by American tourists this season in Amsterdam, "Where's the Celtic Stadium in the City?" "We're not from here – we've come over to support Celtic", I replied. They shook their heads in disbelief. "We thought YOU were the home team! There's ******* thousands of you!"

And finally, being asked by two teenage Celtic fans in Turin on the day before the Juventus game – 'Haw, big man, where are ye goin'?"

"We're away to see the Shroud of Turin", I replied. I will never forget his response.

"Is that here?" he asked. And he wasn't kidding. Words fail me. Now the Nottingham Forest thing has turned full-circle, and it's up to Cloughie's protégé, Saint Martin, to steer us to further adventures. Thanks for the memories, and here's to the Champions League next season – that's if we can manage to do another 'Ajax' result. Slainthe!

PAUL CRAIG, Shawlands, Glasgow

THE year was 1970 and Celtic were in the European Cup final again, this time our opponents were the Dutch giants Feyenoord, and the venue? The San Siro in Milan. My father had booked his flight and hotel accommodation and offered the same to my brother, Alex, who being a 19-year-old adventurer decided that he would hitch-hike all the way from Glasgow to Milan. So off he went, all kilted up to try and gain an advantage.

He was doing okay until he met a group of fellow supporters in a bar in Paris. So after much drinking and singing he was about to leave when one of the older guys asked him to join them the next day on the train. Alex said he didn't have the fare, so the old man said that he worked for British Rail and had a family pass that included travel for his son, who didn't come along, and that Alex could pass for his lad. Well, it was an offer too good to be true, so he accepted. So they boarded the train the next day and were singing heartily, when the conductor arrived asking for the tickets.

The old man gave him his pass and said Alex was his son. The conductor asked Alex his name? So Alex replied, "Alex." "Alex what?" said the conductor. And that's when his troubles began. He had not thought about asking the old man his second name, and was kicked off at the next station. He was miles behind schedule, and running out of time, but he pressed on. He finally reached Milan and was struggling to find his way to the stadium, so he asked a policeman how to get to the game. He thought he had made a mistake, as no sooner had the policeman spoken into his radio, than a police car drew up beside them and told him to get in.

"What have I done to deserve this", he thought, as he got in. But when the driver told him they were taking him to the match, he couldn't believe it. They told him that he had missed the first 90 minutes, but it had finished 1-1 and they would be playing extra time, so he could still see some of the game. By the time they got there, there were about 10 minutes to play, and as he got in and found out it was still 1-1 he was delighted, and five minutes later Feyenoord got the winner, and become the first Dutch team to win the trophy. We lost, but at least Alex can say he was there, even if it was for only 10 minutes.

THOMAS GEMMELL, Leeds

A trip to Cologne

IT all started off when a few of us suggested a sojourn to Germany, a place not one of the Bhoys had ever been to. Flights booked, and off we went via Dusseldorf and a train to Cologne. The fun started immediately when I was introduced to a guy called "Thursday" and asked him how he managed to get a nickname like that. He explained that when he was younger, his little brother used to love Tin Tin, I am sure you can all remember the cartoon was introduced as Herge's adventures of Tin Tin only his little brother could not comprehend Herge's and assumed they were saying "Thursdays adventures of Tin Tin" Eventually he was re-christened Tim Tim as he was a dead ringer for the young Tin Tin.

This set the atmosphere for the whole trip and we arrived at our little hotel on the outskirts of Cologne, visited the Dom Cathedral, just about the only building that stood undamaged during the Second World War, a beautiful Chapel set back from the river.

We then set about visiting the local hostelries and heard one of the Bhoys tell the funniest joke ever or maybe that was because we were well lubricated by fine German hops. To cut the joke short, it was about the "Master of Wit and Repartee" and takes about an hour to tell but it's so stupid that it's funny. The night before the match we ended up in a German nightclub and found out that Glasgow's own Del Amitri were playing there after the game and decided to go there and celebrate.

Arriving at Cologne's stadium we found a beer tent and decided to lubricate our vocal cords and could not believe that beer was on tap to all and sundry.

We all thought it tasted quite strange and it wasn't until on of our educated colleagues managed to decipher the German language only to find out we had been trying to get well oiled on low alcohol beer. The game itself was pretty non eventful and we ended up losing 2-0, the only thing I can remember was, the Cologne fans waving some dirty dish cloth with the Rangers crest on it and the large amount of German Celts who came to follow the Bhoys.

After the game it was onto the nightclub and this is where the fun really started. When we arrived there was a crowd the length of Sauchiehall Street waiting to get in and we were Informed by a couple of British squaddies that we had a cat's chance in hell of getting in as the tickets for the show had been sold out weeks ago.

Just to show you how difficult this was going to be for us, a beautiful big Mercedes Benz pulled up and what I can only describe as the Gillette G2 man (I know it's three now, but at the time it was two) and a dame who I would only describe as "STUNNING" breezed by us with a look of disgust and straight into the club.

We were deciding what to do when I noticed this guy beside the Club off loading PA equipment, only thing was this guy was wearing a green T-shirt, my tiny mind was working overtime and decided to use some of my Glasgow charm. I introduced myself to him only to find out he lived in the West End of Glasgow and had just came back from the game himself. I told him we were having a bit of a problem gaining entry and told me to wait there while he went inside.

Five minutes later, Paul came back and said he had spoken to the band and they said we could be guests of Del Amitri. You could have hit us all with a baseball bat when he said that, it was like manna from Heaven. The squaddies were still in the queue laughing to themselves at our predicament, when we nonchalantly strolled by them with Tim Tim uttering "Guests of Del Amitri" we couldn't believe our luck and neither could the squaddies.

Straight through the main entrance but it did stop there, Gillette G2 man was pushing into the bar and looked completely flustered, what with his perfect hairdo and clothes getting ruffled, and his stunning girlfriend got a friendly "how's it going doll, do you come here often?" from Tim Tim.

The best was yet to come, Paul took the five of us to beside the stage and into a cordoned off area where no one was to be found. "What's this Paul?" I asked, he replied, "This is the VIP area, all the drinks and food are free so help yourself and enjoy the show." We all looked at each other and pinched ourselves, this can't be happening, the funniest thing was everyone was staring in absolute disbelief that a group of green and white-hooped pasty faced Glasgow Bhoys were guests of Del Amitri.

I remember us all whooping with delight and doing a Celtic huddle together and jumping all around. We started to get stuck into the pre-concert drink and food and were whooping it up.

We started to get a lot of attention and at one point a guy who I'd never met tried to speak with me.

I can't remember his name but he did introduce himself as an editor for a German music magazine, who explained it was the equivalent to the New Musical Express, a man with a lot of clout, me thought. He couldn't believe how we got into the VIP area and I told him what had happened.

He asked me if I wanted a drink and I told him not to bother as I passed him a bottle of beer from the stocked tables within the VIP area. We had a fascinating discussion about music, football and Celtic and explained in great detail the Old Firm rivalry.

The band were just about to start up and I bid my new German friend farewell and could now list him as a fellow Celt, he said he would write about our fortune and our love of the club in his magazine. We might have been beaten that night but we got a victory with regards to hopefully gaining new fans across Germany. The concert was out of this world and the Dels' rendition of Rod Stewart's *Maggie May* was out of this world.

One of the band, can't remember his name wore the People's' Celtic top signed by the whole team during the whole set. We met Paul after the Concert and we thanked him so much for turning our trip into one of the best nights of our life.

We asked him if we could get our picture with the band and he came back and told us that they would sign our match tickets but could not be photographed because we were wearing Celtic strips and they did not want to alienate themselves from other people in Scotland. We all agreed that this was the best thing to do and to be quite honest I thought that was okay as some people would do that if they were seen photographed with a group of Celts.

To sum the whole trip up would be one of utter disbelief that we could experience such highs and low while watching the Hoops. The lows of the defeat and the highs of what happened that night, none of us will ever forget what happened to us and it just goes to show that where ever you go, there is and always will be someone with Celtic's interest at heart, and it really does make you proud to be part of one big Celtic Family.

GERARD MURPHY, London

The Champions' day out

OCTOBER 17, 2001. To some Celtic fans this date may mean nothing, to others it may be recognised as the night a bit of reality entered our Champions League campaign, but to me it will always be remembered as the night in which pride engulfed my heart.

I had been forcing this date upon myself since the day we beat St Mirren to clinch the league and the chance to play Champions League football. My summer holiday was spent dreaming of an ambition which burned at the bottom of my heart, a chance to go abroad with the green and white army that is Glasgow Celtic.

Although the term "the greatest fans in the world" may have been abused and turned into a cliché by some of the prima donna money-grabbers who we had signed in the past, to me it still meant something, and something that was to allow Celtic Football Club to take over my life.

The dream all started the day that the Champions League draw was made, expectations were growing ferociously high after we had destroyed and humiliated the mighty Ajax of Amsterdam on their own ground, striking a warning to all of Europe's top teams that we were no pushovers from an inferior league; we were a team about to make a mark on European football.

We were drawn against Juventus, Porto and Rosenborg, arguably the toughest group possible. It felt as though fate was determined to give the Champions League 'amateurs' a severe baptism of fire, but to be a Celtic fan, optimism is a necessary attribute; but optimistic we were. Beyond that, arrogance perhaps prevailed as we sat talking about Rosenborg of Norway as if they were nobodies when they were, as a matter of fact, one of the most experience teams in the Champions League.

So, on to the fixtures, it was Rosenborg first at Celtic Park a delightful draw, opening at home against (with all due respect to Rosenborg) the weakest of the three other teams, but things were to change. Due to the tragic events in the USA it was announced that the game was to be postponed as a mark of respect to America.

I had been desperately looking forward to this game and I was very disappointed that it was called off, a very selfish attitude on looking back; when you put things into perspective, what is a football match compared to the lives on 4,000 others?

It was then Juventus in Turin which would kick off our Champions League adventure. Talk about tough!

Celtic's official tour operator, Keane To Travel, had released their adverts with prices of day trips to each of the away games. Porto was the obvious choice – a warm climate, no history of hooliganism involving Porto fans, and it would give me and my dad more time to get saving the pennies. The date was Tuesday, October 17 – I was going to the romantic-sounding Estadio Das Antas to watch my beloved Hoops.

We all know what happened in Turin, but we maintained our confidence and restored our place after beating Rosenborg and Porto at Celtic Park. It was a small break and then off to Porto!

I sat, day after day, in my classes, daydreaming of what it would be like, a completely new experience for me. It was, without any shadow of a doubt, going to be a trip that I would treasure for the rest of my life.

The day had come. I was woken up at 6am by my dad sneaking into my room and playing our Champions League song, 'Hey Hey Baby!' by the unofficial great Celtic DJ Otzi. I sprung out of the bed, got ready in my full gear – Hoops, flag, Sombrero! I was ready to go, our taxi arrived at around 7am to take us to Glasgow Airport for the start of an incredible journey. If anything, it would be an adventure.

Glasgow Airport was a sea of green and white, full of high-spirited, Celtic-daft (some just daft) people. We waited to check in and collect our tickets and once this was done the day could officially begin.

My dad had been abroad before as he lived through our great European days, but even he couldn't keep the Bhoy in him from getting out, singing and dancing and raring to go. It was the on to the plane, which looked more like Celtic Park than a Boeing 747.

There was slight apprehension in the air due to the recent terrorist attacks in the USA, but the best way to get rid of this was to sing and sing we did. It was obvious that some light ale had been consumed by the Hail! Hail! on the aeroplane.

We touched down in Porto at around 11am, ready to rock the place. We were warned not to feel intimidated by the police, but intimidated was an understatement. Bumping into Bobo Balde in a dark alley at midnight would hardly compare to these police. They looked mean, what with their machine guns, dogs, batons etc...

We were met by representatives of Keane To Travel who directed us to coaches which would take us to Oporto city centre. Oporto looked a quiet city, very industrial and private, but this was all about to change. 6,000 Celtic fans were about to be let loose on Oporto but in a friendly, although noisy way. I was loving every bit of it.

Our first stop was McDonald's, as the plane food was not up to much. Some good grub was required, some things never change. The place was rocking, the girls behind the counter were stunned to say the least. Everything was in good humour, though. You could only feel for the poor people of Oporto who had probably never seen anything remotely like this in their lives.

We had around four hours to explore the city, so we set out to find all the action, and were stopped by a fellow Celtic fan, aged around 25, asking where the local Haddow's was! (It's true what they say, you can take the Bhoy out of Glasgow but you can't take Glasgow out of the Bhoy!). When we found out the guy was serious we didn't know whether to laugh or cry. A polite "No pal, not seen one yet" was all it took from my dad to send the poor guy away on his search for a carry-out.

After landing in the 'Riviera' (down by the riverside) where all the action seemed to be taking place, we indulged in a good sing-song and swapped scarves, souvenirs etc... with some Porto fans. It was brilliant watching all the action unfurl. The highlight of the day must have been the Champions flag being hoisted up the town flagpole. We had taken over.

It was around 5pm and time to start heading for our coach, which would take us to the Estadio Das Antas. The buses were rocking all the way through Oporto. We sung our way to the ground in hope, anticipation and knowledge that we were on our way to see the mighty Celtic. We were top of our Champions League group. 'All' we had to do was get a draw in Oporto and we were well and truly on our way to the second phase.

Easier said than done. After marking our territory with banners etc... we bare-ly had time to sit down and watch the game, the first song of the match rudely interrupted by a goal from Clayton after one minute. We were shocked. This wasn't in the plan. But much worse was to come.

We were being ripped apart for the whole first-half, and just on the stroke of half time, Mario Silva blasted the ball home to sink our hope of any points.

Some people were shouting abuse at certain players and criticising the formation used, but it was clear we were playing no average team. Some of the football being played by Porto was out of this world. Perhaps we weren't all we built ourselves up to be.

The score was 3-0 and I was distraught. This wasn't what I had dreamed of, but it dawned on me, the Champions League was an experience. It was not as if we were being beaten by St Johnstone or Motherwell. It was Europe's finest, teaching us a lesson, so we sang and sang, leaving the Porto fans bemused. I have never felt so proud to be a Celtic fan when we were, to a man, singing Over and Over.

Even back at the airport, we were still singing our songs of hope and joy. It was farewell Porto but, at the same time, we will be back.

Celtic missed out on qualification by a very small margin and won the respect of the whole of Europe for our gallant efforts and excellent fans. Thank you, Martin, thank you, Celtic.

KEVIN BRIDGES (age 15) Hardgate, Clydebank

WHEN I went to the Juventus game on the plane people that were Celtic fans sang, then on the coach to the hotel there were lots of people that had Celtic tops and scarves. At the hotel there were Celtic fans too. That night when we went out there was Celtic fans in all the pubs singing Celtic and Irish songs but the Italian police kept closing down the pubs.

But we got to one eventually then the next day when we went to the Juventus ground it was raining. In the last minutes of the first half they scored and then at the start of the second half they scored from a header before Davids was sent off. Then Petrov scored from a free kick and when Celtic scored from the penalty everyone was hugging and kissing each other. We looked like we were going to draw but the referee gave a silly penalty to Juventus even though the Juventus player dived and Valgaeren did not touch the player at all, but they scored from the spot.

But at least Celtic gave it their best shot. When I was on the coach you could see people squashed in buses. That was my first game abroad and I will always remember it, even when I am an old man.

PIARAS CONNOLLY (age 7), Kenilworth

Chapter Nineteen

We're on our way to Paradise

GROWING up in the Republic of Ireland, you support Glasgow Celtic Football Club. It really is that simple. True, English club sides have a huge support base throughout Ireland, not surprising given the great players from Ireland who have graced such clubs, but it's nothing like the fanaticism that surrounds Celtic. Anyway, if you don't only support Celtic, you support United and Celtic, or Liverpool and Celtic. You get the picture.

This is the background in which I grew up and, as a result, I have always been proud of being a Celtic fan and proud of the great Irish players who have played so well in the famous green and white hoops. So it was that once I was old enough I wanted to go to my first game at Celtic Park. I had seen Celtic on their pre-season tours of Ireland, but it's not the same … At any rate, it wasn't hard to find friends who wanted to make the trip with me, nor has it ever been since.

By this stage, I was a member of Celtic supporters' club in Dublin (one of the many). Through it, I met with many other Celtic fans to watch matches, always creating a great atmosphere and to discuss any and all other matters concerning Celtic and, in particular, the relationship between Celtic and Ireland. I don't think I need go into the details as they're well catalogued and I could go on forever.

So, like God knows how many other Irish people before me, I signed up for tickets at the supporters club, and myself and three of my mates were ready to make the journey. It was Aberdeen – an evening kick-off.

Being students, trips like this had to be done on the cheap. So rather than fly over and stay in a hotel, we were embarking on a 24-hour bus and boat trip that would see us leave Dublin at 8am and get back at about the same time the next morning.

From the time you get on the bus, the bug builds! It starts off slowly, and isn't anything too intense, more a tingle, I suppose…. But it builds. It builds all the way to Belfast, through busy roads and quiet roads, through small and big towns and through the beautiful countryside for which Ireland is renowned. It builds because everyone on the bus is wearing the colours, because the music that plays over and over again is Celtic and Irish, music that, through repetition, threatens to get on your nerves, but never quite does.

And the bug builds because you hear older, seasoned veterans of many a bus and boat trip recall old games and old drinking buddies. It's an incredible buzz as the bus stops to pick up other Bhoys all along the way – first Whitehall, then Balbriggan, and Drogheda, Dundalk, Newry, the outskirts of Belfast … the list grows. Men and women, boys and girls, standing on cold street corners at various hours of the morning, all united by one thing, by a love of one thing; Glasgow Celtic Football Club.

And then you pull into the port in Belfast and the whole scene really does hook you. I had heard all the stories of how many Celtic fans travel from Ireland for every home game (and for away games too, I suppose). I have heard them and I have listened to them, but it's a different story altogether when you see all the buses. Buses from the four corners of Ireland, North and South, East and West. Buses decked out in green and white, the green and white of Celtic.

And then you notice all of the cars as well, cars filled with people of all ages sporting scarves, jerseys etc... Suddenly all of those facts and figures about Celtic and Ireland become real, and you truly know what it means to be a part of it all. You know that Celtic is more than just a football club, it's a way of life to a lot of people, and you've just become one of them.

The boat itself is a sea of green and white. There are people of all ages, from the old men sipping away in the corner to the young boys and girls running from corner to corner and back. We found ourselves a nice little table, not too far from one of the many bars, and settled in for the craic. Plenty of it there was too. You find that everyone chats with everyone else, and there are singsongs all about you.

The bug I mentioned, well, it has grown a lot stronger. The sight of all the young kids on that boat convinced me there and then that the link between Celtic and Ireland, already over a century old, will continue for a long, long time into the future. It has to be remembered the people on that boat weren't the fair-weather supporters who support one (successful) English team and another the next. Rangers had won the last nine league titles in a row and were threatening (unsuccessfully) to break the record of the legendary Jock Stein-managed Celtic sides.

It was probably about 2pm when we finally touched Scottish soil. We had already been on the road/sea six hours (seven if you count getting in to Dublin city centre to meet the bus in the first place), and it is at this stage that tiredness does set in. You've had a few pints on the boat and you want a few more to help you through the next two-and-a-half or three hours on the road, but some law or other prevents this.

So you listen to the music and you have a chat or you try to catch a few winks, but it's not easy. For starters, you're now really up for the game, and as a first-timer you can't wait to see the stadium, the pitch, the players, the Huddle, etc... All the while, you need to answer nature's call. It's one thing I remember clearly from my first trip to Celtic Park. There's no toilet on the bus and the driver won't stop every five minutes or we'll never get a few pints in the Barras.

This is a phenomenon that has haunted me, and many another with a weak bladder, on every bus and boat trip I've taken since. Without doubt, this is the hard part of the trip, and for a while you wonder if it is all worthwhile, all of this for ninety minutes of football.

Then you make it to Glasgow and you remember with Celtic it's never only ninety minutes of football. I'd be lying if I said that Glasgow is a beautiful city that rises from nowhere out of the Scottish countryside, it's not. But still, there's something amazing about being a Celtic fan in the Barras. This is especially true on matchdays. It's hard to describe.

You have the pubs, overflowing with Celtic fans, everyone singing and shouting, trying to be heard over the music and the calls for drink; the way that every pub is the same, but different. The same because they're all filled with

Celtic fans and the same ubiquitous music, different because different fans have marked them in different ways. Nobody can say the wall-to-wall Celtic memorabilia of Baird's is the same as the simple image of the 11 Lisbon Lions and Big Jock in Bar 67, or the murals of Hoops…

This is what greeted me and my friends when we finally made it to Glasgow, and this is what has greeted me ever since. I remember we arrived first at the Squirrel, and from there we did a little Celtic pub crawl on the way to the ground, checking every five minutes that we still had the season-ticket books, given to us for the day by members of our supporters club.

By the time we made it to the ground, we had probably had a few too many but, by God, you sober up when you see Celtic Park come out of nowhere. We were almost running by the time we got there, stopping only to pick up one souvenir or another from the seemingly endless rows of hawkers selling flags, scarves, hats and anything else with enough room to print 'Celtic' on.

I remember us laughing at the fact that no matter what you asked for, the answer was always "Fiver, pal."

Then we entered the stadium itself. We ran like lunatics up the steps, hoping not to miss anything. We needn't have bothered, for the players were nowhere to be seen. Having said that, I still remember my breath being taken away by the sight that greeted me when I first looked down on the hallowed surface of Celtic Park. What a sight, as the stands filled up. The colour in the stands, seeming to separate the magic that occurs on the plain, green pitch from the black night of the real world.

Of course, we couldn't sit still once we got there, though curiously the bug, which had plagued me (in a nice sort of way) all day was gone, even as I waited with baited breath for the players to arrive. After all of this, the game itself was a bit of a blur.

I remember the great feeling as I witnessed the famous Celtic huddle for the first time, and I remember cursing my luck when Aberdeen took the lead. Apart from that, I don't remember all that much. I remember us coming back to win well. However, I was a little overawed by the whole spectacle, and it was only as I got used to my surroundings in subsequent games that I found myself able to concentrate on the game itself, rather than all that happens around it.

After the game, I was on a real high as I floated away from Celtic Park and back towards the Barras. We had time for a quick two pints and they were very much enjoyed as the four of us chatted non-stop about the match and the amazing stadium. And I remember well the fervour we had when we discussed the singing of 'Walk On' when the Celtic players re-appeared for the second-half.

After that, it's just a long trip home. A long, contented trip home. You get the bus to Stranraer, and then the boat (a much more sombre affair than on the way over!) and then the bus again from Belfast to Dublin, and then home … I can tell you, I had the mother of all sleeps that morning.

I did similar trips a number of times, and they all followed a similar pattern, sometimes toughened by a rough sea, other times speeded by a fair one. There is something special about a 3pm kick-off because it means we leave the GPO in Dublin at 3am. This is some craic, because the GPO is situated on O'Connell Street, right in the heart of Dublin, and it's packed at that time of the morning.

Being a Celtic fan means that you always get a great send-off from the drunken crowds, though some young lady nicked my favourite Celtic cap from my head one night. If she still has it, she's welcome to it... Anyway, that's pretty much the lot of a Celtic fan as he makes his way from Ireland on limited income. And it's the lot of a lot of people. Nowadays, I live in London and whilst I watch matches with a couple of supporters clubs, I try to make my way to games independently. It's a lot less tiring than those first trips I took, but better? Not really...

COLIN O'FLAHERTY, Clapham, London

MY story is short but sweet. It tells of my very first trip over to Parkhead and I had such a good time I have made the journey since and am off again for St. Patrick's weekend.

Last April a group of friends and I were travelling over to Glasgow for what turned out to be one of the highlights of the 2000/01 season. The trip had been planned some four months in advance! After mentioning it in work I found out that a past president of where I work (we are an accounting institute) would be travelling over too. The man in question is one Mr Jimmy Donnelly, an ex-Belfast Celtic player. So when it became apparent that we were to attend the same match, Jimmy proudly told me that he and a few fellow ex-Belfast Celtic team-mates would be walking out on to the pitch at half time. When the time came I cheered and hollered and was so delighted for Jimmy to see his proud face on the big screen at half time.

Little did we know when we booked our trip, that we were to witness Celtic defeat St Mirren at home only to win the Scottish Premier League right in front of our very eyes. The atmosphere was electric and words cannot describe the emotion I felt just being there, standing in the Jock Stein Stand cheering and clapping for my favourite Bhoys. At one stage I looked to an elder man standing to my left and tears were spilling down his cheeks. I found that I too had tears in my eyes. Many people have asked me since about Celtic Park but I still can't express in words exactly how I felt that day.

When I arrived in Glasgow I knew that between the 18 of us that travelled together we would have a mad time. Little did I know that it would be myself who would take centre stage on our first night.

We travelled over to the Brazen Head on the Friday evening for a few pre-match beverages and basically to enjoy ourselves. The atmosphere was electric, as most of us punters had rightly predicted that the next day Celtic would be Scottish Champions. So while enjoying the songs and banter I found myself standing up on a pool table singing to my heart's content. Next thing I know there is a big lump of a lad (slightly intoxicated) trying his best to get onto the table (I wasn't alone). Only he proceeded to fall and decided to take me with him. I ended up falling off and landing on broken glass and stabbing a vein in my arm. Next thing I am in an ambulance on my way to the local A&E. Three stitches later I was back in my hotel ready for the next day's wonderful events.

So now when people ask me how I got on in Glasgow I simply reply, "Brilliant and look, (pulling up my sleeve) I have the scars to prove it!"

GRAINNE BYRNE, Nurney, Co. Kildare

Chapter Twenty

A Grand old song

LONDON, AUGUST 1961

At Simpson's in The Strand, Glen Daly had just finished what was reputed to be the best roast beef dinner in England. But as the other diners drifted away in the direction of Shaftesbury Avenue in the heart of the city's theatre district, the Glasgow entertainer was staring intently at his menu hoping for inspiration.

He had remembered reading somewhere that the great songwriters of the 20's and 30's had jotted down lyrics on train menus as they crossed from New York to Hollywood. However, on this occasion he had conveniently disregarded the fact that his name was Daly not Gershwin.

He was due back in Pye Records' Marble Arch Studios in an hour or so to record *The Celtic Song* but at this late stage a final version of the second verse had still to be completed.

"What a time to issue a club song!" he thought.

Rangers rampant, no major honours since 1957, the Kelly kids struggling and the most loyal support in the land being gradually reduced to the hardcore 'Faithful'.

It had all started so simply. He had been touring with The White Heather Group billed memorably as 'Half Irish, Half Scots, Half Daft'. In Thurso a Pye talent scout had suggested that he make a demo with Jimmy Shand Jr. The next thing he was in London making his recording debut with 2 football songs and 2 hymns!

Earlier that day he had recorded *The John Thomson Song* about the tragic death of the legendary Celtic goalkeeper:

> 'A young lad named John Thomson
> from the Wellesley Fife he came,
> to play for Glasgow Celtic
> and to build himself a name'............

He had been a boy of 22 when 'the prince of goalkeepers' had been fatally injured at Ibrox. The Calton had gone into mourning when the news had come that Saturday night that Thomson had passed away at the Victoria Infirmary. People had gathered in small, sombre groups to mourn and remember. A few 'Glesca' hard men had even cried.

The priest at Sunday Mass told his congregation that John was a member of the Church of Christ. A good Christian prepared to meet his maker. Some folk said that it would maybe put an end to some of the bigotry, but old habits die hard.

Sam English, the Rangers player involved, had never really recovered from the events of that sad September day. He played on in England but the crowds were cruel and he finished up in the Clyde shipyards.

Daly reflected on how strange life could be. He too had worked in the yards, an apprentice electric welder working alongside ex-Ranger English - a man of great dignity and decency.

Time was getting short now. But at least that was a rousing opening he already had:

"Sure it's a grand old team to play for…"

The dream of countless generations of schoolboys and their faithers! He'd heard the old men in Abercromby Street talk about Sandy McMahon, 'the Duke' and the exultant street celebrations in the East End when the Celts won their first Scottish Cup in 1982.

He recalled their praise of the team:

"Don't be kidded wae the knickerbockers and striped jerseys son. They boys could fairly play. Took the country by storm. The crowds had never seen fitba like it!"

Images of his own boyhood heroes filled his mind. That picture of Jimmy Quinn he had so treasured.

Quinn – the mighty man from Croy. Playing the Rangers on his own, promoting everything from Bovril to embrocation. His playing partner the famed 'Napoleon' McMenemy, a general who never met his Waterloo.

Then there was the atom that even Einstein would have had problems with. "The Mighty Atom", peerless Patsy Gallagher. They called him 'Chaplin's Double' a footballing genius who could save the day by somersaulting with the ball between his legs into the opposition net.

He fondly remembered the greatest of them all:

Jimmy McGrory the "Golden Crust". World record goal scorer, the man who gave birth to the Hampden Roar and the finest gentleman to come out of the old Garngad. Started to cry when they tried to transfer him to Arsenal. Daly wondered if McGrory wished he'd gone now. It was sad to see him struggling to give some direction and success to young Celtic sides lacking in confidence and talent.

It was a pity that Jock Stein had gone to Dunfermline. The big ex-miner had worked wonders with the Reserves. He seemed to have it all. Leadership, shrewdness and respect of everyone at the park. But he had ambition to manage, to have his own team, to make his mark on the game at the highest level.

He reflected on some of the lyrics again:

"When you read the history, it's enough
to make your heart grow sad, God Bless Them!"

That was the trouble. It was mostly history now. But what a history!

Six-in-a-row

Record Scottish Cup winners

Exhibition Trophy

The Coronation Cup…

His granny Mrs McCann had remembered them starting up:

"Held a meetin' in wan o' the big rooms in St Mary's Hall. Somethin' hid tae be done tae feel the weans".

He could hear her now singing the praises of Brother Walfrid, the saintly Doctor John Conway and Mr Glass who owned the draper's shop at Bridgeton Cross. Telling how the unemployed men had given their labour to build the park, pushing seemingly endless cartfuls of debris along the cobbles of the Gallowgate. What vision and courage these people must have possessed. Grinding poverty, prejudice and the greatest football team of the day. They took them all on and won.

Sad that it all had gone sour when Walfrid went to Whitechapel and the Poor Children's Dinner Table had been gradually neglected.

He tried to think where he had first heard the song. Of course, the Clown Prince of Paradise and good pal Charles Patrick Tully had obliged the company one night in the Kenilworth Hotel where a group of fellow choristers enjoyed a 'slight refreshment' courtesy of Celtic FC. No wonder Bob Kelly felt Charlie's' expenses were a little high. He smiled as he recalled the magical Irishman and his soft brogue as he sang:

"We don't care if we win, lose or draw,
Darn the hair we care.
Because we only know that there's
Going to be show
And the Glasgow Celtic will be there"

It was hard when they got beaten. Having to go into factories, mines, shipyards, aye, and theatres where there were plenty who wouldn't let you forget that the other team in Glasgow were the top dogs.

Did the directors really realise how much the support needed to taste some success? And how long could they hope to hold on to players like Crerand and McNeill before the big English teams came to lure them away? But even now there was something magical about them. Event it if was only the jerseys. Fast, skilful passing, exciting, attacking play. That had always been the Celtic way even when things were tough.

He really had to get on with it now. To get something, anything down on paper.

"I suppose something about them being the best team in Scotland is a start. And maybe a wee bit about players and why we support them. Och, who knows perhaps a miracle will happen and they'll come out of the wilderness and do something in the cup or even the league".

He quickly jotted down a few lines and made his way out of the restaurant wondering, as he emerged into the warm city evening, if anyone would buy the record. He thought too of the venues back home where a Celtic minstrel would most definitely not be welcome.

For Glen Daly, however, it wasn't about money or his career. He was there because he was a Celtic supporter. Just like the immigrant founders, Brother Walfrid's hungry children, the supporters who walked to away matches during the Depression and all those who over the years had made their way to Paradise.

He felt privileged to be representing all of them and those who would come later to carry on the tradition.

As he walked into Pye studios he was determined to give them something to be proud of. The record company hadn't exactly pushed the boat out. A small studio with meagre accompaniment of accordion and drums. But Glen felt instinctively that this song might just be something special. And after all, didn't the team traditionally come out on top when their chances were written off? Jack Emblow, the famous Jazz accordionist played the first few bars of the

227

intro. Glen Daly moved closer to the mike and the Celtic Song echoed down the years.

To the slopes of Hampden as Billy McNeill's late header secured Stein's first trophy. In the tunnel of the Estadio Nacional in Lisbon where Bertie Auld's defiant chorus unnerved Herrera's Inter Milan.

Nine – in – A – Row...

The Centenary Double...

The Treble in a new century....

In victory and defeat...

And as Martin O'Neill once again held the Premier League trophy aloft in a jubilant and packed Celtic Park, 60,000 voices sang along with a voice from a time before most of them had been born. Glen Daly needn't have worried. His song had passed the test of time and its message had endured. For all of those in green and white it was still a grand old team to play for and support.

TERRY DALY, Lenzie

Granny's hero

HAVE you ever sat and listened to your gran's stories? I have, many times. My gran grew up in the 'half way', which is in Cardonald, Glasgow, during the war. She has stories of fear, like the bombing of Clydebank that she watched from her bedroom window; stories of hatred, like Hitler against the Jews; stories of laughter, like when their homemade raft sank ... My favourite stories are of her favourite football team, Celtic.

When I stand in the kitchen while my gran washes the dishes, I love to see her eyes light up when she talks about Jock Stein, Billy McNeill and my granny's hero, the one and only Mr Jimmy 'Jinky' Johnstone himself. For this story, I'm going to re-tell some of my gran's stories.

My gran still laughs when she remembers the time "...Jock Stein chased Jimmy Johnstone up the tunnel..." To let you understand, the great and respectable Jock Stein had subbed the quick and nifty Jimmy Johnstone. Jinky wasn't pleased about this, so when he came off the pitch he threw his football shirt at the 'Gaffer'.

Naturally, Jock Stein wasn't too pleased so he chased Jinky up the tunnel. I was reminded of this incident not that long ago when Dick Advocaat subbed one of his players, and the player shouted abuse at his manager.

Another fantastic story is one about their journey home to Celtic Park after they won the European Cup. The team were travelling on their bus through the streets of Glasgow.

They expected to come home to a hero's welcome ... there wasn't a soul in sight, that was, until they turned the corner on their way to Paradise. The street was packed with green and white fans. This was truly a great moment in any football player's life.

I have to admit, though, that not all of my gran's tales bring a smile to my face. There is, of course, the tragic incident that occurred about 70 years ago. It was that of John Thomson.

To commemorate the Celtic legend, all primary schools in the local area of

Cardenden compete annually for the trophy that bears the goalkeeper's name, who tragically lost his life while playing for the club. My gran says the atmosphere across Glasgow, if not Scotland, was one of sadness and great loss.

This next story is not one of my gran's, but one of my own. After hearing all these stories of Jimmy Johnstone, I was wondering what the hype was all about. I eventually found out when I watched a video all about Jinky, then I knew.

He is the best footballer I have ever seen. He wasn't half bad looking in his day either! It seems that, whoever, dons the No.7 jersey is someone of great skill – Henrik Larsson, of course.

I was saddened to read recently that Jinky is suffering from Motor-Neuron Disease. I understand that this can be most painful. My best wishes go out to Jimmy in this time of great need, although it has to be said it sure doesn't hold him back from regularly attending Celtic matches.

I fully understand why Mr Jimmy Johnstone is my granny's hero.

CLAIRE HOWELL, St Luke's High School, Barrhead

Paradise on high

One day my Granddad sat me down and told me of his life,
Of all his former joyous days, his past troubles and strifes.

He told me of the first ever Celtic team he saw,
And how their exploits on the field had filled him full of awe.

How from on his father's shoulders, the pitch could just be seen,
But he had fallen in love with them, then a Bhoy of just thirteen.

Then times they changed and he changed too, but one thing did not alter,
For his love of this team in green was destined not to falter.

Soon the day had come to tell his son the epic Celtic tales,
All the great players he had seen the Mochans and McPhails.

And before long my Dad was standing there beside him at Parkhead,
Cheering on their heroes from the famous Celtic end.

Then my Granddad watched with joy as my old man brought me up,
And we sang the songs together when we won the leagues and cups.

And so he then confessed to me that his heart near burst with pride,
To see me fall in love, like him, with a great Celtic side.

So nowadays when the hoops score, I give a smile and sigh,
For I know Granddad's smiling too from his Paradise on high.

RYAN JP McGUCKIN, Glasgow

The managers

Where would Celtic be,
Without the most important key,
That made them the team they are now,
Yes, you guessed it,
You know what I'm going to say,
It's the guys who made them fit,
To play for the team called Celtic!

The managers have come in plenty
Starting in 1888
Willie Maley is secretary,
Helping them win the league,
But, the big man to start with,
Is Jimmy McStay.

But come in 1940,
A former player steps in,
It's Jimmy McGrory,
Who gives the team more chance to win!
Getting nearer our time,
In the 1960s,
Jock Stein succeeds Jimmy,
They are doing so well,
It's gimme, gimme, gimme!

Billy McNeill takes over Jock's place,
Ex-player David Hay,
Takes over Billy's case!
Again with the changing,
Billy comes back and David is gone,
But, then time goes on,
And Liam Brady steps in!

The managers go on and on,
Until this present day,
Martin O'Neill takes over,
And he is still at Celtic,
Now the month is May!
Now you know the importance,
That isn't just the players,
The managers of Celtic,
Won't come in pairs,
There is only one at a time,
They are the Celtic fans who care!

CARLYN COYLE, St Luke's High, Barrhead

230

The best fans in the world

I WANT to tell you about my favourite corner of Paradise and the amazing fans who surround me, in effect what Celtic is about – the fans, the humour, often conscious, sometimes unconscious, the focus, the camaraderie and the passion. I want to tell you about the characters that sit near me, not to decry them but rather as terms of endearment. I'm not going to say where in the ground this is because you'll recognise them. Why? Because you'll find you're sitting next to similarly amazing people.

This is key to what being a Celtic fan is about – the humour, tolerance, the feeling of belonging to a huge extended family, which, just like my family, has its eccentrics, its rough diamonds and its black sheep.

Take the two guys that sit just in front of me. One keeps up a constant stream of abuse at, say Alan Thompson. He doesn't just pick on Thompson. All the players are abused equally week in, week out. Anyway, he'll give Thompson 'pelters' and his mate just sits nodding wisely. It goes like this:

"Thompson, you're just a big numptie!"

"You're a balloon! A buffoon!"

"Celtic class?!?!"

"Gaun, ya big jessie!"

Thompson beats three players and slots the ball home for a last-minute goal against Rangers.

The guy continues without any delay, or pause for breath.

"What am I always saying'? Eh? Eh?"

"That guy's a genius with a football!"

His mate nods away wisely.

To the right of me is the bloke who quotes Shakespeare, mostly to himself. He can produce a quote to order for virtually any situation. So, when the team's under pressure, it'll be something like:

"Screw your courage to your sticking point and we'll not fail," or

"Now is the winter..."

He usually ends with "All's well that ends well" if we achieve a victory. A defeat (thankfully rare) brings:

"What's gone and what's past held should be past grief."

To the left is this other guy who is clearly a Ron Atkinson disciple. I call him The Tactician. He's forever shouting:

"Four at the back, Martin!"

"Down the channels!"

"In the hole!"

On occasion he'll even use some of Atkinson's beauties:

"The midfield's outnumbered numerically," or

"Pull him off, Martin! Look, Martin's pulling him off!"

Just behind me is the old-timer.

"Lubo's a very good player, don't get me wrong, but he's not as good as Bertie Auld," or

"This team's not a patch on the Lions, " or even

"What this team needs is a Wullie Fernie or a Bobby Collins or a Johnny Divers."

"WHO?"

"Aye, I thought you'd ask that. Just one of the best midfielders we ever had but he never got the recognition he deserved..."

He keeps everybody well stirred up. But my favourites, and I love them dearly, sit two rows down. The 'Farmers' Wives' I call them. Two rosy-cheeked, sturdy matriarchs. (They've probably got nothing to do with farming but they certainly fit the stereotype). Anyway, as soon as the ball crosses the halfway line, every time they shout: "SHOOT! SHOOT!"

Because that doesn't happen they continue: "C'MON, TAK'M AFF!"

They'd have the whole team substituted within 15 minutes. Then, inevitably, about two or three times during the game: "GOAL! GOAL! Oh no, it's not," says Mary. "I'll need to remember my glasses next week."

"You say that every week," says Frances.

I hope I've given you a flavour of my corner of Paradise. I told you you'd recognise them, the people who keep you entertained if the game goes a bit quiet, the best fans in the world.

PAUL BREMNER, Elgin, Morayshire

What's in a name?

WULLIE was the happiest man alive. His wife Senga had just given birth to a beautiful baby girl. No man could have been prouder as he puffed his way up the hill to Martha Street to register his new baby's name.

"Are you sure that's the name you want to give your baby?" the registrar looked over her glasses at Wullie.

"Oh aye, hen. The wife an me huv discussed this stacks o'times." Wullie nodded his head. He recalled many times how Senga had said "Wullie, you 'n' me huv goat two o' the maist common names in Glasgae, when we huv a wean ah want tae call it sumthin exotic and unusual." Well you'd have to try hard to find anything more special than the name he gave his baby. Wullie became aware of the registrar looking at him,

"Any wean o' mine wid be proud tae huv that name" he said.

"Well it is your choice of course, but what about the baby when she's older" she asked.

"Nae worries, everything will be okay." Wullie left Martha Street feeling 10 feet tall, clutching his new baby's birth certificate in his pocket.

"How ur ye hen?" Wullie asked Senga.

"Oh fine an the wean's been that good so she is." Senga continued, "Ah've bin thinking aboot whit tae call her. Whit dae ye think aboot Daphne, or Summer or mibbe Petunia. Nae wean o' mine will ever be called Senga, it's pure common so it is."

"Dinnae worry aboot it hen, ah've taken care o' aw thae problems fur ye"

"Ah thought ah'd gie ye wan less thing tae dae when ye get oot o' here"

"Oh Wullie how could ye! If ye've called that wean efter yer maw ah'll bloody kill ye!"

"No don't fret pet. Ah knew fine ye wanted sumthin different"

Wullie produced the birth certificate and handed it to Senga. At the same time he opened his present for the baby. Wullie draped the green and white Celtic scarf around the baby's cot. Senga's wail and subsequent tears could be heard throughout the ward.

"Dinnae greet hen, ah know fine it's emotional fir ye. Ah thought it'd be guid if we could just call her Lissy fer short. A kind of pet name, if ye like" Wullie peered into the cot "Ye like that jist fine, sure ye dae. An ah bet ye yer jist loving that wee Celtic scarf roon yer cot tae."

Senga was drying her tearstained face "Dinnae ye jist bother wi a' that Celtic rubbish. She's a lassie. Ah want her at dancing an ballet no up Parkheed wi you"

"Away wi ye wummin it's no called Paradise fer nothin. She'll love it so she will" And so she did!

Every Saturday Lissy could be seen with Wullie up at Parkhead cheering on the Bhoys. Not for her were bedtime stories of princesses and dragons, she went up to bed listening to tales of Celtic heroes, of games won and cups and trophies of days gone by. Her bedroom was a shrine of green and white and she loved nothing better than to watch her heroes in action. Senga was pouring tea for her and her friend: "Ah don't know what ah ever done tae deserve it, ah wanted a lassie tae dress her up in frocks and lace no fitba strips and boots."

Mary her pal replied: "Ah know, mind it's as bad as in ma hoose, sure the only difference is that ma two ur up at Ibrox at the weekends. Mind efter aw, at least Greig's a boy it disnae seem so bad."

Of course Lissy and Greig were great pals and enjoyed playing football together, Lissy always being Jinky Johnstone and Greig being John Greig from Rangers. Their mothers were always complaining "We're just a couple of fitba widows," they moaned. As they grew older Lissy and Greig's friendship turned to love. Soon the young couple announced their engagement with notices put in both the *Celtic View* and the *Rangers News* so all their friends knew about it. The wedding itself was a great event and as Lissy said, "This is a marriage of compromise and partnership." The biggest argument was the colour scheme.

"Ah want green, ah've always wanted green bridesmaid dresses wi' yellow roses in their hair." "No way," Greig said, "It's ma wedding tae an ah've always wanted tae have red, white and blue colours."

A compromise was reached. Wullie wore the kilt in Celtic tartan, and Greig's dad Tam wore a kilt in Rangers tartan. Senga wore a lovely blue suit and Mary wore the same suit in green. The two bridesmaids were in matching dresses, one green and one blue. The happy couple stuck to the traditional dress with Greig wearing a black suit, but with a Rangers tie and Lissy wore a beautiful white dress and carried a bouquet of yellow and white flowers bound with green ribbons. This was after all a marriage of partnership and compromise. Before too long the young couple found they were going to have a baby. Of course it brought back all the talk of names.

"Ah promise that ah'll never register the baby's name withoot ye," Greig vowed.

"Aye too right ye widnae, ma da did it tae ma maw an yer da did it tae yer maw an look at the states they made o' it," Lissy replied. A bouncing baby boy was born and the two young parents went to Martha Street to register the birth.

"Are you sure that's going to be the baby's name?" the register asked. "Oh aye we've even goat oor ain pet name fer him, hiven't we? - Wee Hal," Lissy cooed at her newborn son. "Well I just need father's and mother's full names for the birth certificate."

Greig took a deep breath, "Fathers name: Greig McCloy Jardine Miller Jackson McDonald Conn Stein DJ Johnstone Baxter - surname Logan, an his mither's name is Lisbon Lennox Simpson Craig Gemmell Clark Murdoch McNeill Hughes Johnstone Auld Chalmers – surname Logan."

Greig looked at the registrar, "Oor das loved the fitba."

"So it would seem," she replied "Well that's the certificate printed now," and she gave it to Greig,

"Oh my wee love," crooned Lissy, "that's it official now. Come oan love, let's take wee Henrik Amoruso Logan home." Like they always say, what's in a name?

ASHLEIGH WILSON (age 13), Drumchapel, Glasgow

The day my dad played for Celtic

THE week before my dad's big day, my mum asked me if I would like to go with her and Grumpy to buy a present for my dad's birthday at the Celtic Superstore. She also told me that the under-16 Celtic team was playing at Celtic Park. She said it would be nice to take Grumpy to see this game, as he cannot manage to go to the big football games.

It was the morning of the big day. My dad got up at 6.15am and got ready to go to the golf. He left at 8.15am. My mum, my little sister, Paula (age 2) and myself got up and had our breakfast. My mum was running about like a mad woman, trying to get all of us ready. At 8.55am we were all ready and we all got into mum's car. We dropped Paula at gran's and picked up Grumpy. He was very excited and my little sister looked a little bit sad as we were leaving.

My mum said, "We're going to the football, do you want to come?" and she said, "No football." Finally we were on our way to Celtic Park, but my mum had to stop at Sainsbury's to get some petrol and some money.

We arrived at Celtic Park at 9.45am and my mum parked the car. We waited in the car until 9.55am and then we headed towards the Celtic Superstore. When we got there the sign on the window said it didn't open until 10am. Finally we got into the shop, my mum bought me a new hat and an autograph book and my Grumpy bought me a new scarf. When we came out of the superstore and we headed towards the main entrance and the guy told us we had to go to the left of the building and go through the revolving doors.

We went through the doors and another guy told us to take the lift up to the Kerrydale Suite. We just got out of the lift when we met my auntie Anne and auntie Louise. They told me that they were going to the Barras for some shopping and when they were driving by Celtic Park they saw my mum's car and thought to themselves, "What is Marie doing at Celtic Park?" I asked them if they wanted to stay to watch the match and they said okay.

We went and had a cup of tea and I had a can of coke. We were sitting at the table and then I looked round and saw auntie Kerry and her big brother, Paul. They told me they had come to watch the football match. I went to the toilet and my mum told me that a guy came round with a bucket, collecting for charity and my auntie Kerry said she didn't have any money. Auntie Kerry never has any money.

One time she came to our house and my mum and Auntie Kerry decided to have a Chinese takeaway. She told mum what she wanted and then said, "Marie, I don't think I have any money." My mum paid for it.

After about 10 minutes a Celtic steward came into the Kerrydale Suite and told us that the match would be starting in 10 minutes. He took us through the stadium and showed us where our seats were. There were some players on the park but I didn't know any of them. I heard someone shout my name and I turned round and it was my friend, John Michael Clements. I then had a look at the match programme and I couldn't believe my eyes! No.1 - Frank Queen!

I shouted: "That's my dad!" I looked towards the goal net and who was there - my dad. I felt so proud and I couldn't believe my mum and dad had played this joke on me - but it was a nice joke. My dad and the other players then came of the park and went to get ready for the big match. After a few minutes the players all came back on to the park. I saw my dad and I thought he looks like a real football player. His team had a Celtic Huddle and then the match began.

After about 10 minutes, my dad's team were 3-0 up. He hadn't touched the ball much. He then threw the ball to Tommy Burns who made a bad pass and was tackled by Tosh McKinlay. Tosh was through on goal, just my dad to stop him scoring, he let fly and my dad dived to his left and made a great save. We all cheered. My dad looked very happy. After 30 minutes, with my dad's team 4-0 up, the ball was crossed into the box and the centre-half on my dad's team touched it with his hand. Penalty, said the referee.

"Oh, no," I said to my mum, "dad is going to let in a goal."

The No.8 put the ball on the spot and kicked it at the goal, dad dived to his left-hand side and pushed the ball round the post. He had saved it. My dad had saved a penalty at Celtic Park. I jumped and jumped and jumped and screamed and screamed and screamed. The referee blew his whistle for half time with my dad's team leading 5-0. I went down to the side of the park and gave my dad the biggest hug I could. I was so proud of him.

The referee started the second half, after 48 minutes the score was 5-3 and my dad was angry. He kicked the ball into the Jock Stein Stand and starting shouting at the players in his team. My mum said 'Oh no, he's going to get sent off."

The next incident came after about an hour. It was a penalty for my dad's team. I turned to my mum and asked who was going to take it, and when I looked back my dad was running up the park.

"Mum, mum, where is dad going?"

"I don't know," she said.

I looked round again and he was placing the ball on the penalty spot. My dad was taking a penalty at Celtic Park. I was so excited I could hardly watch. My dad ran up and smashed the ball high into the middle the net. He had scored a penalty at Celtic Park. I jumped and jumped and jumped and screamed and screamed and screamed.

At the end of the game I ran on to the pitch to give my dad another hug. We got our photos taken with Tommy Burns, Danny McGrain, Bobby Lennox and Steve Chalmers and I got their autographs. Later on back in the Kerrydale Suite,

I asked my dad if this was the happiest day of his life. He said, no. He then said the happiest day of his life, will be the day I play for Celtic. I hope I do.

STEPHEN QUEEN (age 7), Hamilton

Celtic, ma team

Thi furst time ah went tae see Celtic
Ah wis twelve
Ah thought Parkheid wis brilliant
Ah wis dead excited
Celtic wir playin' Hearts
At half-time wi got a pie an' bovril tae heat us up
Thi atmosphere wis great
Dead noisy
People wur cheerin' an' shoutin'

Ma favourite gemme wis when Celtic beat Livingston 5-1
Ah wis watchin' it own thi telly in ma livin' room
Ma da' wis watchin' it tae
When Henrik Larsson scored his hat-trick
Ah couldnae believe it
Ah wis jumpin' an' shoutin' an' huggin' ma da'
It wis brilliant watchin' ma team, Celtic

KENNETH MILLER, St Joan of Arc School, Glasgow

Number One

There will be soft rains and the smell of the ground,
As Celtic players call for sound.
And as the ball hit hard, goes into the net,
The crowds clap their hands as the two teams met,

Celtic will wear their gold and green,
Standing so tall, so proud to be seen,
As Rangers stand with the blue and the red
Celtic are thinking we are ahead,

No one would mind rain or sun
If Celtic win they're number one,
And at the end of the game the whistle blows,
The crowd so happy in their rows,

Celtic have the cup at last,
The final goal goes in like a blast

CLAIRE McKINNEY (age 14), Glasgow

Chapter Twenty-one

A fairytale in New York

ALPHABET City in the Lower East Side of Manhattan is a melting pot of various ethnic minorities, and the cafes, bars and shops in the area reflect the cultural diversity of its residents. Beside the Korean deli is a Vietnamese restaurant. Adjacent to the Ethiopian restaurant is a shop, which sells an array of Indian Saris and dodgy looking safari suits. This cultural melting pot was also the temporary home of at least one homesick Celtic fan, myself.

Although I was blessed to be living in the Big Apple, I had to put up with watching the Celtic matches via satellite in what turned out to be a magnificent treble-winning season. Here's the story of one of these days... I woke to the sound of the alarm clock ringing in my ears... well, the theme tune of "Thunderbirds", if the truth be told. My first thoughts were of being late for the kick off, as I thought I might have set the clock for the wrong time. I've never had to wake up at 5.45am for an Old Firm match before, and I'll tell you, It isn't much fun either. The opportunity of a work placement in New York for a year was too good to miss, but I didn't even consider the possibility of the quiet confidence that was emerging at Celtic Park since Martin O'Neill arrived.

For the first time in a while, it looked like we could actually mount a serious challenge to Rangers in the league. With this in mind, I jumped out of bed like a spring lamb, showered, shaved and headed over to Ethels' Diner on 63rd and Broadway to meet my new found friend Jackie and gorge ourselves on the finest bagels and cream cheese in N.Y.C. Jackie was already there and looking dynamite in her Celtic jogging suit, although I suspect the thing had never seen a jog since leaving the wrapping paper.

Maryhill born, bread and buttered and a Celtic fan since leaving the womb, she was the ideal person for sharing the experience of a Celtic-Rangers game when you're 4,000 miles away from home. We chatted like chimpanzees and shared our gut wrenching, diahorrea-enducing pre-match hypothesis, whilst agreeing how important the first old firm game of the season was. By 6.45am, we were enjoying the buzz from Ethel's freshly ground Colombian and ready for the big kick off. We hailed a cab and headed straight to what is becoming a Mecca for Celtic fans in New York, the Parlour Bar.

This joint wouldn't be out of place on the Gallowgate, and it had the entire pre-match atmosphere to boot. The teams were just coming out of the tunnel to the cheers of the 60,000 fans as we arrived, and It almost felt like Paul Lambert was waiting for us to walk in to the bar before saying to the rest of the Bhoys, "They've arrived lads, lets go"! The Parlour was as usual, filled to the gunnels with Celtic fans, a strange sight in New York at seven o'clock in the morning. I don't' know where these people came from, as I'd only ever seen a handful of Celtic jerseys since arriving in Manhattan seven weeks earlier. I guess they all must be normal Joe Soaps like myself.

Bus drivers, pPostmen, labourers, bartenders, Wall Street brokers and childminders like Jackie. Here we were all gathered together in solidarity and a sea of green, to express our celebration and love of the Celts as we played our bitter rivals. I noticed two guys at the end of the bar with Rangers tops on, which was strange, but refreshing to see, given the sectarian divide, which can often spoil this fixture at home. It didn't take long for the collective tension of the 200 hostages of fortune in the Parlour Bar to turn into sheer delirium. 60 seconds, to be precise. "Sutton...he's done it!" shouted the commentator from the 45-inch, wide screen, digital, surround sound, napalm stereo Celtic experience TV in the corner.

The place erupted into a frenzy of cheering and group hugging. We were still cheering when Petrov headed in the second seven minutes later. By the time Lambert added the third after only 12 minutes of play, I was lying under a mass of green and white bodies in scenes reminiscent of a school "pile on" or that Clash gig at the Apollo in 1979. Faces of utter joy and disbelief filled the bar. I noticed that the two Rangers fans were heading out the door and into the obscurity their team so richly deserved that day. Their beer glasses were still half full which confirmed to me that this was our day to savour. Things got ridiculously better in the second half with Henrik's glorious chip over Klos, after nutmegging Bert Konterman. Everyone, including Jackie and myself were up on the tables by this time, singing our hearts out.

Some were in tears; all were genuinely in shock, like we had just witnessed the Second Coming. I couldn't help but feel a sense of sadness, even in an atmosphere that would've rivalled a Rio de Janeiro nightclub in Carnival week. Although it was great to be where I was, I still missed the flag sellers, the smell of the hamburger stalls, the steady stream of fans making their way to the ground, the pre and post match drink in McChulls and watching the match highlights on TV in my mother Glasgow. By the time Sutton scored the sixth in the dying seconds of the match, the crowd were already engaging in some tabletop and bar top singing and dancing, Coyote Ugly style.

Shortly after the final whistle, we joined in on a celebration conga around the block to the tune of the Celtic Song. Jackie and I left the Parlour Bar around 11am, but not before hearing our auld Celtic hero and TV pundit, Charlie Nick offer his post-match analysis with that cheeky smirk on his face which said, "we shall not be moved". The rest of the panel looked totally scunnered. Ah... the simple pleasures in life...

We followed Brendan Behan's footsteps down Broadway in the Manhattan sunshine and sung all the songs that needed to be sung on such a glorious day. Nobody paid much heed to the two Glaswegians with matching green and white hoops. More importantly, it felt good to be sharing the whole experience with someone who could also empathise with the pain that we've all suffered over the recent years. A Ying and Yang kind of thing if you know what I mean. I felt that I'd found my long lost soulmate in life. Tom O'Reilly's in Lexington Avenue was jumping as per usual with the traditional afternoon music session in full flow. The musicians have apparently been playing music there for the last twenty-five years, and it showed.

Bold as brass, I fired up and gave the patrons a rousing rendition of the "John Maclean March", followed by the "Four Leaf Clover". Jackie sang along in front of me like a demented groupie, whilst doing that mad dance that only Celtic fans can do, half military march, half pogo, with the obligatory bottle of Bud in hand. We eventually made our way down to Greenwich Village and stopped at a little Café called Sin-e, (Shinny), which happens to be Irish for "that's' it".

The most amazing music was drifting out of the open door and there was a throng of people squashed into the place, which wouldn't have been much bigger than a living room. All we could see of the singer from outside was the top of his guitar and an Afro haircut, which would grace any episode of Starsky and Hutch.

We went in and squeezed up to the front, where this guy, who went by the name of "The Human Jukebox" was performing. He was a young, thin, shabbily dressed and dishevelled fella about 22-years-old, and was belting out any requests that the audience could throw at him. He sung everything from Hank Williams, Motorhead, The Stranglers, Euan McCall, Abba and Napalm Death Spirit, but the guy threw in the towel when we asked him for the Willie Maley song! Jackie stood up and gave us the most beautiful rendition of the Johnny Thomson song, and even the androgynous, contemporary, Junkie chic, Jack Kerouac lookalikes stopped talking to bear witness to her beautiful lilt.

We spent the rest of the night sitting in a corner, singing obscure Celtic songs, much to the annoyance of the bohemian clientele. Mobile phone texting is a new phenomenon to me, but Jackie was an expert. Her thumb was moving faster than a bee's wing, as she sent, then received a text of a brand new Celtic song, straight from Maryhill to her mobile in New York, which went like this: (to the tune of "the wearing of the green"), "Oh now tell me mister Konterman when you opened up your legs, And Larsson stuck the ball right through then chipped it in the net, When you went in at half time, you were losing three to one, Sutton, Petrov, Lambert and the Gers are on the run". CHORUS Oh the wearing of the blue, oh the wearing of the blue, You came here with your arrogance and you went home gubbed 6-2."

Jackie and I said our goodbyes and parted with a Celtic huddle on 5th Avenue around 1am. I swaggered back to my apartment like a rubber John Wayne and crawled into bed fantasising about the Bhoys playing Barcelona, Juventus and Bayern Munich in the Champions League next season. I fell asleep with the image of that beautiful operatic music "The Chaaaaaaaaaampions" wafting through the stands of paradise and dreamed of the Bhoys taking to the pitch with the roar of approval from the 60,000 souls bearing witness to yet another magical piece of Celtic history.

Yes, our day had come, and even more was on the way. More importantly for me, I was going to be back in Glasgow to experience it all myself, and boy was I going to savour every minute of it. Even the flag sellers and Hamburger stalls on the way to the ground

PETER DEVERS, Nurney, Co. Kildare

MY story begins in 1990, when I was 6-years-old I went to my first soccer practice and right then, I fell in love with the game. I loved the excitement that came with each goal and I loved the pride that came with stopping an opposing striker in his tracks. It wasn't until I was 13 that I began a love for watching the game. I knew about Celtic and Tom Boyd (Tommy is my hero, I am also a defensive back) but when I read the Celtic history, the team charter and read about the great players that have graced the pitch at Celtic Park, that was it. I was hooked.

There was only one problem, I couldn't watch Celtic here in Canada. My best friend and fellow Celtic supporter told me about a pub that allowed kids in to watch Celtic matches. I don't remember the date but I do remember it was Celtic versus Aberdeen. The atmosphere was incredible. It is a very small lounge, maybe a capacity of 200 people when it's packed to the rafters like Treble day 2001 or any Old Firm match.

The people who frequent this pub are mostly Scottish immigrants who grew up in or around Glasgow and are diehard Celtic Supporters. When Henrik Larsson gets a breakaway and buries it in the net the people in the pub go mad or if Joos Valgaeren gets carded for an over-aggressive tackle the people boo. Going to this pub is the closest to being at Celtic Park as I can get for now, I plan to someday make a trip to Glasgow and surround it around a Celtic versus Rangers match so that I can cheer Celtic to victory.

I love Celtic and that was my story of how I came to love the greatest soccer team ever to take the pitch.

CRAIG McFEE, Port Colborne, Ontario, Canada

Sybaritic synchronisation

AS he surveyed the vast, smog-covered sprawl of Los Angeles from his office high in the business centre, Eddie prayed for 8am to come, hopefully signalling the end of an incredibly turgid meeting with his executives and allowing him some time to himself. But clearly the meeting was going to run over.

"Look you guys, carry on. I'm going out for some fresh air."

Mary had endured a hectic, stressful day in her District Nurse role, visiting this somewhat primitive part of Zimbabwe. She would have to stay the night as a guest of her resident assistant, Munya, and complete the inoculation work tomorrow. As darkness descended fast, she consoled herself with the thought that, around 6pm, she'd be lying soaking in a refreshing bath, listening to the radio. Then she remembered. This was a part of the country without electricity!

Dave was sitting at his computer in the lounge of his pleasant bungalow in the suburbs of Wellington, New Zealand, and looking rather distraught. Jane, his wife, appeared in her pyjamas.

"Dave, it's gone three in the morning."

"I know. The server's down."

"What are you going to do?"

"Don't know," Dave replied.

Eddie was now speeding along the LA freeways, a look of utter determination on his face.

Mary's assistant, Munya, appeared at the bathroom door, carrying a radio. Talk about adding salt to the wounds, thought Mary.

"I've signed on with another server," Dave said to Jane. "It's just a matter of waiting to see how long they take. Fingers crossed!"

Eddie sped into the car park of a sports bar, jumped out of the car and was in and seated in a flash.

"It's a wind-up," said Munya.
"Yeah, a good wind-up. But not particularly funny at the moment, Munya," replied Mary, glumly.
"No, no!" said Munya, laughing. "A wind-up radio. You know, clockwork."
Mary was delighted. "You're a genius."

"Dave! Dave!" shouted Jane. "It's on."

To the strains of 'It's A Grand Old Team', a full-house of 60,000 at Parkhead, Eddie via satellite TV, Mary thanks to the BBC World Service, Dave through the world-wide web, and many thousands more just like them all over the world, cheered as the Celtic team ran out the tunnel on to the hallowed turf of Paradise at 3pm precisely.

DAVID BREMNER, Elgin, Moray

FOR me to write a story involving Celtic could be one of many. In fact a lot of the decisions I made in my own life have been influenced by our famous football team. I reside in America and have done for over 6 years now and if it wasn't for the fact that I can watch every game live I don't think I could have made my home here. I first arrived in America in 1995 and was living in a place called Cape Cod, which is about 2 hours south of Boston.

When living there I had no way of keeping up with the football scene as the Irish community there was quite small, until one day I read in an Irish paper that there was a Celtic supporters club in Boston so obviously I called and spoke with Billy Ramsey, whom I thought didn't particularly sound like a Tim but has become one of my closest friends, and he told me where the games were shown. Once I knew where to watch the games. I had to travel to Boston on Friday nights and stay in a hostel, and from there I would watch the games on the Saturday. But as I became friendly with some of the lads the need for me staying in the hostel was dropped and the real season began.

While that wasn't a vintage year for us I remember we had some good times along the way and there were probably some good times that I can't remember! It was at the end of that season when the very first North American Federation convention took place in Las Vegas and oh what a time that was. It was a turn around for me as less than a year before I didn't even know I could watch the Celtic games and now here I was in the Nevada desert surrounded by about 1200 other people all inflicted with the same addiction as me, Glasgow Celtic.

To make my turnaround even more prolific I went from the obscurity of Cape

Cod to the pages of the *Celtic View*. I met with Jimmy Johnstone and had him autograph my arm, which I had made permanent the next morning as I had it tattooed on. That act though could have turned fatal as my friends later told me that as I slept they were going to write Ally McCoist instead!

But as it turned out while it was a decision made while intoxicated it is one I will never regret and it is with honour that I can look at the signature every day and remember that great player and that great weekend in Nevada in 1996. I would also like to thank Matt McGlone for writing about my tattoo in the *View* and letting my father find out about it before I could tell him myself. It is what followed that convention though that proves to me that Celtic has carved out my path in life.

While at that convention I met with a fellow called Paddy Joe Walsh, another lifelong Celtic Fan who lived in Connecticut and was looking for a bartender in the bar he managed. So I hung up my tool belt in Cape Cod and went behind the wood in Avon Connecticut. While that experience didn't last all that long it would lead to a very pivotal part of my life. Living in Connecticut didn't allow me enough opportunities to watch the Celtic games so I moved to Boston put back on the tool belt and was able to watch for the first time in my life, every Celtic game live on television, paradise. Everything in Boston was good and we endured another Vegas trip together but later on that year the winter in Boston was cold, very cold. It was then that I got another lucky break, The guy who owned the bar in Connecticut also owned one in Tampa, Florida and he called me in December offering me a job.

I thought about it for about 5 seconds and once I found out there was a Celtic Supporters club in Tampa I once again hung up my tool belt and headed for the sun. This is where my life changed as it was while bartending in Tampa I met a beautiful girl called Tamyne who now, four years later is my fiancée. This may seem like a happy ending but it does get better. My now fiancée Tamyne is a daughter of a famous footballer Steve Wegerle, who is not a household name in Europe but his brother Roy may be. Steve played for Feyenoord and signed for them in 1970 after the European Cup final. It was there he played with a famous manager of ours - Wim Jansen.

While his time in Holland was relatively short, he moved to America to play in the then widely supported NASL (North American Soccer League) which boasted players like Pele, Beckenbauer, Hay and many more. During my future father-in-law's time with the Tampa Bay Rowdies he played a few pre-season games against Nottingham Forest who could boast of players like Robertson and O'Neill. They all were quite friendly and I was lucky enough to witness this in Florida January 2001. Celtic were over in Florida for a winter break trip so with it being my first chance to see my beloved Celtic in the flesh for the first time in over 5 years myself and about 5,000 others took the trip to Florida. I had since put back on my tool belt and me and my fiancée had moved to Chicago which, of course, also has its own Celtic supporters club. Back to Florida, Celtic had arranged a friendly with the Tampa Bay Mutiny for the Friday night of that week but also had a closed doors game against the University of South Florida on the Wednesday night.

And with Steve Wegerle's help, Steve, myself and another friend of mine, Paddy O'Kane, were lucky enough to be three of the maybe 2 dozen at the game.

After the game the three of us walked across the pitch and it was there where we were introduced to Martin O'Neill. He remembered Steve from their encounters many years before and was very gracious in inviting us to dinner with the team. We, for some reason, declined but myself and Paddy soon realised we had made a mistake and followed the team bus to the restaurant and sat at the bar while the team ate. I must say though while at the bar we were joined frequently by John Robertson and Steve Walford who weren't allowed to smoke at the dinner table!

After a while and a few drinks later I had to relieve myself and went to the bathroom, and without being too graphic while standing doing my business a familiar face came and stood beside me to do the same thing. I was dumbstruck. I was standing next to Henrik Larsson, in Florida and, of all places, in a bathroom. I quickly washed my hands and shook hands with Henrik and thanked him for everything he had done for Celtic and for all of us. He was a bit taken a back as, until then, no-one in the restaurant had a clue who any of them were, but he was polite and friendly. When I sat back at the bar and told Paddy of my encounter his first question was " had he washed his hands before you shook it" I replied that he washed them after I shook hands with him.

Paddy's response "Yes! Let me shake your hand!" This all basically shows that without Celtic being a part of my life, it would not be the same and I would not change my life for the world. Celtic truly are a great team and no matter where in the world you are you can keep connected with Celtic, whether in your thoughts or now through modern technologies. And my advice is bide your time as good things come to those who wait. I have been extremely lucky and hopefully so too can many others.

DAIRE BARRY, Chicago, USA

A Celt in the Savannas

NO matter the venue, no matter the stage, no matter even the teams, there is a special magical air attributed to European nights. As twenty-two of the most talented players from across the continent grace one pitch in a bid to determine for whom the night will end in desperate heartache and for the other to experience the extreme ecstasy which will live vividly in the memory, well until the next night anyway. And disappointingly, in recent years, all too many of these have concluded in the former for the men in green and white.

Lyon, Bordeaux and Valencia have all travelled down London Road undeservedly singing the sweet song of success. The particular experience I want to share with you did end in a momentous victory, albeit they were to depart from their debut season in the Champions League in grand old fashion.

For a week I'd been gathering up my football comrades in St. Ignatius, a tiny indigenous Amerindian village in the South of Guyana, where I'm currently spending my gap year teaching English to secondary students. (However, I save my best lessons for coaching the football team the great Martin O'Neill 5-3-2 philosophy.)

At the beginning of the night, my friends knew nothing about Celtic apart from the fact that they wear green and white and that I used to rabbit on about them for hours. But by the end of proceedings they too were to feel the great passion and pride that goes with supporting the club.

Our viewing arena could not have been more of a contrast to the electric bedlam pre-match all those thousands of miles across the Atlantic: the 7 Star Shop (and no I didn't name the shop for them, it is sheer coincidence), a small mud-hut at the centre of the village, one of the very few buildings to have electricity. As the sun set behind the shop, the spotlight turned to the TV. As the teams were announced there was a feeling of no hope amongst my adopted followers. "Look, Del Piero, Trezeguet, Nedved and even Buffon's on the bench. You can't touch these men!" they said.

The game started. I was straight to my feet (I seem to have an inability to sit while watching a big game) oooohing and aahhhing, but embarrassingly seemed to be the only one taking such an interest. How feelings were to change. When Alessandro Del Piero exquisitely struck that free-kick, the silence in Glasgow's East End was mirrored in my wee mud hut. I realised at this point how they saw the supposed minnows outplaying the giants, but it was all so unfair. But then it was Joos to the rescue.

Greeted by roars he brought subdued Amerindians to their feet, which was quickly followed by bubbles of relieved laughter at the reply showing O'Neill's reaction: the mimicking of the headflick in perfect sync with the big Belgian as if to say, "Now go on Joos, just how we practised it." The Irishman was fast becoming a cult figure.

Although it was Chris Sutton who was to prevail as the outstanding player with his double and that bulleted half-volley to put Celtic 3-1 up. I'll never forget the sight of one of the onlookers actually falling backwards as if he had been blown away by the ferocious power of the shot. From then on the place had turned into a bit of a party, and even David Trezeguet's lesson in a finishing master class went without the blink of an eye-lid. The tune of the Martin O'Neill song and the confused words of the "Fields of Athenry" boomed loud for the next half-hour until, well, we all know the outcome, don't we?

At the point of discovering the result in Oporto the scenes at Celtic Park were once again reflected all those many miles away. Some looked so dejected that they embarked on the ten-mile walk home early to sulk and reflect on a traumatic evening. At full-time, with the place packed to capacity they simply nodded to me before engaging in a torrent of applause in akin to the way in which they would greet a Brian Lara century. I almost expected the steel drum to kick into life as they celebrated their new-found love.

I left the 7 Star Shop that night fully attired in my Sunday Best (which does of course bear the number 7) and oozing with supreme pride. How my great feelings for the club had successfully been shared with so many, away from all the hatred and bigotry of an Old Firm derby. It's one of those magical nights which will live long in my memory not only for the fateful heartache but also for seeing those people celebrate and appreciate Glasgow Celtic Football Club. And, I leave you now (once again celebrating after the clinching of the Championship) with something slightly more than a whisper of "Hail! Hail!" coming direct to you from the Rupanami Savannas, Guyana. Keep the faith.

RORY HAMILTON, Helensburgh

MY wife and I came to Ireland for the first time and stayed in Killiney with a friend. I have never really been much of a "football" fan until this trip. We had some great food and drink and my friend mentioned there was a great game about to come on the television. He asked me if I liked football, and of course my reply was yes. Well it was not the football I was thinking of. It was soccer. His favourite team is Celtic, so we got ready to watch the first game of the season (July 2001).

I have never seen so much skill as I have seen in those players like Larsson who had just come back from and injury recovery 6 months earlier, and there is a multitude of other players that were just dancing around the other team. They made it look like it was of no effort at all. I was truly amazed. I could not sit still. I was jumping up and down when they scored and yelling loud and all the other craziness that goes with that kind of energy.

Needless to say I had to go get on the Dart for a trip into Dublin and get myself a Celtic shirt at their pro shop in the mall. I treasure that shirt and love the way that it fits me. I had the best time watching you guys play, so much so that when I got home (California, 11 hours away on a plane) I had to go to your website and become a member.

I now get all the info and updates and have also purchased Satellite Television so I can see the White & Green play. I also have put the team photo as my background on my monitor, and screensaver. I would love to come and see them play, they have opened my eyes and heart to a new sport. Although a new computer would be great too, seeing as I am in the Networking world. Someday I will get to see a home game and complete this newfound love for "Football" and the Celtic Football club, HAIL! HAIL!

ROBERT E.SMITH III, Laguna Niguel, California

I'M not very good at compositions at all and I'm not such a good English speaker but there is one thing I can say about football: for me there are two teams, the Romanian national team and the best club in the world - Celtic. I am a little bit different from my friends who support teams from Romanian league or teams like Barcelona, AC Milan, and Real Madrid who are big clubs... I support Celtic! And, of course, the question is why?

Nobody here (well at least I don't know yet although I didn't find anyone) supports Celtic and everybody asks me why do I support this team? Well, I just love them... I discovered Celtic when I was 16-years-old and since then there isn't a single day in which I'm thinking about them. First I liked the Scottish and Irish music and I wanted to find more things about these 2 great countries and so I found about Celtic.

I've got my room full of Celtic posters, I have a Celtic jersey, scarf cap, and calendar, CDs with songs, *Celtic Views* etc. and all are from Scotland because here I couldn't find anything about them. I made my parents mad because I need money for all this things and a jersey is very expensive here.

My girlfriend was mad as well because the only thing I was talking to her was about my team and results. And, of course, I got my friends mad about the same thing. Now everybody I know (parents, friends) know something about Celtic because I talk non-stop about them. When Henrik Larsson had that horrific fracture in France (Bordeaux) I couldn't do anything for 3 days. I cried and I just stood in my room watching the posters and didn't want know about anything... but when they got the Treble... Man! I was the happiest and the most proud person in the world and I was wearing the jersey with pride. And when they beat Juventus 4-3 everybody said that they didn't know Celtic were such a good team and they played classy football. This thing only made me prouder that I'm a Celtic supporter...

Well I would really want to tell you more about my favourite team but I really need to go because I'm sending this email from my job and my boss is not happy because I'm not working.

CODREA MARIUS, Cluj-Napoca, Romania

A call from Neil Lennon

I DON'T often get calls from international footballers or members of the Celtic football team (well I'd never had one to date but you can but dream). This is the story of what felt like a dream but was in fact Celtic "playing" with new technology. It's 6am in the morning. I'm asleep. I'm in a hotel room. I'm on holiday in Australia. My mobile phone starts to ring (beep, beep).

Not surprisingly awoken from sleep, I stumble out of bed to find the phone (to put it beside the bed would assume I expected a call in the middle of the night - it was in last night's handbag under a pile of clothes). I don't get to the phone in time so call my voicemail in a panic to find out who had called and if they had left a message.

It was Neil Lennon to tell me the Celtic game had been moved by 15 minutes and not to be late! The first thought was "wake up, your dreaming". But as I look around everything is still as it was when I went to bed last night. I'm still in a hotel room in Australia. It is still 6am in the morning. As I slowly gathered my thoughts I realised that if I had been back in the UK, it would have been 5pm and a good reminder not to miss the game. Celtic were obviously experimenting with voicemail messages to mobile phones (without knowing that I wasn't in the UK and my phone works in Australia).

So no it wasn't a dream (no personal message from Neil Lennon - just a recorded message to thousands of fans) but for me it was a very EARLY morning call while Celtic experiment with new marketing techniques and new technology. I'd still like a personal call from someone in the team but try to avoid my holidays next time guys - we all want to dream in peace.

CATRIONA FERRIS, Guildford

ME and my older brother Martin have been great and faithful Celtic fans from our childhood, and even though lots of our buddies from this part of Europe at our 'tender' days were keener on the English clubs, which was and probably has been sort of fashionable as it is, we never tended to follow the trend and always fought the others, of course for fun – as all the lads do.

Perhaps because of the fact that part of our forefathers on mother's side came from Scotland, but we didn't know it, that's not the point though. Years back, after the revolution in this country (and before my first 'allowed' trip to Scotland to see the Bhoys in flesh at last), Celtic played Kiev. The away game was live on the local TV so I can leave it to your imagination how 'antsy' we were and how much we couldn't wait.

We had left for another town to see our granny and after spending one day and night there, we literally made a dash for our car to be back just in time for the kick-off. That was all happening in a hurry and with our thoughts fairly pre-occupied we started to act like absent-minded fools. Firstly, Martin couldn't find his car keys, then I realised that I'd forgotten my wallet with all my cash at granny's so we were forced to turn around, no matter what names my brother was calling me and how cursing he was.

After roughly 30 miles we were stopped by speed cops only to discover that he had left his driving licence behind so we changed our seats. Some 5 miles from our destination we were nearly out of petrol and having taken the so-called shortcut there was no filling station around, but the two of us eventually made it. When I hurried to switch on the telly it suddenly dawned on me that my TV set had not been working the proper way with its screen being pretty blurred, so we headed to our mother's to catch the second half at least. But we DID make it to see the Bhoys Live at last

OTA KOPRIVA, Prague

Fear and loathing in Paradise

I FOUND myself standing in the heart of the jungle submerged beneath a canopy of rich green, just ninety minutes now stood between Celtic and an historical Treble and the noise, as you could imagine, was literally deafening. Most Celtic fans would have given their right leg to be standing, albeit with some difficulty, where I was on such a great day in the Club's history. While I'd claim to be as passionate as the next fan they were more than welcome to my place in this so-called 'paradise'.

Quite frankly I would have given any part of my anatomy: my legs, my ears, even my testicles, to be anywhere but there. There was no point moaning about it though, and anyway my mates would have been first to remind me that such an idealistic trade off was simply not possible. OK, so perhaps I am exaggerating just a wee bit here. It's true there were certainly worse places on Earth I could have been on cup final day than Kecil, a tiny tropical island located just off the northeast coast of mainland Malaysia.

Indeed many people would regard sun-drenched Kecil, with its long white sandy beaches and sapphire blue surrounding sea, as something akin to paradise on Earth. Yet for all its superficial beauty let me inform you that Kecil also has a dark and ugly side...namely it is home to some of the biggest, ugliest, scariest creatures, known to mankind.

So maybe that's just my opinion, but while I am no expert on the subject I should point out that I have been to Ibrox before. Even if this frightening fact has not put you off Kecil there is just one other small thing I should mention

247

about the island - it has a strict alcohol ban! Quite frankly, every living creature in the small island of Kecil is big. The ants are almost as big as beetles, the beetles are almost as big as rats, the flies are almost as big as small birds, and the small birds are almost as big as medium-sized birds.

Fortunately I never had any close encounters with big birds while on Kecil, evidently one of the few advantages of staying on an island with a strict alcohol ban. While I also never came across any fleas while on Kecil, I was beginning to wonder was this where the distant ancestors of the great Jimmy Johnstone had once hailed from. While I'm no fan of flies, beetles, ants, or any other named creepy crawly, I can handle them all, except that is one small fearless beast - the dreaded spider. Everything about them 8-legged buggers terrifies me, from their long hairy legs, to their big fangs, to their deadly speed. Needless to say Kecil was home to a fair few spiders and, needless to say, these spiders were just a wee bit bigger than the ones you get back home.

As soon as we arrived on Kecil I had a short glimpse at the dense jungle behind the beach and immediately clocked hundreds of them, all lounging around in their self-made hammocks in wait for their next human victims no doubt. It seemed that every tree on the island was colonised by the beasts, each chilling on webs the size of goal nets. Now I've heard of bird eating spiders before but when the birds on Kecil were bigger than average, surely it follows that the spiders on Kecil have appetites that bit bigger than average. Having a fear of spiders, or arachnophobia, as it is known, is not unusual.

However I have never liked to admit that I had a phobia. A phobia, defined as an irrational fear or mistrust of something or someone, undoubtedly carries with it negative connotations, a reflection of an element of weakness in one's personality. While some phobias are downright obscene, e.g. homophobia or xenophobia, others are quite simple ridiculous, e.g. pogonophobia - an irrational fear of beards. Perhaps I have no right to pass judgement on a pogonophobe, but surely it would take the arguing ability of a leading QC lawyer to convince me that someone who mistrusts those with beards could also think rationally. Although it seemed like an eternity, we were only to stay on Kecil for four days.

While most of the island is covered in dense spider infested rain forest, our accommodation and all amenities were located conveniently next to the beach. There was in effect absolutely no need to wander into what the brochures described as dense virgin jungle...or so I had thought. While Saturday 26 May 2001 will forever live fondly in the hearts of Celtic fans everywhere, it will forever remind me of the day I had to live out one of my greatest nightmares. One of the obvious disadvantages of staying on a remote tropical island some 6000 miles away from Glasgow on cup final day is that you are simply not going to see the final.

As Celtic fans, my friends and I were all obviously gutted that we would miss out on witnessing one of the greatest moments in the Club's history - or so we had thought. During a few mid-afternoon soft beverages at our favourite alcohol free bar we found ourselves talking to the owner about how disappointed we were to be missing the cup final that day. Much to our surprise he told us that he would have been able to show the game but unfortunately the bar's satellite connection had recently been down. He informed us that there was one other restaurant on the island that also had a satellite connection and would certainly be showing the game. There was just one small thing; the mentioned restaurant was on the island's only other resort - on the opposite side of the island! On the one hand there was nothing I wanted more than to watch the game that could see Celtic clinch an historic Treble.

On the other hand there was nothing I wanted less than to have to confront my biggest fear and venture into the jungle. In reality I had no choice, like a fly caught in a web there was simply no getting out of this problem, any attempts to wriggle free would simply have been in vain. While it was only late afternoon and the game was not due to kick off for another five hours or so I had to move fast if I was to get to the restaurant showing the game without my mates finding out about my arachnophobia. The general consensus was that we would aim to get to the restaurant an hour or so before kick-off for a few cheeky soft drinks to settle the pre-match nerves.

As Kecil is some seven hours ahead of British Standard Time, the game was not due to kick off until 10 p.m. that evening. While my friends didn't appear to have a problem venturing into the jungle under the cover of darkness with the one torch we had between the five of us, there was simply no way I would be joining them. Going into the jungle in broad daylight was a daunting enough prospect in itself but at least I'd be able to see the enemy. Going into the jungle with only one torch and the moonlight for guidance was a bit like Mo Johnston's transfer to Rangers, it was simply asking for trouble.

According to the map of Kecil in my guidebook the other resort was some 2 kilometres away. While such a distance may not seem very far bear in mind this was merely a distance as the crow flies. I was not a crow but a humble human being with no wings but only two legs, and a deep-seated fear of those with eight.

The journey through the jungle may have not been too far, but to someone with arachnophobia the jungle is massif! Anyway, I hadn't seen any crows anywhere on Kecil, although I wouldn't like to imagine why. I have never had to think twice about getting kitted out in all my Celtic gear before going to watch a game, but like they say, one should never say never. I was going to be wearing green, with green being the predominant colour in the Jungle. I would be completely blending myself into the natural surroundings. If I was a soldier involved in jungle warfare such camouflage would obviously be necessary, but I was merely an arachnophobic Celtic fan about to live out one of his worst nightmares. Did I really want to blend into my surroundings and have all sorts of creatures thinking I was but a tree, crawling up my legs and laying eggs, or setting up homes in my ears and nostrils?

For a moment I considered going dressed in loud colours, this way I would scare off any small beasts on the lookout for a new home, but I soon dismissed the idea. The only loud item of clothing I could find in our beach hut was an awful orange Hawaiian style beach shirt one of my mate's had once purchased, I presume for comic value. Now I could have gone to watch the cup final wearing orange, but I have always prided myself on having good taste. If I was going to be eaten alive in the jungle so be it, but I would not been seen dead wearing orange. As soon as I stepped into the dense jungle a wall of noise hit me from all angles. There must have been billions of creatures in that jungle to make such an intense level of noise and all of them must have been on the lookout for someone, or something, to mate with. To say I was nervous as I made my first strides into the unknown is a slight understatement.

Usually I get butterflies before a big game, but today's little venture coupled with a certain cup final had seen me reach new levels of nervousness. I felt terrible. I decided to block out from my mind the fact I was in the jungle, while I had to see where I was going I didn't want to look too closely at any tree or shrub for fear of spotting a giant spider. I kept my head down and ran as fast as I could and some 20 minutes and 2 km's later I had reached the Promised Land that was Abdullah's alcohol-free restaurant. I had arrived with plenty of time before the kick-off, some three hours.

Being a bag of nerves I couldn't stomach any food so I decided to get a jug of the strongest soft drink they had. With no Irn Bru in these parts I settled for a jug of Fanta. A jug or three later and it was finally kick-off, though the lads hadn't arrived yet. While they may have bottled the moonlight trek into the jungle, the most likely explanation for their absence was that a satellite connection had been re-established back at our resort. In other words, I would be going back alone and in darkness. I couldn't concentrate much on the game now. I saw Jackie hit the first and then saw Henrik grab a superb second, but it was hard to enjoy the moment. Everything reminded me of what awaited me following the match. When Henrik smashed in the third from the spot I imagined the ball to be my face and the net a giant web I would undoubtedly walk into later than night. With the Bhoys clinching the Treble I took comfort in the fact my last moments on Earth had been happy ones.

I decided to have another jug of Fanta for the road, much to the bemusement of the restaurant owner who pointed out that if I had any more I might turn orange. With that frightening prospect I decided to give the Fanta a miss and head straight back. Fear of spiders may be an awkward phobia, but fear of turning into an orangeman is surely a healthy one. With only the moonlight to guide me I stepped back into the jungle. Once again the wall of noise immediately hit me, but then I heard something else. Maybe it was my imagination, maybe it was the Fanta, but to this day I swear, above all the noise, I heard some words faintly whispered.

While I didn't catch the full sentence I clearly heard something about Zed and catching a big fly. With that I made a swift U-turn back to Abdullah's and ordered a big jug of Sprite. I braced myself for what was going to be a long night of soft drinking, while secretly hoping I'd find a big bird willing to take me under her wing. Well my mates hadn't shown up so I had nothing to fear did I?

PAUL TULLY, New Southgate, London

It was in the year Wim Jansen made Celtic Champions. Me and a friend travelled to Scotland for two weeks and we stayed in a camp site in Balloch. It was a rainy Monday that I bought a newspaper. I saw a picture of a green and white shirt and my heart started pumping faster.

I read the article and came to the conclusion that this glorious sight was Celtic. I saw this beautiful green and white home kit with the green leafed clover and it felt like falling in love.

So I said to my friend, this weekend we are going to Celtic Park. The next weekend we went to the station and asked a clerk how to get to Celtic Park, the man went nuts because he appeared to be a Rangers fan but he told us how to get there. So we arrived in Glasgow and the hunt for Celtic match tickets had begun. We walked for a while and saw a horde of green and white supporters so we followed them.

We caught the eye of some supporters because we wore Feyenoord shirts. So we started a conversation and were welcomed very warmly by the fans, we told them that we had no tickets and they said to us, stay here.

They walked to a guy that sold flags and scarves and spoke to him. The guy with the flags waved to us and we walked to him. He started chanting a salesman tale of flags and scarves and asked if anyone had two tickets for the Dutchies. After a while of chanting and singing, a guy sold us two extra tickets and we were in. We were stunned at the stadium and its beautiful supporters, then it appeared to be the day that they unfurled the flag of the Champions (how lucky can you be?) It was the most beautiful day of my life and from that day on I never wore another shirt other than the green and white. See you in Paradise this year again.

DENNIS DEN BOER, Schoonhoven, Holland

A van called 'Cara'

"IT was a cold and wet December day when we touched the ground in JFK..." Well actually, these were the lyrics coming from my walkman, for we were in fact landing in Boston's Logan Airport on a clear and hot July day, another Antipodean beginning his grand overseas experience – the "Big OE". I was typically attired in backpack, jeans, walking boots, All Blacks' cap, and pride of any kiwi's sartorial selection, the home town club rugby shirt – in this case, the green and red of Celtic RFC, Timaru, South Canterbury, NZ.

I looked across the arrivals hall for a glimpse of my Yankie friend, who I had met in an Irish bar back in Christchurch. She was this gorgeous raven-haired beauty called Cara doing a bit of travelling down under and we shared a taste for beer, sports and adventure. Anyway to cut a short story even shorter we had swapped numbers and here I was looking for a place to layover, en-route to London to join the rest of my countrymen. "Ughhhhhh!"

Something hit me under the ribs and sent me sprawling across the shiny linoleum in the baggage hall. Partly from the force of the impact, partly because I was overbalanced with my backpack and partly because I was blindsided, but whatever my excuses, I went over like a powder puff – bloody embarrassing. "Hiya buddy – you must be Chris, Cara's holiday romance" boomed this big American voice from a six foot four, 230-pounder who introduced himself as Larry - real name John. But being the biggest Boston Celtics fan in the world he had picked up the tag of his favourite player, legendary Larry Bird.

"Hi" I said, trying to appear as un-winded and unhurt as possible, "You are Cara's big brother?"

"Yeah, nice to meet ya Chris, she's got the car out front, let's go."

Cara blushed as we recounted the crash tackle at Logan. I did interject that there was no "romance" as alluded to by Larry – he admitted he was teasing, digging Cara in the ribs – she blushed even more noticeably – such a babe! Anyway, I stayed at their family house, was treated to some superb New England hospitality, and somehow in the wee small hours, whilst ploughing through our second bottle of Bushmills, Larry decided he was coming to London too – he was between semesters at college and had always wanted to go. Fair enough, the more the merrier. Feeling worse for wear the next morning we piled into Cara's beaten up old Taurus.

We acquired an extra seat on the BA0238 flight to Heathrow, and after bidding Cara fond (more than brotherly in my case!) farewells we boarded an uneventful six-hour flight to London. Uneventful that is, except that we sat next to this skin-headed bloke from Glasgow with a shamrock tattoo on his neck who upon seeing my Timaru Celtic rugby shirt and Larry's Boston Celtics tee-shirt exclaimed "You boys over for the game in four weeks too?"

"Er, what game?" I said, barely understanding the accent.

"The first Old Firm game of course" he said, looking both surprised and menacing in a way that only a tattooed, skinhead Glaswegian could...

"The old who? Is this cricket or rugby" I replied, knowing by the way he winced perceptibly, that I was in mortal danger.

"Where you two boys from then? You not ken the Old Firm of Celtic and Rangers?" he asked.

"Oh, I'm from New Zealand and my mate is from the States. Never heard of the Old Firm."

Somewhat happier that we had an excuse for our ignorant blaspheming, he launched into an animated and enlightening discourse on the Old Firm and what it meant, and how much he hoped Martin O'Neill could turn around Celtic's fortunes. We liked the dude, and he liked our Celtic shirts, although I think the idea of a club being called Celtic Rugby Football Club and being based in small town NZ freaked him out. We touched down, bade our farewells, and Larry and me were herded into the "Foreign Rabble" queue at Heathrow. There we were in London, me a country boy, wide-eyed and full of expectation at the coming adventures, and Larry, a cynical yank who'd seen the bright lights of NYC and LA but had never left America.

I did have a slight advantage of having some contacts from my university rugby days who were already over here, drinking beer, playing footy (the oval ball sort) and working behind bars. We figured out the Underground map and noted the position of the almost worn-out (from countless Antipodeans touching in homage) "Earl's Court" label above the circle with green and blue lines going through it.

A bumpy and exciting 45 minute ride later (trying not to look like tube-virgins); we climbed the stairs from the station and emerged into a fine West London autumnal afternoon. Hmm, perfect beer-drinking weather, I thought – I noted Larry was checking out the passing skirt. Anyway we managed to find 58 Hogarth Road and we were informed by a dishevelled looking bloke who reeked of illegal substances that my old mate Tommy was "down the pub" apparently. We dumped our backpacks amongst the strewn array of beer-cans, footy boots, pizza boxes and old copies of "NZ News UK" and headed on down the street to the "Prince of Teck".

Tommy was playing pool with a chick wearing a Scotland rugby top and jeans (I couldn't help noticing – or averting my eyes when she busted me) that made her look like a major minx. Too late. Larry was in there in a flash, flipping me a shiny mauve banknote (twenty quid I quickly learnt) giving me instructions to buy some beer, or something – his words trailed off as his attentions turned to the uberbabe in question. Eight hours, ten pints and some great craic later, the four of us were staggering back to the flat. "So when are ye visiting Glasgow then?" the sultry Fiona queried. I think she was asking me too, although she seemed snuggly entwined with Larry (Damn, that boy works fast...)

Turns out the Kiwi (plus token Scot) flat had a van parked outside that one of the blokes, who was off back to NZ, wanted to sell. It would be ideal for a tour around Britain and Fiona decided she'd be our tour guide as far as Glasgow – she had leave due and wanted to get back to see her parents. After a heavy sleep I waswoken by a boot, kicking me in the ribs. "Come on kiwi, we've got a van to check out" Larry said, in far too happy a mood for such an early hour (1130am) on the morning after. He'd pulled! Tommy drove us round West London for an hour and we check out "Cara" – as I had decided to dub her if we should part with the £1,100 being asked for.

All seemed OK – four good tires, and not too much smoke from exhaust, no major leaks and most important, a kick-ass sound system. I was itching to get out on the motorway in a new country with some good mates, my sunnies on, the windows down and U2 blaring out at 120 dB. As CW McCall once said – "Let them truckers roll, 10-4". A week later and we "Head out along the highway... Lookin' for adventure". Well actually, we're heading out of Manchester and we're not looking for adventure, just a sign that says "Glasgow", or "Scotland" or "North" or even just "Out of bloody Manchester". Fiona thought we were on the A635 (roads at home only have one number and no letters) whatever that is.

The petrol light was on and I thought Cara was overheating – come on baby, get us to the next service station. It was getting dark as we finally spotted the friendly and welcoming green glow of a BP sign. Relieved, we pulled in. Larry went off to buy a map as I soothed Cara with some water and oil. Apparently we were in Stalybridge and we needed to head back to the M60. We decided to find a pub to eat and rest before the nightly fight for space on the two mattresses in the back of the van. And there it was. Another sign. This time it really was a sign. The sign for Stalybridge Celtic FC, in fact. Fiona was amused – apparently it's "not the real Celtic". Er...

"What do you mean", Larry and I interjected almost simultaneously. We enlightened Fiona on the international usage of "Celtic", be it for small town rugby clubs or NBA basketball franchises. She wa impressed, I can tell, because she ass silent. Then she announced triumphantly. "Well, I'll take you two to an Old Firm game and show you the real Celtic".

Old Firm rang a bell – that Scottish guy on the flight from Boston had mentioned the term – apparently some huge soccer rivalry. Being from a country where only asthmatics and ex-pat Brits play soccer, I found that the words fierce and passionate were incongruous to the word, soccer.

Then again, the whole point of my travel was to broaden my horizons, so I was always willing to try something new. And besides, I was starting to find the Scottish accent quite sexy! "Oh yeah Fi, let's go to one of them Celtics games"

Larry responded, interrupting and agreeing with my thoughts. The next morning we were back out on the motorway north, U2 still hammering out their bombastic anthems, Fiona trying to hear her father speak over the din.

"Yeah dad, got some pals, they'd like to see an Old Firm game... Next one's in two weeks... great..."

It transpired that tickets for that game were sold-out but as Cara pulled into the outskirts of Glasgow after 10 days of touring the Peaks and the Borders, we still had hope. Alas, unless we had a spare 300 quid, no chance for tickets. Fiona wasn't perturbed. "Never mind, we'll watch it in my old local, O'Leary's Bar. You can meet some of the wildlife..." she smiled knowingly. So there we were standing in the crowed and raucous bar. There was an almost tangible electricity in the air, an atmosphere of expectation and excitement but tainted, albeit almost indiscernibly, with the smell of fear (or was that last night's Guinness residue in the carpets being heated to room temperature?)

All around me were smiling, friendly (despite outward appearances of the infamous football thugs I had seen on the telly back home) people, who, every so often cast nervous eyes towards the big screen in the corner before returning to their football management, gossip, and merriment. Once the game began however, a reverent hush descended. All eyes on the screen. At this stage I, along with every man woman and child was transfixed. This really was big. The crowd roared with either delight or anguish at every bounce of the ball, depending on which colour the bounce favoured, green or blue.

The game was seconds old when suddenly... "And it's Sutton. Yesssssssss". The pub erupted into a fervour I have seen only surpassed twice before at a sporting event. And both of these times happened in the next 12 minutes, as first Petrov, and then Lambert stuck the ball into the Rangers net. 3-0 against the arch enemy and I could see from the unbridled joy on the faces around me that this meant absolutely everything to them. Needless to say, Celtic won easily. Make mine a Guinness. I was converted, or maybe I already was.

Maybe the Celtic fraternity extends to every little Celtic club in the world, be it rugby, basketball or soccer. All I know is I'm now one of many Celts around the world who check the Scottish football results religiously and get a lift every time the Buoys open up an industrial-sized can of whoop ass on them Rangers (as Larry said at the time!)

CHRIS CASEY, Kingston-upon-Thames

I REALISED very quickly my dilemma. And, as I thought what had initially started out as a great opportunity at a tremendous price was going to end up a very expensive experience, and all in the name of the famous team in the green and white.

The lady from British Airways had quoted me £344 for a trip of a lifetime and I had the choice to book it there and then or lose the chance forever.

The deal would be gone at midnight. It was within moments of reading out the old credit card details that it dawned on me that I was flying back in the middle of an Old Firm game and...well there are some things money can't sway and it was time to do some re-arranging.

My wife and I had arranged a date of August 29 for our wedding day and I wanted to visit all my family in Canada before I accepted that a thumb that had swivelled precariously over my head for a number of years was just about to fall full force and my chance to travel would be gone forever!

And, for that price to be able to travel on six planes from Glasgow to London and Toronto and Vancouver and back was too good to turn down.

A long story cut short, I was soon on the phone to American Airlines and had arranged what would become known to my wife-to-be as a 'diversion' from Toronto to New York the day before the game. Total cost $382. Hotel for the night $240. Now how would I hide that Visa card?

And yet if a wife could only understand. I made that trip and it was an experience that opened my eyes wider to just how huge this thing that is Celtic really is. If you could see the fervour and excitement of these ex-pats, their arrangement for such events, the way they welcome the visitor from home and the atmosphere of it all in the most unlikely setting.

The game was a Scottish Cup tie in 1997 and I found the internet site for the Manhattan CSC and on arrival had made my way to The Triple Crown. On that first day there had been half-a-dozen folk around the bar and I wondered how this large bar, just off one of these huge wide New York streets, could have any association with what was happening the next day at 2.30pm eastern time.

I found myself asking if the tellies could pick up Scottish soccer games. Within seconds I was sitting back, sipping a beer and watching highlights from the Premier game at Aberdeen from the week before! Ah, home at last!

I wandered around the Empire State building the next morning with my hat and scarf. I couldn't work out how, here we were a few hours from a Rangers game and no-one had any colours on. But, I'll never forget as I drew up in a yellow cab at mid-day, all my luggage in tow for a 7pm flight home, the sight of hundreds of Celtic fans waiting to get in to this bar as New York madness erupted all around.

People of every colour, horns blazing, office workers stopping to stare. It was the strangest sight, like a fish out of water. Suddenly my early morning shyness gave way to an explosion of pride. I was among my own again and there were loads of us. Inside all the familiar songs were roaring out. I joined in. The televisions were showing past encounters and a wonderful mix of Scottish and Irish voices reverberated off the high ceilings and the game began to rapturous cheering. I remember 10 minutes in, the channel stuttered and the place went silent. Suddenly there was this guy on skis belting down a slope and a voice from behind yelled out, "Thank the Lord, Di Canio's still on!"

And back it came. We won that Scottish Cup tie 2-0 and it sent me on my long flight home happy as could be. But I'll remember it for so much more. I'll remember it for what Celtic means to these far travelled Celts. It means as much and more to them as it does to us at home.

I often think as I make my way towards Paradise of them all getting out of their yellow cabs and gathering so far from home.

They're all singing with the same voice, perhaps a wee bit louder and longer, but then they make their way out into the streets of a foreign city, cities all around the world, until they can some together again under their own Celtic roof and cheer on the team we all love.

ROMANO PETRUCCI, Stranraer

A pilgrimage on paper

BEING a Celtic supporter in Denmark was not easy in the middle of the '90s. Brian Laudrup was the indisputable hero of our soccer nation and in those days he won title after title with Rangers. The fans and the media were all over him and his club in an institutionalised praise where objectivity and critical attitude were almost completely absent. In early 1997 I had grown tired of this. I decided to go to Glasgow and write an article to tell the story of MY club and its supporters.

The occasion for this would be the Old Firm on Sunday, March 16. I arrived at Buchanan Street bus station at 6 o'clock in the morning and all odds were against me. I don't know if any of the locals have ever tried to imagine how scary this so-called "Dear Green Place" can appear at first impression under these circumstances. I had never been in Glasgow before, I didn't know anyone, I didn't have any ticket for the game and I was far from sure that this article I had decided to write was ever going to be printed back home. The only thing I knew was what a shop assistant in World of Soccer at Oxford Street in London had told me the day before: go to East Glasgow. And I vaguely remembered the name of Baird's Bar from one of the few balanced items Danish TV had managed to produce about the Glaswegian soccer rivalry.

I found a taxi. "I'm going to Baird's Bar, East Glasgow", I said.

"Are you sure you wanna go there?" the driver replied anxiously.

"Yes", I responded (this was before I adopted the phonetically more pleasant "Ay").

"Well," the driver said. "I'm not taking you to that part of town. It's a no-go area, especially at this time."

Since I knew of absolutely nowhere else to go, I insisted. He dropped me off beneath the tower at Glasgow Cross.

"That's Gallowgate", he pointed. "But don't go there. You'll get murdered." As if to emphasize this warning his vehicle departed from the square with a hysterical screech. It was now 6.30am and the streets were deserted. I started walking up Gallowgate. It was still dark and the drizzle covered the grey, ramshackle buildings in accurate correspondence with my nervousness.

Still no-one was around. I found Baird's Bar. It wasn't due to open for another couple of hours. I sat down on the front stairs. It had been a tough journey, going by bus all the way from Denmark and only stopping for a short time in London. So I placed my head on my bag and soon started slumbering. I woke up in a different world. The light, although still fragile, penetrated the grey skies from above and exposed a street that was rapidly becoming alive. Around me numerous stalls were being put together and dozens and dozens of green and white scarves, hats and shirts confirmed that I had indeed landed in the right part of Glasgow.

A few yards to my left an enormous lad enthusiastically shouted "Di Canio" every 10 seconds, holding up high a heap of white shirts with the Italian hero's image. It was probably he who had woken me up (the man with the shirts, that is…) Then Baird's Bar opened. I stepped inside, an action which was copied by what seemed like hundreds of other guests. Now I was not alone anymore. And with beer around, one is never far from someone asking you where you're from and what you're up to. I started to converse with a man called Brian.

And it was pretty difficult to tell him my story without sounding a bit like someone who was feeling extremely sorry for himself. He wasn't from town himself. But he introduced me to a local friend, Ronnie McLoughlin - and after having spent less than half-an-hour in the pub and less than fifteen minutes conversing I had been invited to stay at his place for free for as long as I wanted. The rest of the day we continued the drinking, talking and singing, only momentarily affected by the unlucky 0-1 defeat which sealed yet another Championship for Rangers.

The bartender signed me a diploma stating that I had "obtained the standard required to become a true Celtic supporter". Everyone was curious, but I sensed something more profound than the normal friendliness that is part of common Scottish hospitality. I sensed what I would describe as a deep gratitude towards me, not for being Danish and still sticking to Celtic, but for my ambition of telling the story about the spirit of Celtic in my country. I drank for free that day and I met so many lovely people, both at Baird's and down at the Tolbooth Bar, that I have sadly forgotten some of them.

I stayed with Ronnie for three days, rewarding him and his friends with nothing else than my company, my humility and an inexpressible gratitude which was to be the perfect inspiration for my article. It took me a few days to write it, while staying in his apartment.

But not until September 1998, when Celtic had regained the throne of Scottish football thanks to among others a couple of Danish players, it was printed in a newspaper back home. It was never going to be an objective article. It came out as a tribute that at least partly restored the balance in the Danes' perception of what the Old Firm is about. I had to have it printed. I guess I felt that I owed it to the people I met at Baird's. In 1998 I was admitted to the Danish School of Journalism.

Years later this education provided me with the chance to return to Scotland for an internship at The Scotsman in Edinburgh. I often went to the Celtic games and I revisited Baird's and Tolbooth on many occasions. Sadly I never met Brian, Ronnie, Liz, John, Lorraine and the others. I visited Ronnie's old address to show him a copy of the article that I wrote at his place three years earlier, but he had apparently moved. I hope that he and the others will get the chance to read this instead.

THOMAS GRAVGAARD, Aarhus, Denmark

Although I'm Aussie born and bred, my parents are both Paddies
So I suppose it's only natural I became a Celtic laddie
Dad's been a supporter all of his life and weekends are always the same
Sunday mornings on the phone to get the results of the game.
Then one day to us he said
"We're going home for a holiday and a trip to Parkhead"
We took our places in the stand amid wind, snow and ice
But when the players to the park, I realised why they named it … PARADISE.
KIERON MANNING (age 12), Lethbridge Park, New South Wales, Australia

Bhoy from Brazil

BEFORE anything, I have to apologise for my poor English because I'm from Brazil. Beginning my story, I have to say my passion for Celtic started when I was just a little child, about six or seven-years-old.

I think I became a Celtic fan at the first time I saw Celtic play, because of the colours green and white, and the different and wonderful shirt the team wear. But my interest grew so much that I always waited anxiously the news from my grandpa who lived in England for many years because here in Brazil, I couldn't follow the steps of the team at that time.

I remember like it was yesterday of the 87/88 season: if Celtic won the next game they were the Champions. In the same day we had here in Brazil a great game between São Paulo FC and SC Corinthians and my father took me to the stadium (he is a fan of Corinthians).

It was my first time in a football arena, I was watching a game between two of the greatest teams in Brazil, and the only thing I could think about was the phone ringing the next day to talk to my grandpa about the victory and the Championship of Celtic. Well, it happened I got so happy that from that day to now Celtic is my official team, followed by São Paulo FC (who won that game). To complete my happiness, later that year grandpa told me Celtic won the Scottish Cup as well.

That is my simple story, it is from my heart even though I still never watched a Celtic game live at Parkhead. Ah, just to end my story, while I write this, I watch the replay of Celtic 3 Dundee 0 on ESPN. That's Celtic on the way to our 38th Premier League title! Thank you.

FABIO CORACINI OLLITA, Sao Bernardo do Camp, Brazil

I HAVE always wanted to be in Scotland; even back before associating with the Gaelic culture was the cool thing to do. Really couldn't tell you why. I suppose for most Americans it's all about roots and connecting to your heritage and what not. Not me, I just have always randomly wanted to be in Scotland. The summer of my 17th year I decided I was going. I was about to finish high school and begin college and I wanted this in between.

I told my parents my plan and got a very sceptical, "Oh really young lady?" for my trouble. The thing was I really did have a plan, I would be 18 by the time D–Day rolled around and as a legal adult they really couldn't forbid or approve of my decision as much as accept it or not. Theoretically I could pull this off and they both knew it. It was decided that my father would accompany me on my little excursion and we would see what might be made of it.

One thing I was terrified to become was the stereotypical American tourist (I really can't tell you what that is exactly, only that the thought of it scares me) and I set out to find what I could about whatever the travel brochures aren't inclined to tell you. The answer was simple enough: the World Wide Web. I got online and into Scottish chat rooms and just listened and waited. Oh, soon enough it filled with talks of Bhoys and Rangers and how the other were numerous dirty names and whatnot (I have to admit that the whole experience really expanded my vocabulary), it was all a little intimidating.

So, curious, I asked what in God's name they're talking about and the immediate response was "Yanks are *****!" So much for American charm! Others, however, were quick to fill me in and one was even so nice as to explain the concept of the Old Firm derby to me (and why Celtic really needed to win). So began my now deep-rooted enjoyment of the team and the game itself. I began keeping up with scores online and on days the Bhoys played the Rangers I was always sure to support my team with white and green. My trip began taking on new possibilities and destinations, namely I had to go to Glasgow and see Celtic Park for myself (I wasn't naïve enough to think I might get into a game, at that point just seeing the stadium would have been enough).

Unfortunately, with the summer's epidemic of foot and mouth disease and other unforeseen missteps my grand plans fell through. I'm in college now and the closest I see myself to the country or my team (oh I may be an 18-year-old American girl but make no mistake, they are my team) or even just the stadium they play in any time soon is to sit with the television in my lap. I have actually never seen Celtic play. Every time a web cam offer comes up I have class and every time I'm anywhere near a TV with ESPN2 the 20 other people in the room want to watch the basketball game that is inevitably on.

I managed to sneak a Rangers game in over Thanksgiving break to watch the names that were familiar from checking scores play and it was one of the most exciting things in the world to me. I can't even imagine what I would do at this point if I saw the team I supported play when I get that excited just watching our biggest rival. I know it'll happen eventually, one of these days I'll be off when the next Web Cam game comes up and all will be pandemonium. More than anything else I wanted to write this so you know I'm here. I've never been to a game, or even seen them play but the men of Celtic are my Bhoys and I'm here rooting for them. Hail! Hail!

JENNIFER FUNKHOUSER, Murfreesboro, Tennessee

SATURDAY, May 26, 2001 approx: 4.45pm. The sun is shining and the skies are blue. People spill out onto the streets singing and dancing, holding aloft tinfoil cup replicas, much to the bemusement of passing by motorists who (have to) stop and see what the fuss is about.

It is not however the streets of Glasgow I'm referring to it is Calle Marques de Urquijo in the city of Madrid, outside Finbar's Irish House, home of the Madrid Emerald CSC.

The Treble of 2001 was memorable for everyone connected with our club, not least the fans. I was no exception. However this triumph was somewhat different for me as for the first time I was unable to celebrate with my closest friends and family. Not living in Scotland meant that I enjoyed the season like countless others around the globe, watching games on satellite television in a supporters' club.

I could go on for pages reminiscing about days (and evenings!) spent in Finbar's which are memorable for me and the other Madrid Bhoys and Ghirls, but they are perhaps too personal in that 'you had to be there' sensations would prevail, but for this piece of writing I have narrowed some tales down to the following;

1) Didier's last gasp 'bullet' header at Dens Park which provoked much joy and knocking over of bar stools! The day the league was won?

2) The CIS Cup semi against Rangers. We couldn't get the match so we watched a tape sent over from back home the next week. One of the year's best nights followed, with everyone treating the match as a 'live' game, even though we obviously knew the score. (That didn't stop me losing the sweep for 1st scorer though!)

3) CIS final. Satellite connection cut off as the teams came out the tunnel! Amid claims of a Masonic conspiracy we had to 'watch' the drama unfold on Teletext! Apart from the goals, the only highlights were the disparaging comments about the referee's ability. My father who was present at the match agreed that our comments were totally justified! (Even watching Teletext we are paranoid!)

4) Clinching the league was special not least because some good Spanish friends had finally made it down to watch a game in Finbar's. They couldn't believe the atmosphere and noise and passion emanating from the fans. Parkhead wasn't bad either! For a staunch Real Madrid fan to comment on the atmosphere being better than he was used to shows he was impressed. He was also able to pick up some expressions that he had never learned in English class!

5) Scottish Cup final was...well it was bedlam. Flags and scarves hung from every roof beam, as did the aforementioned cardboard cup replicas. Full time the champagne was flowing as was a bottle of Buckfast which had been imported specially.

Needless to say our Spanish friends (now fully fledged Celts after one game) disputed the fact that this was wine! Live music had been arranged to ensure the party didn't stop... not that it would have!

As I stated earlier, these stories may not mean too much to supporters back home (although I hope they raise a smile), as they are personal experiences.

The reaction of the Spaniards when there is a game on is priceless. The singing and dancing, the jumping up and down, the watching games from the week before or on Teletext does baffle them somewhat. But what makes more surreal, more special is that the same thing is going on in hundreds of locations around the world, provoking the same reaction from bemused locals!

What I would say is that the function and importance of CSCs outside of Scotland cannot be understated. It may provide amusement for the locals, but it is important that we can live Celtic together no matter where we are in the world.

It brings home that we are much more than a club. This is not anything new to Celtic supporters but living away from Glasgow it has certainly reinforced the fact more.

WE are afar, but WE Shall Not Be Moved!

TO all CSCs around the world especially Madrid Emerald ¡No Pasarán!

TOMMY McCONVILLE, Madrid

MY family immigrated to Canada in the mid-1960s, but growing up I always heard stories about the Bhoys from my father, uncles and cousins. So it was with great anticipation that we gathered at my aunt's house one day in the early 1970s to watch what I believe was the first broadcast of a cup final in Canada. Can't remember who Celtic were playing, but I do remember the great anticipation before the game, everyone sitting around waiting for the kick-off, when for some reason (excitement, I guess!)

I decided to inhale a piece of hard candy I had in my mouth, where it rapidly lodged in my throat and started choking me. Now you have to realise, this was minutes before kick-off, and a decision had to be made: Take me to the hospital, or watch the game. Guess what the choice was? Yes, they chose the game, the swines! Luckily, someone had the bright idea to try to melt the candy by pouring hot water and tea down my throat.

Well it worked, everyone was happy and Celtic went on to win the game! That's what I remember about the first time I saw Celtic play! I also remember, while on a family vacation in 1977,my uncle John Purdie taking me on a tour of Parkhead, including the trophy room and onto the pitch. That was really something! And also being at the opening game in 1977 when Jock Stein came out for a lap in his car and all the Walk-on scarves came out! Pure magic! Going to Ayr on the supporters' bus. Johnny Doyle crossing a waterlogged ball, knocking out the ref and getting red-carded!

My first Bovril, which I still love to this day. All great memories and I've still got that walk-on scarf! C'mon the Bhoys!

JAMES G SWEENEY, Thunder Bay, Ontario, Canada

I WAS born and grew up in Ireland and was aware of Celtic from a very early age. I must confess, though, that I am a rugby fan, but I am also what you might call a fair-weather Celtic fan. The last time I saw Celtic play in the flesh was at a less than rousing friendly against Shamrock Rovers in Dublin a few years ago. I also recall with sadness that the Celtic change strip was indeterminate in colour and design. However, I remember vividly watching the Lisbon Lions on the telly in a Dublin pub.

It is hard to forget that game even now, especially the sight of Tommy Gemmell smashing the ball into the top of the net. What a game. I now live in Montreal. For Montrealers, Celtic matches are made available by satellite by the Celtic Supporters' Club, well managed by Jimmy Traynor. To my shame, I attend rarely. However, the sentiment is always there and a friend from Glasgow, Frank Traynor (no relation to Jimmy), and I often fantasise about my retiring and going off to Glasgow together to take in a few games at Parkhead and either preparing ourselves for the games and/or conducting post-mortems in Baird's Bar. Frank makes the pilgrimage every few years and has me almost convinced that I should place it on the top of my list of retirement projects. Frank is a died-in-the-wool Celtic fan. He is known to entertain his friends in his house on occasion, among whom he counts some Rangers fans. Once they are plied with the requisite amount of the national beverage, he pops a videotape on the history of Celtic (the one with Billy Connolly in it) into the VCR. They have to watch it, no matter how many times they have seen it before.

It is all taken in good humour, but Frank never lets an opportunity to promote Celtic go by. My story begins with my wife who runs a small antique store on the western part of Montreal Island, an area where English predominates and where one is likely to find Celtic (and Rangers) fans. She buys her stock at flea markets, fairs and estate sales. On one occasion a few years ago she was informed by a friend of the sale of the estate of an old French/Canadian woman who had just died and whose daughter was selling off the household effects. The woman was a widow and had lived alone before she died in a large house in Lachine, which has a large French-speaking population.

The sale had all the stuff my wife looks for: cups, vases, teapots, picture frames and a myriad other items. The effects were arranged in the usual lots for auction. Without a thorough preview it was hard to tell what the lots contained as they were stuffed in boxes. My wife had her eye on one particular box, as she had glimpsed a few cups sticking out of newspaper at the top. She bid on the box and seemed so intent on getting it that her rivals backed off and let her have it. She brought the box home and left it in our dining room where it remained for months before she examined it.

The cups, saucers and plates were finally unwrapped one day as spring approached. The box was large and contained much that was worthless after the china, which prompted my wife to dispose of the rest of it.

However, one never knows what treasures lurk in those boxes and so she continued to rummage. Soon after she approached me with a plastic bag containing what looked like St Patrick's Day decorations, thinking that I might be interested. A search in the bag revealed multiple cardboard shamrocks, leprechauns and the like.

There was also a white scarf with shamrocks on it. However, inside that scarf was another scarf in green and white. I was about to dismiss the lot as St Patrick's Day souvenirs when I turned the second scarf over. And there were the magic words "Glasgow Celtic."

A find beyond value. I can't be sure of its age. It was made in England of acrylic material and has one thick and one thin green stripe running the length of the scarf on the outside with the white stripe in the middle. "Glasgow Celtic" is written on one side flanked by two four-leaf clovers with the word "Celtic" underneath. It looks like it might date from the 1970s. The amazing thing is that it was found in the possessions of an old French-Canadian lady with no obvious connection to Glasgow or Ireland. Frank believes that it is a sign from the Celtic gods that I have to make the pilgrimage in order to gain redemption for past neglects.

There is no other explanation for it: those gods made sure my wife got that box with that scarf in it in one of the last places you would expect to find it. I believe him. I am convinced. The scarf is folded neatly in a dresser drawer awaiting the pilgrimage. And when I walk into Paradise and Baird's Bar, I will be wearing that scarf, proudly.

DONAL IRVING, Baie d'Urfe, Quebec

Chris Sutton - the Hoops' hit man

I CAN remember, ever since I was little, listening to my dad's short-wave radio. The radio was old with a coat hanger antenna and if we talked we were given "the look", or in other words "if you know what's good for you shut up!" What's the significance of the radio?

Well, it's the first time I ever heard Celtic. Being born in Canada with Scottish parents, I was told Celtic were the greatest, Celtic are the greatest, and Celtic will always be the greatest! As I got older, I saw a few games, but it wasn't until I was 13 that I got my first taste of a real club.

My dad told me his friend was starting a club near where we live. I was interested and couldn't wait to see my first game in the Barrie and District Celtic Supporters' Club. The game was Celtic v Motherwell on August 5, 2000. I loved the thrill of the game, but was angry at the refereeing. I was mad because Sutton and McNamara were sent off for nothing!

It was in that game that I picked my favourite player. Even though he'd only played a few games, I knew Chris Sutton was going to bring great things to Celtic (and with three trophies in the case, I guess I was right!) I wrote and re-wrote this part because I wanted you to really understand why I think Chris is such a great player.

When he comes on to the pitch I know it's going to be a great game because he tries his hardest. I used to worry when he lost his temper, but now I think it's proof that he cares so much about his team. Although Henrik Larsson is an amazing player and no-one can deny his talent, I don't think he could have scored so many goals without Chris.

Chris is such a strong player and he stops at nothing to give the perfect pass or jump high above everyone else to score that header. If I were up against him, I'd just say, "take the ball!"

My dream is to meet him and go to a game. I am very fortunate because after two years of supporting Celtic, I am finally able to go! I leave in March and it's a dream come true. You have no idea how bad I've wanted this and I've been waiting for eight months!

To meet Chris would be the best day of my life, and I also have to take a photo of Lubo for my dad (Lubo's his hero!) I was planning on writing this big piece on why Chris is my favourite player, but I really can't explain it. I get goose bumps when he comes out of the tunnel, I jump off my chair when he scores and I cheer whenever the camera shows him.

Even though I live in Canada, my walls are covered with posters, and my schoolbooks are plastered with pictures of him! And even when he's not playing, I wear my Sutton scarf with pride! Now my friends don't even ask where I'm going at the weekend, they know that the club is where I'll be!

My sister once said that it's just a game, but to me it's not. I live in a country where hockey is THE sport and the fact that I can't stand it makes me the odd one out. If you even mention soccer here, the only team they know is Manchester United, and to be honest, one of my favourite games was when we beat them! To watch Celtic is my favourite thing to do. It is the only thing I know that can make your stomach turn, your mind race and the fact that the

263

excitement makes you feel like you could have a heart attack is a sign of a great game!

The way I look at it, anyone who says it's just a game should have a nice chat with Martin O'Neill after a Celtic versus Rangers match!

LAURA MULRINE (age 15), Innisfil, Ontario, Canada

ITALIAN giants Juventus were afraid that night when they arrived in Glasgow. The beautiful city of Glasgow had a tremendous atmosphere, and the worldwide known players of the Turin club were prejudiced before the game because they heard the ambience and the fans of Celtic Park.

There are things which carry teams to the top of world football, as football is played in the UK and developed from many sides in Europe and the other parts of the world. We witnessed some teams who were living their heritage, going into the roots of the history; teams such as Liverpool, Celtic and Galatasaray SK (my team) are like castles which won't be destroyed in the future.

Let's get back to that night where the people were shouting for the victory of Celtic FC. The biggest club of the SPL was on the verge of making a rarely seen success in Scottish football. Though the match ended 4-3, defeating Juventus was important, but the team mourned the fact they were not one of the two teams who moved through to the second groups.

And I think it was also Celtic's destiny they were eliminated from the UEFA Cup on penalties, but don't be sad, you are always a big team.

MURAT YUMLU, Istanbul, Turkey

Chapter Twenty-two

A memorable day

The wind was blowing
The sun was shining
As I caught the train
To THE CELTIC GAME

The tickets were ready
The shop was awash
With supporters in green
For THE CELTIC GAME

The policeman all stood
The horses were poised
To herd all the fans
To THE CELTIC GAME

The stewards came across
They met in a huddle
They shook their heads
At THE CELTIC GAME

It's cancelled they said
The stadium's broke
The wind has defeated
THE CELTIC GAME

FIONA BLAIR, Uphall

Heed the baw

IT was a Wednesday night away game at Airdrie. So I finished work early and made my way to the Dougrie Celtic Supporters' bus in Castlemilk where I meet up with the rest of the lads. The usual trip prevailed into to a couple of verses of Hail! Hail! and how many we were going to win by. It was a good night weather-wise; a wee bit cold but pretty clear. When we got the ground we mostly split up and went with our own friends.

My three friends and myself ended up behind the goal nearest the pie stall. Being the youngest group in the club the oldest members would try and keep an eye out for us at away games, making sure we did not get in to any trouble, as if we ever did. The game had begun to take shape with Celtic doing all the attacking as usual, but still to score. The next thing, I look up from biting my pie and here comes Big Yogi with his head down and the ball at his feet charging towards the goal. The thing with Big Yogi was he never exactly knew where the goal was until the last minute, because he always had his head down looking for legs to go around instead of looking where he was going. "SHOOT YOGI" was the cry from the terracing and the big man let fly.

The ball flew over the bar like a rocket and was coming in my direction. I could not get out the way, and the ball skimmed the top of my head. It didn't hurt but I gave it a rub as you do, only to find it was wet and sticky. BLOOD. There was an older Airdrie fan stood by us, who ask me if I was all right. I said yes but he saw the blood and waved for the ambulance men who came on to the terrace and told me I had to go to the ambulance room.

As I was escorted around the track, our committeemen spotted me and thought I had been hit by a bottle or some flying debris. When I got inside the ambulance room I was more concerned about catching the plague or missing a goal than I was about my head. Two minutes later the Dougrie Celtic Supporters' Committee arrived to see if I was okay. And you guessed it. Celtic scored and we all missed the goal. What I got going back home on the bus could not be printed.

DENIS McFARLANE, Adelaide, Australia

IN 1949–1950 I went to Tynecastle to see Celtic play Hearts. I went on a supporters' bus but to my dismay they could not give me a ticket for the match. I just stayed on thinking I could get a ticket when I got there, but to no avail. So what did I do? Remember at the Celtic end of Tynecastle there were tenement buildings overlooking the Park.

I went into the street and rang one of the bells of the top flat. A lady answered and asked what I wanted, I told her I was a Celtic supporter, but very respectable and could not get a ticket for the match. She told me to stand out in the street and looked down at me. She then said that I could come up. She put a stool at the window in the kitchen and pulled the window down. It was the best view I ever had at the Park and I have been following Celtic for close on 70 years, except for the war, as I spent over four years as a P.O.W in Poland.

She only charged me two shillings plus a cup of tea. The only sad part was that they beat us 4-2. How I kept in touch with Celtic during the war was my father sending me clippings about Celtic in a next of kin parcel, which we received roughly every two months but they did not seem to do well during the war. I have two season tickets which I received off Mr Kelly just after the war, I have also been a Pools agent since the start and also have a lot of shares which I bought when Mr McCann was in charge.

JACK MARSHALL, Cathcart, Glasgow,

AS I lay my head down on the pillow I reflected on the day ahead. Tomorrow. Tomorrow would be either one of the best days of my life or the terrible opposite. I knew also that tonight I would have no restful sleep. I had so many thoughts, flowing through my head that I couldn't switch my brain off and sleep peacefully like usual. Tomorrow, ten months of work would be summed up in one fateful day. I was extremely nervous and I wasn't even playing. I was only a supporter. I imagined what the players must have been feeling like. A whole generation of supporters hoped that they would win. A thirty-year-old record lay weighted heavily on their shoulders. Losing was unthinkable.

I woke up around nine o'clock. My alarm wasn't due to go off until eleven. I considered going back to sleep but instead opted for a good breakfast and a long bath. After my breakfast I walked to the local shop to pick up a few papers to read while I waited to go.

The back pages of the newspapers were dominated with our league-deciding fixture. Reading the newspaper only made me more confident. The one article that encapsulated my confidence was the one detailing the bookmaker's odds. We were very strong favourites to win. In fact, we were so strong that it wasn't even worth betting on us to win. After reading the paper, I realised there was still half an hour before my dad was due to pick me up. I decided to put on my jacket, scarf and took the tickets from the mantle, put them in my pocket and sat there staring into my lounge fire, reflecting on the challenge that lay ahead. Surely we would win. It could not be usurped for us.

My dad tooted the horn of the car to signal his arrival. I walked out to the car, as I entered I realised something was unusual. For the first time my dad was just as excited as I was. He turned to me as I began to relax and said. "Big day today…yeah…big day." I didn't answer, but acknowledged his statement with a smile. He then began to describe to me the last league decider he had been at.

It was an amusing story and he told me how he lost his keys to his house and car when Celtic scored. He had jumped about so much that they fell out of his pocket. He was left stranded 40 miles from home. A story that most people wouldn't find amusing but dad said he was so happy about winning that he didn't care, and spent the night in a bed and breakfast free of charge as the owner was also so happy at the score. The story was so long that when he finished it we were only a few minutes from the car park.

The scene was amazing as we reached the summit of a hill a few miles from the stadium because this was the first visual evidence that today was different form all the other games I had gone to. What lay in front of me was a breath taking sea of colours.

The pavements were full of men covered in green and white. What added to the scene were the huge flags hanging out of the car sunroofs. There was a carnival atmosphere around the day. Witnessing the huge mass of people all dressed similarly, in green and white made me feel very nervous. I realised this was not only special to me but also to many others. I had something in common with a huge mass of people. We were all experiencing something special, something that we wouldn't forget for a long time.

We parked the car where we usually did when we came to the football and joined the river of colours. The streets heading towards the stadium were filled. By the time we were there, there was no difference between roads and pavements. Both were walkways. The few cars engulfed in the mass of people were stationary, as I passed, and probably remained so for some time.

We turned a corner and there it was, like the coliseum in Rome. A huge edifice on an otherwise flat landscape. Celtic Park loomed over us. The shadow it cast made an extremely hot day seem cooler and duller in its shade. This was only the second time I had ever appreciated the size of the stadium. From inside echoed chants and songs. I was desperate to join in.

There was a long queue at the turnstiles. It seemed half of the stadium was trying to enter at the one time. Eventually, after a short while we entered. Now the sound was more than an echo. It was much louder. As I walked up the stairs into the stadium my heart pounded in phase with the drums beating all around the stadium. With almost a sense of relief I reached the top. I was here at last, inside the stadium. In front of me again was a mass of colours, brightened by the blinding sun. I stood for a moment and gazed starry eyed at the colours then turned and made my way up the second flight of stairs that led to my seat. At that moment I had my back to the pitch. I could hear the deafening chants. It was so loud I could feel the vibrations strumming through me.

As I reached my seat the man who had sat in front of me for two years greeted me. He shook my hand and said, "we'll do it today." I nodded in recognition. Even after two years I didn't know his name. We didn't talk very often, only the odd friendly remark during the game. We all began singing in chorus. This lasted until the teams came out. Then we sang louder than before. With scarves held aloft we sang. At the top of my lungs I shouted 'You'll Never Walk Alone'. The game had begun and nobody could stop us now.

After about ten minutes of shouting and singing my throat was throbbing. I didn't care, however. This was our day. It was better very suddenly. Henrik Larsson hit a shot from twenty-five yards and it went into the net. Celtic Park erupted in fits of joy. The whole stadium jumped up and down in frenzy. Sixty thousand people locked in a fit of madness. One of the very few opportunities to see frown men express their true emotions. No feeling macho or acting manly. No, just sheer raw emotion. A kind that very few people who don't have a passion for football ever experience. Where else do you witness 60,000 men cuddling and jumping up and down with other men?

After Larsson's goal we sang for about an hour. Then Celtic scored again and any tiny amount of doubt that there was there was erased. We were presented with the trophy after the game. The moment when Tom Boyd held the trophy above his head was one of the greatest images inscribed on my memory.

We left the stadium about an hour after the game had finished. When my dad and I left the stadium was still half full. We emerged from the stadium into a mass of people with scarves and flags fluttering as they headed home. We returned to the car through the hustle and bustle of people. When we began our journey home, it was on the motorway that I realised the extent of Celtic's victory. Every car in a mile long tailback had a flag or scarf hanging from the window, car horns also proclaiming our victory to anyone who didn't know we had won.

The long line of cars with flags and banners hanging from them looked like a parade. When we reached Coatbridge the atmosphere was amazing. The streets were literally matted with flags and banners. There were also people on the road dancing and singing.

There was no room at all on the pavement. It was a surreal atmosphere. When I returned home I told the other members of my family about the unique day I had had. I was so proud to be a Celtic supporter. I have always been proud to be a Celtic supporter but today it was a different kind of pride. It was a kind of pride that I will never experience again in my life. We had made possible what many believed was the impossible. We had conquered the unconquerable, and no journalist, or TV presenter could take that away from us. W had stopped 10 in a row.

The 9th of May 1998 was a day that I will remember until my last day. It was a day when 9 years of ridicule from my so-called friends who supported another team was ended. A day when a record, which my dad grew up watching being made was kept intact. A day when a year of joy and hardship finally came to a conclusion. One swing of fate and this essay would have told a different story, a story of sadness. I'm sure I would have entitled it, "The Worst Day of My Life" Instead I remember this day as a very happy one, probably the happiest day of my life. Even four years on I still look back and smile. I still have a vivid image of Tom Boyd with the league trophy above his head. Most young Celtic fans would agree with me. It was the best day of my life.

I will look forward to the day when I am walking down the Gallowgate towards Paradise with my little boy by the hand and I turn to him and say. "I remember my first league decider..." And I will tell him this story.

CHRISTOPHER SANAGHAN, Airdrie

A day in my diary

SATURDAY, May 9, 1998

Woke up at 6am by my recurring "10-in-a-row" nightmare, and lay in bed staring at the ceiling for around 30 minutes before finally admitting I'm not getting back to sleep. My stomach is churning and I'm starting to sweat. I hold my arm out and my hand is shaking, my nerves are shredded. I feel completely wrecked, and for once drink isn't to blame, last night I didn't touch a drop.

6:30am, with my wife and kids still sound asleep, I get up, get dressed, and go for a walk. My overbearing feeling is that I can't take any more stress.

I feel I'm about to explode. My mind is in turmoil, and all of a sudden these last nine title-less years don't feel so bad. I can't remember them ever make me feel like this.

On the way to the shop I see a few other guys I know are Celtic fans who probably, like me, are at their wit's end, and decided an early morning walk is the only cure. Probably, like me, they'll have discovered it hasn't worked. On the way back I say to myself repeated Hail Marys and various other prayers. It's always been my belief never to pray for anything for myself, so I pray for all other Celtic supporters worldwide that this would be a day for them to remember.

My wife is awake when I return, and when I enter the house she just looks at me and shakes her head. I'll give her due, she knows better than to say, "It's only a game." Breakfast is on the table, maybe she doesn't understand after all; how I can I possibly eat with my stomach in the state it's in. I sit down and stare at it for a while, before she finally pulls it away and tells me to phone my brother.

My brother is a few years younger than I am, and, if it's possible is even more fanatical about the Hoops than I am. He's still single and tells our mum that he will stay that way until Celtic win the league, and maybe then he will settle down. In my worst moments I picture a lonely old man, but surely that's all about to change

269

today. Anyway, it's now 9am, and after a few phone calls I've managed to round up a few mates, organised a taxi, and we're on our way to the Gallowgate in Glasgow. First stop, as always, is the Mecca of bars for all Celtic fans, Baird's Bar…. and it's absolutely heaving. The volume, of people and noise, is overwhelming. We fight our way to the bar and manage to get a drink but it's just too busy, so it's one pint and then over to The Hoops Bar. It's full in there as well but we find a space and settle down. After another beer I'm starting to feel a bit more at ease, a temporary alcohol-induced calm sets in. The video is showing old Celtic games, the Bhoys in the pub are belting out the songs, and getting louder with each one. The atmosphere around the whole Gallowgate area is absolutely amazing, wall-to-wall Celtic fans at various stages of nervous disorder.

Then I notice behind the bar the standard Hoops Bar polo shirt for sale, but with an additional logo saying "CELTIC - PREMIER LEAGUE CHAMPIONS 1998". I don't see anyone buying; a sign of nerves amongst the faithful, nobody wants to tempt fate. I ask the barmaid how much, "A tenner", not bad, but not for a shirt that might be thrown away in a few hours' time. I still can't get rid of that gut wrenching feeling that this could all end in tears. It's an amazing rollercoaster of emotions, one minute we're Champions without question, the next it's…well I can't even go there. But for now, I'm on a high.

Eventually it's time to walk to the stadium and again I feel my confidence starting to wane as the kick-off draws nearer. What if! They'll fly that bloody helicopter right over the top of us; there's nothing surer. I can't even contemplate it. But, as we approach the stadium and I hear the singing, I get another rush of positive energy. I read in one rag the next day that around the stadium was silent and nervy before the match, but whoever wrote it wasn't underneath the North Stand. Ten minutes to kick off and this place is absolutely bouncing. Hail, Hail is giving it laldy, being sung as loud as I've ever heard…. And that's saying something. The punters in the graveyard will be complaining if this continues. Once again my spirits soar. This is our day and nothing will stop us.

Climbing the stairs to the top tier has always been a long struggle, with me not being in peak condition anymore, but today someone must have carried me up because I'm at the top I and can't remember getting here. I make the last few steps before finally being able to see over on to the pitch, and it's a picture that will live with me forever. I don't think I've ever known an atmosphere like it. In all my years of following Celtic, this is the pinnacle. The whole place is a mass of green and white, and the noise is unbelievable…. I can't hear myself think.

I find my seat and it's hugs all round with the guys who sit around me, and whom I've spent a long agonising season with. We all encourage each other.

"This is it…. Come on, this is it." And then the teams come on the park and the whole place, which is already at fever pitch, erupts. The Bhoys go into their Huddle, and it gets louder, then the Huddle is over, and it gets louder, and then the whistle blows to start the game, and it gets even louder. Whatever happens now, I'll never forget this atmosphere; this is something special…. And it's only just begun.

Five minutes gone and the St Johnstone keeper comes to the edge of his box to clear the ball, but doesn't make a very good job of it. Lambert brings it down nicely on his chest and plays it forward to Henrik. "Come on, Donnelly, make a move for him." But Henrik has other ideas, a quick shuffle and he leaves the defender, another and he creates a yard of space, and then he lets fly. I knew the moment it left his boot it was a goal all the way, this stadium gives you that level of view, and when it did...bedlam, bedlam, bedlam! The guy next to me grabs me and we jump up and down, shouting "WE'VE DONE IT, WE'VE DONE IT". The whole place is going mental, people falling over each other, grown men screaming, the stadium is shaking...shear relief as well as unadulterated joy. Our dreams are coming true.

We've got the start we needed; now it's time to kill them off. A second goal soon and we can dispel all nerves and start the party in earnest, but it's not happening. Someone tells me St Johnstone are threatening, they're in our half, but I don't know, I can't look. Then when I saw George O'Boyle head over an open goal...oh Jesus. Surely after Dunfermline last week this can't happen to us again?

Half time. 1-0. I wait for the longest 45 minutes of my life. John Higgins brings his World Championship Snooker trophy onto the pitch, he gets polite applause but nobody's really interested. No one is talking about the other game in Dundee. Unusually, no half time results are announced from the tannoy, that can only mean the Gers are winning, but that'll not matter, tell me it'll not matter. The second half is scrappy but Celtic look to be in control. Then their keeper makes a great save from Donnelly and the nerves are back, maybe it's not meant to be. As long as it stays 1-0, it's sheer panic when St Johnstone get into our half, and you can see that panic transferring to the players.

"Come on, Celtic.... get a second!"

65 minutes gone and time for a substitution, on comes Harald Brattbakk. I've spent countless hours in the pub arguing with my mates to give this guy a chance, "Listen, he'll come good" I tell them, "wait and see.".Oh how I would love that time to be now.

75 minutes gone, we're nearly there, if we lose it now I'm packing football in. More scrappy play in our half then Boyd wins a tackle, runs 30 yards with the ball at his feet, and plays a perfect pass along the wing to McNamara. Some joker comments, "Who's the guy in the Tommy Boyd mask?" Then I see Harald Brattbakk make a run from the centre spot between the two central defenders and into the box, and Jackie has seen him so all it needs is the pass. Everyone stands up.... Come on.... Please.... And the pass is perfect. He can't miss, and he doesn't, passing it under the keeper and into the net. If it was bedlam before then the place goes absolutely berserk now, everyone just loses it, except Harald, who remains cool.

People generally say the best moment of their lives was the birth of their kids. Well I'm lucky enough to have three Bhoys who are the centre of my life, and was fortunate enough to attend each of their births. It would be fair to say they were highly emotional and very magical experiences, but they don't come close to how I'm feeling right now. There is no way we're going to lose it now. For 10 long years I've waited for this moment, and it isn't really sinking in that it's finally arrived.

The last 15 minutes of the game are just a blur; all I remember is bouncing up and down and singing at the top of my voice. I look at the tunnel and see Tosh McKinlay celebrating already. When the final whistle eventually goes I can feel tears in my eyes and try to hide it, but I'm not alone. I can't describe my feelings, I don't have a strong enough command of the English language (being a Scot), but I know I'm going to have one hell of a party and it's not going to stop for a very long time. I can't wait to see my wife and my family, I can't wait to see my brother and my mates, I can't wait to get back to work. But for the moment I'll just share these feelings with 50,000 other Celtic fans around me.

The players receive their trophy, and as I watch and enjoy their lap of honour, a part of me wants to leave now and get back to my local to be with my mates and begin our celebrations. But I hang around a bit longer to soak in the atmosphere. Lots of fans are on the park, making the most of their day to remember. As I leave, a woman says to me this was her first match. My first thought was "how the hell did she get a ticket?" and my next was, "I hope she doesn't think it's like this all the time".

Around the stadium the atmosphere was total euphoria. The streets were a sea of green and white scarves and flags. People in cars were tooting their horns, colours draped out sunroofs and windows. My thoughts turned to the 10th flagpole outside the Louden Tavern…. with no flag, ya beauty.

Eventually I make it back to my local, and from there I'm afraid the whole thing becomes a blur, my recollection of events somewhat clouded. But one thought I do remember having at the time. "I wonder how much those shirts in the Hoops Bar cost now?"

DAVID QUIGLEY, Cumbernauld, Glasgow

Where were the Likely Lhads on 9 May, 1998

The Players:

John'o: The school-teacher for whom every trip to Parkhead is a religious pilgrimage - each weekend up there is relished and savoured … and sanctified by several pints of Guinness!

Mark: The lucky mascot - the smile gets wider as the pints get bought! Celtic never lose when he's at a match - he should probably really be given an honorary season ticket by now!

Pat: The man behind the Peterborough Celts machine … also the man who tells his sons to not do as he does on the Glasgow weekends - that'd be drink too much then!

Tony: Respectable family man … until we cross the border - then the devil descends! A mad Celt in every way - there's nothing better than the 'Tony' roar as another goal goes in!

John: The Cambridge student who is best known for … decorating the college laundry in all shades of green and white every time he hangs up his numerous Celtic jerseys to dry!

Richard: The 6ft gentle giant … who also turns into a 6ft raving loony once we hit Glasgow city limits - even his brother gets scared then!

Various other squad members turn up now and again - but the six first team regulars are the main players to feature in all the legendary Celtic stories that we've been part of over the years!

The Story:
WE could talk about one of the first ever trips to Parkhead - the fact that we complete the journey to Glasgow in a ten-hour round trip makes it all the funnier that one of the first matches we went to saw us leave Glasgow at about 6pm on the Saturday, and return to Peterborough on 6am on Sunday ... the reason for the delay - erm ... we stumbled across a pub near Newcastle! Or there was the time that the final leg of the journey from Scotch Corner was completed without the full complement of gears - arriving in Glasgow with merely first and second gears is a feat Pat is determined never to repeat!

No-one ever forgets a trip to Parkhead but the match with Aberdeen in November 1996 which put us top of the league sticks in the memory. The fact that we were in the temporary stand and the rain belted down all afternoon meant it was a legendary experience.

However, at this match John was nursing a broken arm and it needed protection from the rain so we found the ultimate plaster cast waterproof accessory ... a Tesco carrier bag!

And then there are the numerous Sky television experiences in Peterborough - on at least two occasions a Celtic goal has been followed by the Sky viewing card falling out of its box! There are many things that make our Glasgow weekends a brilliant experience but what follows has to be the ultimate, the greatest feeling that perhaps anyone will ever experience...

9 May, 1998 (6.00am)
The adventure begins ... today Celtic would make history and we were to be there. The fervour surrounding the last game of the season with St Johnstone was intense - we had no match tickets but there was no way we were not going to be in Glasgow on the big day. People said we were mad, crazy, whatever and guess what ... we didn't disagree! This was the day that 10 in a row would become a magic 1⊕ in a row! It says something that, for people who don't do mornings, we were all wide awake as soon as the alarm went off at the ungodly hour of 5am! By 6am we were all assembled and seated in the back of our Volkswagen minibus.

(6.01)
Surprise, surprise John falls asleep! A man probably capable of falling asleep in the middle of an earthquake never fails to let the lads down as soon as we hit the road ... zzzzzz! Tony now lays odds of even money on the likelihood of John staying asleep until Scotch Corner.

(8.30)
Like an oasis in the middle of the Sahara desert, salvation emerges for the Peterborough Celts - or just the prospect of a nice fry-up as we hit Scotch Corner. Well, not literally hit - the driving isn't that bad!! On any other day, a greasy hamburger this early in the morning would barely be touched let alone relished like it is now! A quick cuppa and we're off again surging towards Glasgow in the style of Henrik Larsson surging into the Rangers penalty box - or just foot on the accelerator and go!

(11.30)

We arrive in Glasgow and see the Theatre of Dreams. Celtic Park. As someone not-so-famous once said, 'the only reason God put Ibrox in Glasgow is so that we can appreciate the true majesty of Parkhead!' And today, although we didn't know it quite yet, would be quite majestic! We drove into Sauchiehall Street and checked into the Kelvin Park Lorne Hotel. After that we proceeded to check out the beauty of the Botanical Gardens (mothers and wives skip the next few lines) - we all know that's a load of rubbish but we have to keep up a pretence! What did we do ... we found the nearest pub!

(1pm)

John'o is disappointed to learn that he hasn't even made the subs bench for today's game against St Johnstone - ah well, he doesn't mind too much as another pint of Tennent's heads his way! As we get nearer to Paradise the pubs are more packed than ever - we squeeze into a few venues along the London Road to sample the atmosphere! Sadly, Richard isn't with us today - much to his disappointment and frustration he is in the wilds of East Anglia on a Geography fieldwork trip. He still gets the odd bit of stick from anyone who knows that his answer to the question 'Where Were You When We Stopped The Ten?' will always be "in the middle of a mucky field in Southern England!"

(2.45)

Approaching kick off - suddenly five pints prior to the most crucial game for Celtic in a long time doesn't seem like the greatest idea! We also managed to lose Mark but somehow we were sure that he had found his way into Paradise by hook or by crook! Thousands of people were outside Parkhead - like us no tickets but sensing something big was about to happen.

(3.00)

Kick off!

(3.02)

GOAL! Super Henrik puts us in front - and 10,000 people now know what it is like to jump around like a loony and celebrate something we can't actually see. But it's a fantastic feeling! Tony does his 'victory dance' as Pat, John and John'o revel in the moment!

(3.30)

Radios are blaring out nineteen to the dozen, and the BBC Broadcasting Unit is besieged by Celts as news spreads that they have live pictures of the game. Pat gets a look-in to reveal that the TV 'screen' is about the size of your hand - still doesn't prevent a throng of people itching to grab a look!

(3.45)

Half-time! Poor communication between the ground and the fans outside means that we think Celtic have scored several times and that, for some bizarre reason, Craig Burley has scored two penalties! It's like a game of Chinese Whispers with 70,000 people - 'half-time, one up' can easily translate to 'Gascoigne sent off' and generate some humour among the Celts outside the ground!

(4.10)

Nervous!

(4.15)

Nervous!

(4.20)

Nervous!

(4.28)

GOAL! And the man bearing the Good News is ... Harald Brattbakk! Delirium descends as surely nothing can stop us now - strangers become the best of friends as everyone gets a hug. Or a kiss! Grown men have a tear in their eye as the Promised Land is upon us! Wim the Tim has delivered and we are the Champions!

(4.47)

CHAMPIONS! The final whistle blows and the party, which in reality had started 19 minutes ago, can officially start!

Not one of the Peterborough Celts has said that 9 May 1998 was not one of the greatest days in our little history of supporting Celtic. The night was long and we celebrated well into the night and the summer was one of sunshine and smiles! The season had been tense but exciting, edgy but spectacular and the fact that we were kept in suspense until the last day of the season must have been God's way of having a little laugh at our expense. It must have been fate that Celtic were to clinch the title at home in Paradise in May 1998 ... and we have all thanked fate numerous times for doing us a very big favour and helping us have a massive party that day!

JOHN BOLAND, Peterborough

IT was May 9, 1998 and this day was very special to me because I was to make my First Holy Communion but there was a problem ... hat was the last day of the season and I had not missed a game all season, so I was not going to miss this one.

All through my Communion all I could think about was seeing Celtic lift the trophy. As soon as the Mass had ended I got all my pictures taken then I rushed home, got changed, left my Communion party and off I went.

The game was fab. We won 2-0 over St Johnstone and so far that has been the best day of my life (except when Celtic won the Treble)

NICOLA PEARSON (age 12), Coatbridge

One fine day (Celtic Park 1998)

I HAVE to get up early so I go to bed
Because in the morning at six I am off to Parkhead,
To watch one of the greatest teams
To score many goals and fulfill all dreams.

We get up at an early hour
Because today we have to travel far
Across the ocean to a different place
Today I wish the time would race
Our club members- Emanuel, Muff and many more
Try to predict the final score
But whatever happens we will not really care
We will be able to say that we were there.
This Saturday is so exciting to me
Going to a match and Scotland to see.
Standing outside Celtic Park
Is a time to remember, a time to mark
Stalls selling flags, badges and more
And lots to see in the Celtic Superstore,
Everything of Celtic which you can buy
Pyjamas to boxers, right down to a tie
Seat number 7, area 118, row UU
We have to go and stand in the queue
We give our tickets and then we go
To the South East Stand way down low
My Daddy runs to go to the loo
I will see the pitch in just a minute or two
I shut my eyes, I shut them tight
Soon I will see an unbelievable sight
To go up those steps is another story
These are the steps to dreams and to glory.
All of a sudden I can see
A sight that is so new to me,
The atmosphere is electric and flags fly high
Thousands begin to sing The Fields Of Athenry
I take my seat and the others do too
We look all around us and admire the view
The whole stadium starts to roar
On the pitch the Celtic Bhoys pour.
Celtic form the Huddle, the other team prepare
I can see Henrik Larsson, you would know by his hair.
Burley, Donnelly, McNamara and the rest
This is Celtic, they are one of the best
Hail, Hail the Celts are here
Everyone would shout, everyone would cheer.
When we see the green and white
We roar and scream with all our might.
Celtic scored so many that I lost count
But as I remember, five was the amount.
I knew they would win, they always do
Okay I will admit they lose a few
But they will always remain one of the top clubs
If they have players like Boyd and Alan Stubbs

I cannot believe it was over so fast
I wish that it would go on, that it would last
Going back home, everyone started to dose
Until finally our eyes slowly did close
It is a grand old team to play for
And a grand old team to see
And if you asked a million more I think they would agree.
Back we go to the Falls Road Celtic Bar
From here to my house it is not far
When I get home and into my bed
The day's events spin through my head
I will never forget it no matter what
To go back again I would give all I have got.
Once you go, you can't stop going again
It is a chance in a million, it's hard to explain
Paradise is just what it will always be
A second home is what it is like for me
My Daddy says he will take me again
I just cannot wait, it drives me insane!!

CLAIRE CANAVAN, Belfast

A memorable day

Oh, the Rangers men said 'Come see us play
As we'll make it 10 by the month of May'
But we stood firm and we stood tight
As we stood by the Bhoys in green and white.

We went to church on that Saturday morning
To give all the Rangers players a warning
That Celtic would come out today
And show the world how to play.
And the singing and dancing had begun
When Henrik Larsson made it one
We could see the flag being flown today
Flying over Paradise way.

With every shot and every pass
The Celtic pressure would surely last
With the Viking Harald in his glory
He made it two past the St Johnstone goalie.

The tears of men and the tears of boys
Couldn't describe all of our joy
The ten-year wait had come to an end
As the Championship trophy was home again.

And we can only thank one brave man
Who restored the faith of a million fans
He brought the pride back to Celtic men
The unforgettable Dutchman, Wim Jansen.
DANIEL McDONAGH, Scarborough, Ontario, Canada

The 6-2 weekend

MYSELF and my now wife, Amanda had lunch together for our first date, which I followed with several pints. We had to go back to work, which was a bit of a struggle but only for an hour and a half.

My flight from Dublin was at 6.30pm and Amanda said she'd give me a lift to the airport. As her car was parked in Whitehall, we had to get a bus to pick it up. Suddenly it was teeming with rain and booms of thunder seemed to fill the sky. Of course by then I was so hyped up and a wee bit merry I didn't have the exact money for the fares and didn't want any change, just get me to the plane. This confusion I could do without. We got to the airport where I said I'd meet her in the bar after she parked the car. I had a few JD's and said I'd phone her when I got back. "Enjoy yourself," she said, little did I know how much I was going to 'enjoy' myself.

The flight to Glasgow was quicker than usual or so it seemed, just long enough to have a couple of complimentary cans. There to meet me were some friends, who gave me a bottle of Bud for the journey and invited me out for dinner and would collect me about 9 o'clock.

I arrived at the Georgian in Coatbridge – now home of their own CSC – where I had long since established a home from home under the good care of the Rossi family and staff (Rangers fans included). I might as well have a beer while I washed and changed so I'd be in fine form for dinner.

I don't remember being collected for dinner and I had chicken something or other and when asked which wine I'd prefer "Bordeaux", I replied. Nice choice in an Italian restaurant, topical I thought seen as how we were playing Bordeaux in Europe. I was 'quietly' dropped back to the hotel with Charlie and the Bhoys singing in my ear.

After checking in at the Clock, Saturday morning I got a train into town to meet up with friends who lived in Battlefield. Many pints were sunk with Scott and his mates among whom were a few of the blue variety (season book holders) and then we all trooped back to his flat with a carry out. At this point I feel I must stress I DO NOT drink Buckfast. I recall after a lot of slagging about the result the following day (or hours later) that Scott inviting me to stay in his spare room "No, I've a chance of a ticket if I'm in Coatbridge, but none if I'm here", was my reply.

At half past four in the morning I poured myself into a mini-cab bound for the Georgian. The driver had other ideas, when I realised it was the red light area we were driving through, I roared "It's Coatbridge I want, not a bloody hooker". "There's road works around", "I don't give a damn, just drive to Coatbridge."

When I got back into the hotel, after banging on the door several times and explaining to the night porter who I was, "I'm Johnny Martin, from Dublin", I seen a note attached to y key. I knew straight away that it was from Gerry about a ticket. "Phone Gerry, URGENT", it read. A bit too late now I thought, it seemed to have a rapidly sobering effect on me. Straight to bed.

Surprisingly enough I awoke at 9.30 in the morning showered and phoned Gerry. "Do you still wasn't a ticket for the game?" "Aye", I replied. "Good, but it'll cost you twenty quid"; I could have bitten his hand off for it. "I'll see you in the Clock at half ten with the ticket" says Gerry, "No bother" says I. Breakfast was a blur of hands, tea and toast.

I floated down to the Clock, no hangover, just excitement and anticipation. And a lovely day to boot. The walk down to the bar is a wee bit special for me, resplendent in my Celtic top. Past St Augustine's where I originally came to bury Tam, who had been a good friend of mine, and whose family I still keep in touch with. Then past the Bank's Social Club, cross the road under the 'brig' by the bookies and into the bar.

It was heaving', a massive sea of green and white. Then in walks Gerry, gives me the ticket and I now know I'm going to lose my 'Old Firm' virginity tag. A couple of beers, with no time for more on the bus. The same bus I go on each time I travel over for a game, the Townhead Connolly CSC, a great bunch of people, they couldn't do any more or make you feel more welcome. By now the butterflies in my stomach are having butterflies. In to the ground and I'm sitting twenty yards from the bluenoses right behind the goal.

What happened in the next 90 minutes of football was too much for me to take in at that moment. I had to buy the video when it came out to watch the game again, and again and again. I was hoarse from the singing and shouting. I'm sorry, Fergus, but many a ballad was sung that day with deep and true meaning behind them. After the final whistle as I left the ground I seen one of the lads off the bus, "I walked in to Paradise and I've caught a glimpse of Heaven", I said (although I couldn't remember). I just walked back to the bus speechless and unable to really understand or take in what I and 60,000 others had just witnessed. Kevin and Gerry hugged me, I looked totally dumbfounded and was just waving my arms about wanting to cheer and sing but nothing seemed to be appropriate enough for the moment. All the lads said after that they'd try for a ticket for me anytime I came for the Rangers game. I was their lucky mascot. That's too much for any Irishman to carry.

The journey back to Coatbridge was ecstatic, the roadway lined with green and white and we were cheered as if we'd played. The pub was bouncing when we got back and we were cheered and patted on the backs. What voices we had left were put to full volume with the favourites of many young and old men and women from Ireland and their descendants in the West of Scotland. How many drinks I had, who knows, but I wasn't really that drunk, maybe drunk on euphoria. This is what it is all about. This day seemed to be in me from an early age, it was just a matter of getting the chance for it to emerge.

Again I had to bang on the door of the hotel to get in; I'd no idea what time of the night it was. This time I decided I was hungry and wanted a toasted cheese sandwich. As I walked into the kitchen, cries of "you can't go in there" came from the friendly night porter whom I'd christened John (easier to remember if it was the same name as mine). I found the bread, walked into the fridge and came out with a catering size block of cheese and picked up a carving knife. "Where's the toaster" I shouted to 'John', who looked decidedly frightened. At what I wondered. I suppose the sight of a big drunken 'Paddy' in a Celtic top carrying a huge block of cheese under his arm, waving a knife looking for a toaster in the early hours of the morning would make a lot of night porters around the world wonder if there were easier ways of making a living.

Monday morning down to the Clock for a curer. People all over were buying ALL the papers. It did happen. I even spotted myself in one of the photos in the paper. My good friend Kevin drove me to the airport, both of us with smiles that could be worn for a year. I arrived back safe and sound after seeing my beloved Celtic trouncing Rangers in one of the most thrilling games of football I have seen. Before that, Ireland beating Russia 3-0 in 1974 was probably my most memorable game. I had bunked off school for the afternoon.

Anyway the memories of that weekend will live with my family and me for eternity. A big thank you to Kevin, Gerry and everybody in Coatbridge who knows me, with our whom I would never have been able to write this and thank you to all at Celtic Park, with out whom something would be missing from my life.

JOHNNY MARTIN, Blackrock, Co Dublin.

A perfect day

I went down to me local that fine August day
To cheer on the hoops, cause I knew they could play
And what I did watch brought a smile to me face
Cause we had poor aul Rangers all over the place
Sure with his first touch Chris Sutton did score
And from Paradise there came a big roar
Then Stan the Man he struck number two
The Rangers defence, sure they hadn't a clue
Up stepped big Paul Lambert and hit number three
I jumped outa me seat and kissed the TV
Then after the break with his still dreadlocked head
Henrik the legend, he left them for dead
Cause for number five he jigged and he danced
Then with a great lob he buried his chance
And just when we thought it didn't get any better
Up stepped that man Sutton, our new goal getter
By the end of it all poor Rangers were sick
We were dancing and singing "Bye Bye Dick!"
We drank and we laughed and we all felt so proud
We just flaming wished we were there in the crowd
To see the great Celts blow them Rangers away
It'll stay in me mind as a most perfect day!

ARRAN FEERY, Glasnevin, Dublin

A special Celtic moment

BEING only 14, I haven't experienced many historical Celtic moments in my lifetime. However, one of the moments which will live in my mind forever, is when Celtic defeated Rangers 6-2 at Parkhead. It was August 2000. Celtic Football Club were not highly rated when playing Rangers - home or away.

We had a poor record of victories over our arch-rivals but we had a new manager, Martin O'Neill who had achieved success at Leicester City, our best striker (and arguably our best over-all player), Henrik Larsson was back to full health after he sustained a double fracture of his left leg and O'Neill had signed key players in that fantastic game: at a cost of £6,000,000 Chris Sutton from a miserable spell at Chelsea and pacy Belgian defender Joos Valgaeren who had caught O'Neill's eye at Euro 2000.

Celtic fans learned of what skills Dutch winger Bobby Petta possessed, who had a dismal time under the Barnes/Dalglish regime.

Probably most importantly, Celtic Park re-discovered the pride factor they had longed for. Under O'Neill, Celtic players would fight for their place to the bitter end (and that was very pleasing to see).

In the first game of the season, at Tannadice showed Celtic's new team spirit. Henrik Larsson had opened the scoring with a fantastic left-foot curler but Dundee United brought it level. Celtic refused to take anything less than the maximum three points and they did just that. From a Stephane Mahe blocked shot, Sutton scrambled home the winner. O'Neill's soldiers were on the right road. Many thought Celtic still weren't good enough to beat Rangers but I had a feeling this was to be a memorable match for more than one reason...it was my first Old Firm game and deep inside I thought the Bhoys could do it.

Even the night before, I was excited about the match and in the morning I couldn't wait. Inside the stadium the atmosphere was electric. All there was to see was a sea of green, white, and gold to equal around 53,000 persons and a smidgen of red, white and blue to equal about 7,000. Everyone was singing one of two songs: Walk On or Follow, Follow.

When the Bhoys emerged from the tunnel with the Rangers players, they were greeted with a cheer I had never heard before at any other match. As they went into the Huddle, an even louder cheer erupted which easily drowned the small boos from the Lisbon Lions' end.

At that time, to be honest, I was quite nervous about losing the game because even though everyone says it is only a game and it shouldn't really matter, it does to me and when Celtic lost in the past I would in a way feel embarrassed and sympathetic to our players because it must upset them to hear all the chants made against them for losing. When the match began, it was as if a force had overtaken me because I couldn't stop myself from singing and chanting comments at the Rangers fans. We had hardly settled into our seats when Chris Sutton netted our first of many. The feeling we all had was indescribable: joy, happiness, thankfulness to name but a few.

From that point on, we were in control like I hadn't expected. The Rangers players were misplacing passes constantly and their goalkeeper making mistakes which could have cost them dearly. The young Bulgarian midfielder

Stilian 'Stan' Petrov netted our second and nobody could believe it. I literally was jumping for joy and laughing at the expense of the Ibrox men and their fans.

It is amazing how, when the boot is on the other foot, how your opinion changes so drastically!

The unlikely Paul Lambert scored our third of the game and deservedly took a bow to the crowd. Rangers threatened to come back at the newly affirmed Parkhead outfit and did well to bring the score to 3-1. We still had the upper hand in the game and the players were hungry for more out of the men who had killed their spirits so many times in the past. Henrik 'The Ghod' Larsson then hit the back of the Rangers net twice to bring the score to 5-2 with not much time left. The perfect day was rounded off in style when Stephane Mahe rampaged down the left of the Rangers half and crossed in for Sutton to calmly steer the second for him, eighth of the game and sixth for Celtic.

The final whistle seemed like hours away when the fourth-official held up the neon board stating there was three minutes to be added to the regulation 90.

And there it was. It put an end to the misery of the Rangers players and fans but after the whistle blew, I wanted to do it all over again. I didn't get out of Celtic Park that day until about 15 minutes after because everyone was cluttering the staircases to sing some songs to the five Rangers fans who hadn't left even before the whistle.

I believe that mauling of Rangers was the turning point in Celtic's history. It gave us the confidence to believe we weren't just a stepping-stone in Rangers' way to the league trophy. Ironically, we went on to beat Rangers over and over and to win not only the league trophy but also the Scottish Cup and the CIS Insurance Cup - The Treble, our dream.

That dream was now a reality under Martin O'Neill and with that attitude, even when the current team and O'Neill are gone, we can maintain that amazing playing quality...for years to come. I know that would make the winners of that CELTIC 6-2 RANGERS game, my favourite one, proud.

LAUREN McCLOSKEY (age 14), Whiteinch, Glasgow

Cascade

THE 3rd of May 1986. I can see it's going to be difficult to explain the significance of that day. It was about ownership I suppose. Of course I knew all the stories of triumphs and tragedies at Celtic Park, Hampden and in Europe, but they weren't really mine. I'd watched my Dad debate the relative merits of McStay, McNeill, Jinky and Auld and wanted to be part of it. And I loved the family reviews of Saturday's game after Sunday Mass, as reassuringly familiar as mass itself.

"Disappointing again, Ter eh?"

"I dunno why we bother"

"Aye you do".

I had some first hand experience of what it was all about by then, don't get me wrong. My first Cup final was at Hampden Park, 1984. feels like yesterday. It never occurred to me we could lose, it really didn't. The chaos of colour and crowds, that complete feeling of being lost in the present, just being there. It was a grand old team. I did know the history. I don't remember my heart going 'woah, woah, woah', but I won't swear it didn't. We'd turn up without tickets, imagine trying that now? A policeman sorted us out. You need the worst of times to appreciate the best. Mum's maxim. Didn't stop me tearfully vowing never to set foot in the Granite City. Still can't warm to McGhee or Strachan even now, if I tell the truth.

1985 was my reward. I'd been reassured we would win this time with my Dad's assertion that "the Bhoys always win the one-off competitions." The 100th Cup final qualified as such; we were destined to win. And how we did. It was perfect. Provan's free kick sailing high into the net, the look on McGarvey's face as he wheeled away from goal. You don't forget those things. That's part of it anyway, but there's more to it than that. I'd better start form the beginning.

I didn't become a Celtic fan so much as become aware that we were a Celtic family. It was always there, the colours, the stories, 3pm on Saturday afternoons. I wasn't allowed to go to the games when I was small. The reasons varied. "it's too crowded", You'd be bored to tears". I learnt that sitting on the doorstep, Celtic scarf and mournful expression in place helped no end to fevered such decisions.

Ok, I'll admit allowing Tommy Macken to put me down as a Hibs fan. A primary 4 class survey on football support. By way of mitigation I can only say that Hibs were lying a poor 3rd place in our school poll. It's a terrible excuse, I know it. That aside, it was always there. The time the four of us kids got my dad's football collection down form the loft. Spent ages gazing at the wicker basket, the anticipation delicious. Siobhan, the youngest, thought we might find treasure. Sean, older and slightly more realistic, hoped for Jimmy McGrory's boots. Newspaper clippings from Lisbon '67, written before we were born, were enough for us.

1986 was a strange year though; everything was changing, new experiences coming without explanation or invitation. Duran Duran were no longer the centre of our universe. "Nobody," I was informed by girls who knew such things, "listens to Duran Duran any more". I was, then, nobody. Exams were vying for our attention against stiff opposition from The Pogues, Talking Heads, The Eurythmics. I was 15, nearly 16. Prince's advise to 'party like it's 1999' seemed sensible enough. Another lesson; vodka whilst odourless, was not, contrary to school legend, undetectable to parental senses.

I'll be honest with you; I didn't like the changes. Celtic, of course, remained ever present and Mum and Dad, whilst seemingly oblivious to their children's need for the right clothes, sufficient funds and unlimited freedom, remained admirably sensible concerning football.

"Scottish Premier Division. Season 1985-86". I wrote it neatly in green pen on my calendar, circling the first match, Celtic v Dundee, P.D (A). I'd put the games in my diary as soon as the fixture lists were out. We discussed each on the school bus with confidence and authority.

Pittodrie was difficult; hardly anyone wins there, Mo Johnston would get top scorer, we would win the league. It was important to get reassurance from the experts, particularly in the face of taunts about Celtic's ability to grab a draw from the jaws of victory. I sought a definitive answer from the man who knew.

"Do you think we'll win the league Dad?"

"We could do"

"Yeah, but do you think we will?".

The secret was to pursue this line of questioning until reassurance was provided. It could take some time.

"Whether they win or lose we'll still have to go to work in the morning".

Dad's attempt to lessen the hurt of possible failure. He had to say it and I loved him for it.

The season started well enough, a draw away to Hearts, another against Rangers. Only two points dropped in the first eight games. The New Firm the main concern. Show no fear. It was difficult to account for the dismal performances that saw us lose 3-0, 4-1 and 3-0 in consecutive weeks. The post Mass analyses suggested Celtic only had themselves to blame. Davie Hay's admission troubled me; "Everyone at Parkhead has to take a long hard look at themselves, no-one more so than myself." I knew better. I'd turned off the radio during the Ibrox game. I vowed to do better, bought a Celtic badge for my school bag and traded achievements for good results. Fifty lengths in the pool for a victory on Saturday, running home without stopping for a goal. It didn't always work I have to admit.

Hearts were doing something I'd never known in my lifetime, they were winning everything. It was difficult to be concerned initially, but their games without losing was becoming impressive. Had they no respect for tradition? Living just outside Edinburgh ensured that none of this was spared us. Maroon scarves and title-winning memorabilia appeared everywhere. They'd been top of the league since Christmas, on a superb run. Celtic could never catch then we were told. I hoped Celtic didn't read 'The Scotsman'.

It came to the last game. Would you believe it? Three points and four goals between us and glory. Three lousy points. We'd lost nine in a month for God's sake. Still there it was, a statistical possibility.

I spent the night before at Karen's house. We'd spend a lot of time there, me and Claire, when her Mum worked nights. Karen's interest in football was, well, lacking, as was Claire's. I was glad of their indifference that night I can tell, losing myself in cheers, Cider and school gossip.

I got up early that morning, leaving Karen and Claire to whatever tedium was left for those without football. The enormity of the day hit me on the number 65 bus. This was it. Glory or failure.

Look at the team we had though? I settled on glory.

Paul McStay was my favourite, no doubt about that. The Maestro. Shy and skilful. The best. I like Aitken, brave, committed, and the subject of my favourite 'Feed the Bear' chant. McClair too; witty, smart, not a bad striker either.

Danny McGrain was different. I'd watched him with awe and respect since I was small. He'd been a Celtic player for, well forever it seemed.

I was home by lunchtime. As always we gave our pre-match preparations careful consideration. The pros and cons of wearing our colours. How best to show faith without tempting fate. It was a tricky one. Mum was encouraging, "Whatever happens they've done well. We can be proud of them".

"Except if Hearts win too, and we lose the league", Sean's remark, my eldest and most pragmatic brother.

Radios upstairs, in the kitchen and front room tuned in. we waited.

284

Have you ever had that intoxicating feeling of fear and excitement? There's nothing you can do, and so much to win or lose. I swear I'd make a wonderful Pathological Gambler, that feeling is priceless.

Archie McPherson, as always, started things off.

"You've just made the best possible start to match day by tuning into Premier Division football live on..."

We cut in, finished Archie's words for him, as tradition dictated.

"Radio Scotland. 92.4 to 94.7, FM, and 8, 1, 0 medium wave".

Archie continued,

"Live action from Love Street and Dens Park on what promises to be a pulsating afternoon"

Last glance at the papers, and review of all possible outcomes. I checked Siobhan was clear. She's the youngest you see, so was less experience in these matters.

"If we win and Hearts draw, what happens?".

"They win"

"Uh-huh, and if we win 2-0 and they lose 2-1, who wins?"

"Us?"

"No, they still win, it's 4 goals remember?"

We were all set. And it was 3 o'clock.

The match itself is a bit blurry, I once read that hyperventilation can do funny things to your memory. I do remember the goals.

"1-0 Celtic. That man again, McClair. Talk us through that Archie".

Archie did. Why couldn't Dundee just score? And it continued as we stood, paced, fretted. 2-0, 3-0.

"Lovely skill there, from the penalty area, McGrain, McLeod, McStay, and Aitken all involved. Put away by Johnston for Celtic's 3rd"

We were 4-0 up at half time, and still the goal we needed didn't come. Dad had enough.

"I'm just away out to, eh, get some milk".

A deafening silence at Love Street, louder still in the house. We didn't dare say anything. It was said for us.

"Oh, Drama at Dens! High Drama at Dens!".

We tore over to the radio, couldn't get near enough to the possibility.

"Albert Kidd scores"

Silence. Who was Albert Kidd?

We got the answer we needed. It was happening.

Six minutes to go, 5-0 up, and then.

Roars from the radio, deafening, I thought it was over. "Dundee's second, and now , surely, the championship is bound for Parkhead. Archie?"

And it was over.

We grabbed our scarves, tied one round Kerry, remarkably keen on football for a Border Collie, and tore off down the street, shouting, screaming. We found Dad driving back up. He'd turned off the radio, but didn't have to ask. Sean and Ferg scrambled up on to the roof, scarves raised above their heads.

Celtic had won. We had won. And it was perfect.

MAIRE. K. COONEY, London

We've won the league again...

Celtic went to Love Street for the season's final game.
To win in style with goals to spare, their clear and simple aim.
Their fans were out in numbers to support the Bhoys in green,
But the drama that unfolded surely none have foreseen.
Celtic scored four first half goals to make the points secure,
Perhaps Hearts celebrations were a little premature.

McClair scored number five, a deflection off his knee,
The thoughts of players and fans alike now turned to Dundee.
Hearts required a draw at Dens to fulfil their title bid,
But with only seven minutes left, up stepped Albert Kidd.
He rammed the ball into the net, to put Dundee ahead,
Hearts Championship ambitions were hanging by a thread.
Their hopes were finally buried when Kidd, he scored again,
Meanwhile back at Love Street, they were singing in the rain.

And so it seemed the Scottish press was in for a surprise,
For against the odds, the Title was bound for Paradise.
The Bhoys in green and white nipped in, when Hearts seemed set for Glory,
To add another chapter, to the Glasgow Celtic Story.
MICHAEL O'LEARY, Coatbridge

A splash of Cologne (a true story)

THIS story is true and happened to me during the first round, second leg UEFA Cup game against Cologne in 1992/93. I think it was either August or September and the opponents were an unpredictable and inconsistent side, struggling domestically but currently leading Celtic 2-0 from the first leg.

I was with my friend of 20 years, Danny McLoskey, who was carrying his arm in a sling following a fork-lift accident at work, which broke "just about every bone in my forearm", as he liked to remind me, particularly when it was his round at the bar.

We purchased tickets for games on a regular basis and not being season-ticket holders, we had the luxury of picking and choosing our games, when funds and commitments allowed. What appealed about this game was that firstly, neither of us had been to a European game before and, secondly, we genuinely believed that Celtic would overhaul the two-goal deficit and go through.

Armed with this optimism we took our places in the old 'Rangers End' of Celtic Park, which was still the terraces, about halfway up and directly behind the goal Celtic were shooting at in the first-half. We arrived about half an hour before kick-off, as a combination of nervous anticipation and Danny's dodgy arm required us to leave that little bit earlier than usual.

The game got underway and it was obvious Celtic were well up for this tie from the word go, possibly because of the stinging comments in the German media during the week about Celtic's chances but, more importantly, the effect of the 'twelfth man' on the players, as the crowd were absolutely deafening throughout.

Celtic scored midway through the first-half and the roof almost blew off the stadium, with total strangers on all sides grabbing and cuddling each other (apart from Danny, who excitedly patted people with his one good arm). The atmosphere was electric and the terraces were bouncing with joyous fans, willing the team to glory.

At that point, Danny and I looked at each other and he said: "We're gonnae dae it, Kev. I feel it."

I nodded and turned back to the game with a big daft grin on my face and a thousand butterflies in my stomach, and joined in on a chorus of 'Hail! Hail!' that seemed to go on for ten minutes.

Then it happened. Right before half-time, Celtic scored again and my life was changed forever. Gerry Creaney deflected a shot into the roof of the net and the stadium erupted once more. I launched myself into the air (no easy task for a big, 'chunky' 16-stone guy like myself) along with everyone else and punched the air with joy.

Unfortunately, my landing lacked any grace or finesse and, having been pushed forward by the surging crowd, the flat step once beneath my feet was replaced by the edge of the step in front of me. I landed awkwardly, going over on my ankle on the step, and instantly knew it was broken.

I went down like a sack of spuds, the colour drained from my face, and looked up to see Danny still jumping around, oblivious to everything apart from the pitch. I slowly tugged on his trousers to get his attention, unable to speak and almost passing out a few times with what I was told later was shock. He eventually saw me and, thankfully, the half-time whistle blew, because if Celtic had scored again I imagined my body being tossed around like a rag doll until the game was over.

Danny went to get the stewards, leaving me leaning against the barrier in the corridor outside to get some air. And he told me later he felt ridiculous going up to the first aid room with a broken arm in a sling and saying, "I think my mate's broke his ankle."

Anyway, he arrived with four weedy-looking St John's Ambulance men in tow, who laid me on a stretcher and carried me (with some difficulty) to the first aid room in the ground. While the doctor examined me (I had clean socks on that day; thanks mum, I knew your advice would come in handy one day), I glanced around the medical room and noticed it was packed with walking wounded, all carrying knocks and bumps to varying degrees from the celebrations.

Then the door opened and a Celtic fan being pushed in a wheelchair by a steward looked at me as he passed and said: "Second goal?" I stared at him and nodded back in agreement, to which he nodded to himself before being wheeled away by the steward. At that moment there was an understanding between us; we were kindred spirits, we were injured in the line of duty, we suffered for our cause and now … we would miss the rest of the game.

The doctor concurred with my earlier diagnosis that my ankle was indeed broken and declared me unfit for the second-half. I protested that I was fine and asked desperately if I could be given a seat in the stand for the second-half, which was half-empty with only a small bunch of Cologne fans occupying a corner of it.

The doctor went away to consult with the stewards and came back with the news that a guy with one leg and a guy with one arm were no risk to security. We could have a seat in the stand if we removed our scarves and sat quietly next to the German fans. We agreed and took our positions (me with my leg up on the empty seat in front) as the second-half kicked off and Celtic charged up the park.

The second-half unfolded with Celtic throwing everything, including the kitchen sink, at a dishevelled Cologne side, and reward came 10 minutes from time when John Collins, from an impossible angle, slip the ball under the Cologne keeper from six yards.

Once again Paradise erupted in noise and myself and Danny, forgetting where we were, erupted too, in front of 50, moody-looking Cologne fans. We turned slowly after celebrating to see every one of the Cologne fans staring at us, and not wishing to have any other parts of our bodies broken that day, we slowly and apologetically rook our seats.

At this point a German who was sitting next to me leaned over and, gesturing to my chest, said: "Scarf." I looked down and my Celtic hooped scarf was sticking out of the top of my jacket. I stuffed it back down and reassured him it would remain there until the end of the game.

Unfortunately, he persisted with his scarf comment and repeatedly pointed to his own scarf and then mine. It slowly dawned on me he wanted to swap scarves, not strangle me with one. We duly swapped scarves and some pleasantries for the rest of the game with a number of the Cologne fans around us, who sportingly praised the Celtic team and crowd for their respective performances.

At the final whistle, we all stayed behind (Cologne fans and all) and applauded the players off the park, before departing to a chorus of 'Always Look On The Bright Side Of Life', and a short trip to the casualty department of the Royal Infirmary, Glasgow, with a warm heart, an aching leg and a 3-0 win in the bag. A truly great night indeed!

KEVIN KERRIGAN, Glasgow

In the early 1970s, Celtic played Leeds United at Elland Road in Jackie Charlton's testimonial match. I was a young lad of 12 at the time and had few opportunities to see my beloved Celtic play.

I had moved away from my home town of Glasgow at the age of six when my father moved the family to Yorkshire when his job moved. Fortunately, my best friend was a rabid Leeds United fan and his father organised some tickets and cleared it with my parents to take me along.

We arrived in good time at the ground and managed to get a good station just to the side of the visitors' dugout. Although this was designated as a Leeds area, there was little chance of any trouble and the stewards had no problems with me wearing my colours.

Perhaps this was because I was a mighty 4'1" tall and could only see over the retaining wall with some difficulty. As the only green and white scarf in a sea of Leads United fans, I was easily spotted by Celtic masseur Jim Steele. Presumably because he was not expecting to see a Celtic scarf there, he soon struck up a conversation with me.

As the conversation progressed, Jim became more and more interested in how I came to be in the Leeds United area of the ground. When I told him my name, an expression of realisation came over his face.

He correctly identified my grandfather (Willie Johnstone), my mother and my father by name. It turned out that he had been a guest at my parents' wedding some 18 years earlier! I still have the clock (since passed on to me) that he gave them as a wedding present. We talked for a few minutes and he asked after my parents and my grandfather (who had moved down to stay with due to poor health).

As the game started, Jim saw that I was having some difficulty in seeing over the retaining wall. Without further ado, after clearing it with my friend's father, he lifted me over the wall and sat me in the dugout between himself and the great man Jock Stein! At half time my match programme was taken to the changing rooms and signed, not only by the entire Celtic team and staff, but the programme made its way round the Leeds dressing room too!

One of the lasting memories is of the refusal of the Celtic fans to return the ball when it went into the small 'Cowshed' stand until Jim went up and pleaded for it to be thrown back. What wonderful memories of a great day out, if only I knew where I put that programme! Oh...and the score? A 4-3 victory for Celtic just to put the icing on the cake.

MIKE SCOLLAN, Wakefield, Yorkshire

IT was spring 1970, I had a ticket for the European Cup semi-final second leg at Hampden because Celtic Park was undergoing renovations. I was 15-years-old and at school we had a pool for the first goal scored. I had drawn Billy Bremner. My uncle took me to the game but he had a ticket for the Stand, my ticket was for the Enclosure. As I waited at the turnstile a rather large crowd was milling around. All of a sudden a group of fans tried to scale the wooden gate, with about 20 people on top of the gate it fell in.

Scores of ticket-less fans stormed in. Once inside none of the walkways in the Enclosure were visible, there had to be 150,000 people in the stadium all singing the usual hymns. The game started and when Jimmy Johnstone ran down the wing the whole crowd leant forward to watch him. I looked at the people behind me and there were three guys that were just football fans – two were wearing their colours the other one was not.

They were two Clyde fans and a Rangers supporter out to watch a great game. (I will let you guess who did not have his scarf) As we all know Leeds scored first and I had won my pool (Bremner). Now the game was on for me, of course, with two great goals by the Bhoys. We went on to the final, which I seem to forget about.

The Bhoys lost out to Feyenoord. My other fond memory was the night we won the league with 10 men. I was a steward at Celtic Park and on that night I was working outside at the Rangers End. Rangers scored in the first few minutes and the cops we were working with were elated. Once we got inside the most electrifying game I have ever seen played out. Murdo MacLeod played his best game for us, and when Johnny Doyle got sent off I thought we had lost the title. But the 10 men played their hearts out and we triumphed.

PAUL DOCHERTY, Caledon, Canada

I GOT the fright of my life when my, normally quiet, mother started screeching "penalty" at the television. She hardly watches it at all except for gardening and "house doctor" type programmes. I'm usually busy playing netball on a Sunday afternoon but this particular day I had a bad cold so I happened to be in when everyone was watching the football on television.

Well, after a while I was getting really annoyed at them all, as I couldn't concentrate on my art homework for all their excitement. Every time I tried to draw, my demented mother jumped up and down, giving the poor referee a hard time and I would get such a fright I would violently jerk my pencil. I decided that I would have to get to the bottom of this unusual and slightly over-the-top behaviour. After the game when my mum was behaving in a more (well for her anyway) ordinary way I asked her gently, as you do with people who are upset or hysterical, to tell me why she had been "carried away" by a game of football.

"It's the Celtic," she said. "They aren't just any old team they are very special."

Well, I thought, my netball team are pretty special to me as I'm a very competitive person, but my mum isn't that type at all so I just could not figure out why she was so interested in them other than she has said in the past that somebody called Stilian Petrov is really good looking!

I asked her to tell me why Celtic are so special to her when it's only a game and she isn't even sporty.

"It all started with someone called Tommy Bonnar," she said.

Did he start up Celtic I wanted to know? Tell me about him I demanded.

"It's really part of our family's history," my mum said, "All wrapped up in the history of the West of Scotland and Glasgow."

That got me really interested, as I was enjoying history at school. Who was Tommy Bonnar? If you know the history of something it helps you understand the present day, my history teacher says.

My mum began the story by explaining that Tommy Bonnar was my great, great grandfather. He was one of the first trainers with Celtic in the 1890s, just after they were founded to help the poor of the East End of Glasgow. She showed me the picture in the book about Celtic and there he was, standing with the team.

The same picture hangs on the wall in Parkhead today and we'll take you on the stadium tour to learn some more, she said. Well, by this time I was engrossed and fired some more questions at her.

"Did you talk to him about it," I wanted to know.

"Hang on," she said. "I'm not that old but I found out that he lived in Westmuir Street, near Parkhead Cross in the 1880s and 1890s. Tommy was married and had a young family and his young son Francis was to grow up to be my grandfather," she said.

"And it was Francis who told us the stories about growing up close to the Celtic."

Francis was the hamper boy and remembered his father, Tommy, bringing home the Scottish Cup just after the team had won it and keeping it under the bed in the house in Westmuir Street for safe keeping. I wondered if that is what Martin O'Neill does with it too!

"Why do you look so serious?" I asked. I told my mother she should be proud and excited at being connected to a famous football team. My mother told me that she had found out through family documents that Tommy couldn't write and had only put his 'x' mark on his son's birth certificate. His occupation on the Census returns of 1891 was listed as "coal miner" and he was obviously a part-time trainer, probably part of a team of trainers, as Celtic didn't have an actual single manager until 1895.

Tommy obviously had to work very hard to keep his young family. Francis, his son, left school at 14 and went to work in a factory but at least he had learned to read and write and survived the First World War, repairing aircraft for the Royal Flying Corps.

Tommy Bonnar's parents came to Scotland to escape the Irish Famine and like all the Irish in Scotland had quite a hard time of it. Two more generations on from Francis, people in our family have every chance of going to University and College and although we feel so lucky to have these opportunities. It makes my mum a bit sad sometimes when she thinks of what a struggle life must have been for her grandfather and great-grandfather.

We are so lucky, I thought, but then I couldn't get my mum to stop telling me favourite family stories about the Celtic. She went to St. Columbkilles' Primary School in Rutherglen and it was famous for having had Bobby Murdoch in the school team. We have another family connection there, my mother told me as her uncle, Terry Heaney was a teacher at the school and together with the Jannie ran the team. When Bobby was only eight-years-old, they included him in the team and Jock Stein and Sean Fallon came watch him play. As Bobby went on to become a Lisbon Lion, all of Rutherglen, but especially my uncle Terry, has always been enormously proud of him.

There is a funny store about uncle Terry and I hope he doesn't mind me telling it here. His sister-in-law (my gran) told me this story when she heard I was writing a story about Celtic. She was looking for old cloths to use as dusters one day and knew there was an old football jersey lying in a cupboard for ages.

She ripped the sleeves off the jersey and used them for dusters as she thought it was a leftover old school strip – the St. Columbkille's strip was the same colours as Celtic's. Months' later uncle Terry searched the house muttering something about "Charlie Tully's jersey."

Well, when the penny dropped my gran innocently asked uncle Terry, "What jersey?"

"The one I was given – I was going to raffle it for funds for the school team."

I think my gran confessed about 10 years later and he has probably never forgiven her, at least he has never let her forget this awful crime as for those under age 60 Charlie Tully was the Henrik Larsson of the 1950s.

My mum and dad carried on the rest of the evening talking about Celtic's glory days and I at last re-started my art homework. I heard bits of their conversation though and felt full of pride too. My family and all the other families who have followed Celtic are part of the history and they are part of ours.

I looked down at my sketches and scribblings and there on the paper I realised I had been drawing a large trophy – maybe now that I know the history, someone would get me a ticket - perhaps this daydream will come true and I too like my great-great grandfather will cheer them on when they win their next trophy. I don't think I'll be allowed to keep it under my bed though.

MAIRI FERGUSON (age 12), East Kilbride

Celtic legends

Pale eyes were distant
In his snow white head
When boldly he said
"Three stories I will tell you son."
Then the unfolding tales began.

In sight of wharfs and lively docks
Whisky is never poured o'er rocks,
Where thirsty fans discuss football
And Celts with confidence would call
To order, a "Young, Loney and Hay" –
The greatest half-back line of their day
And put the barman to the test,
Then relish three halves of the best!

During some frantic five-man game,
Young Tommy McInally by name,
Would twist and turn, then suddenly stall,
Arrogantly sit upon the ball,
No-one was brave enough to tackle
Perchance they'd get into a fankle.
In his shorts, from a pocket neat
He'd produce his favourite sweet –
The young and rising Celtic star
Would nibble a chocolate bar,
And hope with energy replaced
That he may never be outpaced.

Gallacher, as slight as a leaf,
With loads of in-built self-belief.
As slim and supple as a willow,
A strong and energetic fellow.
As prickly as a wire brush,
Created an exciting flush –
He'd leave the skilful skip and tread,

Balance the ball upon his head,
The terraces went wild with fun
When Patsy made his mazy run.
He'd drop the ball, conclude the fete,
Caress the orb into the net.

When told by an excited youth
Based on several seams of truth,
Gems of the famous Glasgow Celtic
Repeated over fifty years hence,
Will contain some poetic licence.

GERARD MULHOLLAND, Edinburgh

Celtic 1 Rangers 0 (1974-75)

THIS is a story they still talk about back home in my home town called Denny, Stirlingshire. It was 1974-75 season and we used to go to Celtic games, home and away, in a minibus every Saturday. I will never forget the mini bus hire firm's - name McKnight from Kilsyth. He had a few buses, all different sizes – 45-seater, 20-seater and so on. The bus we had that day was a converted one he got from Larbert Hospital and it was painted green. We had used this bus many times. It would pick us up at Denny Cross next to the railway hotel and round about one o'clock we would all pile into the bus.

It had wooden seats, which were very hard on long trips, and off we went, all blethering about the game, cans of beer were being passed about the bus. Nobody realised until it was to late the driver had taken us to IBROX PARK! He thought the game was at Ibrox. Tam Forsyth (nickname Wee Furry) and Matt McVicar, who organised the bus, were furious.

We were surrounded by Rangers fans by this time and the bus was getting pelted with bottles, stones, you name it. I was never so scared in my life. They were rocking the bus as Matt and Tam (Wee Furry) held the door closed. I remember looking all round me – you could not see out of the windows, they were covered in spittle. We were stuck somewhere near Govan in a street full of Rangers supporters in a green bus for about 20 minutes, before the police got us out of there and we were on our way again.

The driver got some abuse and we were late getting to Celtic Park that day, though we were just glad to be out of a situation that we would not like to repeat. The game ended up 1-0 to Celtic, so ended up a good day after all. Back home in the pub in Denny, the story was told and retold. Even the Rangers fans couldn't believe it. We had a good laugh about it over the years but at the time it was something else. What a day that was.

PATRICK FERGUSON, London

Scottish Cup final 1989

IT was a sunny afternoon, May 19, 1989 to be precise when the assorted members of the Tommy Burns CSC, Portadown, Co Armagh assembled in the port of Larne to catch the ferry to Cairnryan in the hope that their heroes would compensate somewhat for a disappointing season (after the previous season's Centenary Double) by at least retaining the Scottish Cup.

Ferry operators in conjunction with the local security authorities (anxious to a void a dockside or mid-sea clash of rival Celtic and Rangers supporters, not so much a SeaCat voyage, more a potential Sea Catastrophe!) decreed that we were to set sail on Friday mid afternoon and be housed en masse overnight in the anything but palatial surroundings of the Butlin's Holiday Camp in Ayrshire.

There was one major consolation however - the annual Cannon and Ball Butlin's Holiday Show didn't start until the following week!

The tension at the dockside in Larne was palpable. Scores of police officers had their work cut out ensuring that the rival fans boarded their respective boats (why were the sailing times of both boats in such close proximity I wondered?), exchanging only unpleasantries.

But tension gave way to humour when a diminutive little character positioned strategically at the rear of the Rangers boat (bound for Stranraer), of lionesque-like courage and bedecked in a Celtic shirt (wearing a long overcoat with his back turned to hide his true loyalties from his fellow passengers) gave a thumbs-up sign to the Celtic masses as it sailed past the still anchored Celtic vessel! I often wonder did this chap receive his well-deserved Victoria Cross?

A notable absentee on this particular voyage was Belfast man, Sean Rogan, father of Anton, who travelled regularly with the rest of the punters on the early morning ferry in those days. Invariably he would have a large and captive audience as he proudly showed off one of Anton's medals or perhaps an international cap. We were all spellbound.

More mirth ensued in the Communal Dining Room (and I use the term loosely!) of Butlin's in Ayrshire later that night as about 500 ravenous Celtic fans from Ireland impatiently awaited their evening repast.

However, all pangs of hunger disappeared as a witty wag (one of the very few who hadn't lost his eyesight due to hunger!) announced that the starter course of soup (or was that tepid water with the odd piece of carrot?) was about to be served by loudly singing 'Hail, Hail The Soup Is Here!' as he spotted the first waitress with a tray. Cue another explosion of laughter! Still, soup or tepid water, we ate voraciously.

Saturday morning was exciting! With the pre-match strolls (and dashes to the toilet!) over and recovery from the previous night's hangovers, and groin strains (from attempts to imitate John Travolta at Butlin's Disco you understand!) now complete, we boarded a fleet of buses to take us to Glasgow and the hallowed Hampden. Our bus driver, obviously a risk taker, decided to lay his cards on the table from the off by displaying his red, white and blue trimmed socks to his passengers before setting off!

He was assured by all and sundry that everything was okay, there was no need to worry about his funeral arrangements just yet, and the big-hearted magnanimous Celtic fans had the usual whip round for our pilot as we approached the environs of Glasgow.

So to my first glimpse of Hampden, where my shock at the dilapidated (as it was then) old stadium immediately gave way to amusement as the Rangers fans (vastly outnumbering the early Celtic arrivals) taunted our inability to even try and match their vocal effort by loudly proclaiming that 'You Only Sing In The Chapel'. I'm not bigoted you see, I'll laugh at infantile humour from any source.

One of our number had a Starry Plough flag and had barely unfurled it when a police officer severely rebuked him. Another of our group (the one with the 'O' Level and consequently an intellectual) demanded to know of the officer why Starry Ploughs were out of order while hundreds of Union Jacks and Tricolours fluttered colourfully without inhibition in the Hampden sun?

Cue an insomnia-curing diatribe from the officer explaining the finer points of the Flags and Emblems Act etc, and a clip on the ear from the rest of us for Bamber, our intellectual friend, after the police officer had departed.

That aside, the banter was good among the Celtic fans as we soaked up the sunshine and the pre-match atmosphere., although paradoxically, there was still an underlying somber mood prevailing as barely a month had passed by since the Hillsborough disaster. The main topics of conversation were the imminent return to Parkhead of Mo Johnston in the summer as announced by that morning's tabloids (yes, yes we should have known better I hear you say). But with Mo's return, who needs Frank McAvennie anyway was the common, if ultimately naïve feeling of all Celts on that sunny afternoon prior to kick off.

We also pondered the possibility of young Steve Fulton earning a cup final starting place after his heroic performance against Hibs in the semi-final.

Young Fulton and Billy Stark were finally cast in the roles of non-playing substitutes as it transpired. The excitement mounted as kick-off time approached. Each Celtic player was loudly acclaimed as he made his way on to the field for the customary warm up, each Rangers player was booed, some (need I mention Butcher's name?) more loudly than others.

The game itself, alas, was not memorable save for Gary Stevens' first-half bloomer which let Joe Miller in to fire low past Chris Woods for the wining goal.

Other noteworthy incidents included (thankfully) a glaring late miss by Ally McCoist and the introduction of a certain Mr ("I didn't name myself as sub just to get a medal") Souness late on in the greatest example of how ineffective the sleeves rolled up (and stockings rolled down as I remember) hands-on management approach can be!

Other abiding memories of the game are few and far between. There was a blatant slap in the face for Peter Grant delivered by the Rangers substitute the late Davie Cooper, and Joe Miller successfully running down the clock by audaciously shielding the ball from Souness on the touchline and, even more surprisingly, living to tell the tale! Obviously Joe had never heard of George McCluskey!

The real drama occurred on the pitch after the final whistle. The world and his wife waited for a re-enactment of the Battle of the Boyne in 1690, or at least the 1980 Battle of Hampden. But it wasn't to be, thankfully, as the Celtic lap of honour was strictly confined to the Celtic End of Hampden as Aitken, McGhee, McCarthy (his final game for Celtic), Rogan, McStay, Morris, Grant, Whyte,

Bonner and Miller all in turn showed us the cup.

We were particularly proud of our Honorary Club President, Tommy Burns, who took his bow wearing a sombrero during the lap of honour and who had played his full part in the victory, despite his relatively advanced years and (in those halcyon pre-laser sight-correcting surgery days) losing a contact lens during the game after a clash with Kevin Drinkell. You see, we all knew Tommy personally of course! We had the photographs to prove it! After all, he had visited Portadown along with Davie Provan earlier that same year for the annual dinner dance. He was definitely one of us, a Celtic fanatic!

We spilled out of Hampden in a state of absolute glee, singing and dancing still. Our team had retained the Scottish Cup, exorcised the painful memories of the league campaign and the early season 5-1 league defeat at Ibrox, deprived Rangers of the Treble and the whole event was played out in glorious sunshine.

But the day wasn't finished, not by a long way. As we sat on the bus outside Hampden waiting on the all-clear from Traffic Control (aka the Glasgow Police), new songs were devised with a productivity rate far in excess of anything Stock, Aitken and Waterman ever achieved. 'There'll Be No McEwan's Lager In The Cup' was on of the more witty as I remember.

Then to cap it all as we remained in a stationary position still outside Hampden, a busload of understandably distraught Rangers supporters passed by and a guy in the back seat who made Robbie Coltrane look slim could not contain his disappointment and responded to the temptation to display his abnormally-sized bare posterior against the back window of the bus for us all to see and laugh at.

A veritable book could be written about the celebrations at Butlin's that night but I think perhaps it would not be wise to go down that particular route. I do recall an officious Fulton Mackay (the governor in TV sitcom Porridge) look-alike stepping on to the bus to greet us on our return to Butlin's congratulating us on our team's victory while simultaneously pleading for the holiday complex to still be in one piece come Sunday morning!

The complex was indeed intact on Sunday morning, which is more than could be said for some of the guests! It was a coach load of very tired but extremely happy passengers that made its way down the Ayrshire coast to Cairnryan that Sunday afternoon, all frantic attempts to attend Mass finally abandoned.

I recall a battery of cameras being produced as passed the clubhouse at Royal Troon, the aim being to impress the folks back home as to the quality of our Scottish accommodation! What a weekend and what great memories!

TONY FEARON, Portadown, Co. Armagh

My Celtic story

Our family has had some humorous Celtic moments, like the time when my papa almost flattened my dad when he leapt up, toppling back on his armchair when the full time whistle went in Lisbon against Inter Milan in '67. Obviously, I wasn't there at the time, but it was almost as good when recently Celtic beat Livingston to take the league. At that time I was taking my two friends (who are Rangers supporters) home in our car, from our football game for my local team.

They didn't look too happy when the radio commentator announced it was 4-0 before half time!

This story takes us back to 1973, when my dad was in second year at St Andrew's Secondary School, and guess what, the Champions were in Europe once again! They were in the first round, and they had been drawn against Greek giants, Olympiakos. Celtic drew the home leg 1-1, and now they were to play in Greece to decide who would advance to the second round. It was do or die for the Hoops!

My Dad was devastated to hear the news that the match would be on TV in the early afternoon, during school time! There was only one hope to see the match; he would have to plead with his mum or dad to let him stay off to watch the match on television. Papa wouldn't be so hard to reason with, he would probably say yes straight away like he didn't care one little bit. But my gran was a very different story, she would have to hear all the details, wear you out by explaining, and then she would say no, after all, school is much more important than watching Celtic, isn't it? The good thing was, his mum would have to work that day, all day! So all he would have to do was ask his dad if he could stay off to watch the match, and that would be that!

The next day, the match was on telly, my dad and his pals were in watching the game with my papa. Celtic unfortunately went on to lose the match, 0-2, and get knocked out of the tournament.

In my dad's school, practically 100% of the pupils were Celtic fans, apart from the rumour that the janitor was a Clydebank supporter! That afternoon, there were only one-third of the pupils actually at school! So, the match must have got one of the highest TV ratings ever!

The next day, all dad's pals, and everyone that had dodged school, didn't have a letter to explain why they were off. It was only dad and his best friend, Brendan, who had thought to get notes. My dad and Brendan were teasing everyone else who didn't have a letter, saying they would get the belt, which I think is horrible, and I'm glad they have stopped it.

At assembly, the headmaster was very angry with all the people who dodged school, he organised a belting line for everybody who didn't have a letter. Masses upon masses of pupils joined this line, to get punished by getting a strike on the hand with a black leather belt. It was only my dad and Brendan who didn't join the line, and they were feeling very pleased with themselves! So Brendan checked his letter just in case. Shocked, it read; "Brendan was off school today" in messy handwriting, and it wasn't signed!

Solemnly, Brendan ripped up his note, and joined the belting line, and only dad was left. The headmaster called dad out to read his note, and read it aloud. He said; "Harry stayed aff school to watch Celtic play on the telly yesterday", Dad's face went bright red. He stayed silent and joined the belting line, just to avoid getting himself in any more trouble than he already was.

Luckily, the headmaster was too tired to give my dad the belt by the time he got to the front of the line, so I suppose he got away with it.

My dad learned that papa wasn't such a softie after all, and if you support a team with as long a history as the Celts, you have to take the bad with the good, even if it means risking six of the best! Up the Celtic!

EUAN MARSHALL (age 10), Glasgow

Determination without the grit

THIS little story could probably start with those four little words we see at the beginning of a fictional or children's' fairy tale, but the truth is this is an account of something that really happened. It was 1968 and it was shortly to become 1969, but more importantly we were about to go and watch The Bhoys, play Rangers in our New Year derby game; or were we? My mate's brother-in-law Jim, was our transport to the match, but like all good things there was a price to pay. Jim was a milkman, and in order to be finished early enough for the kick-off, he would need help to make the deliveries.

This wasn't a problem, Willie and I decided the best thing to do was to stay at Jim's on the Friday night, this would allow us to get the best possible start on Saturday morning, (more like Friday night). Willie slept on the couch and I was on the floor in front of the fire, which we kept lit during the night, as outside it was snowing heavily, and it was now about 2 feet thick. All of a sudden I felt myself being shaken about. I immediately thought I was having one of those nightmares, you know the ones I mean, where you are falling and you never seem to reach the bottom of the fall.

But, no, it was worse. It was Jim trying to get us awake, and it was 04:15 in the morning. Margaret, Jim's wife, was in the kitchen, and had the breakfast ready and was filling a couple of thermos flasks with tea and coffee. When we reached the dairy Jim jumped into an electric float (this vehicle resembles a golf cart with a trailer welded on the back), which was empty, I wasn't long in working out who had to load it up. It was now 05:40 and the float was ready to go, Willie and I were sitting on our hands trying to get some feeling in to them, then out the yard and down a very steep hill, towards Coatbridge. Disaster struck as we reached the bottom of the hill, the float hit an icy patch, skidded, spun round and landed on its side, throwing some of the crates onto the grass verge. Between us we managed to get the float righted, (although we had to remove some crates to lighten the load first).

The one bit of good fortune was that only a small amount of the bottles of milk were broken, (no use crying over spilled milk), but we had to return to the dairy to replace them. When we got back to the dairy we found a truck sitting there and after some bargaining, we managed to get the use of it. It was now 12:57 and we were leaving the dairy, our milk delivered, and the truck cleaned up. When we arrived back at the house, Margaret had a beautiful, huge, piping hot fry up, and a big pot of tea waiting for us. The snow hadn't let up all morning, but it was time to don the colours and make for Paradise. Jim had his own way of getting there, and we headed out towards Rutherglen through the backroads in an attempt to dodge the heavy traffic; but we weren't the only ones to have that idea and it wasn't long before we were bumper to bumper, and travelling very slowly.

In the blinking of an eye, Jim had mounted the pavement and was heading up along the inside of the traffic to the top of the road, rightly or wrongly we broke into a very loud cheer, and began singing some of our Parkhead hymns. When he reached the top of the road he bounced back onto the road, and we were now without windscreen wipers, the small drive motor had seized, and the snow had now reached blizzard level. Well I was determined after all we had been through there was no way we were going to miss the match. Ding! All of a sudden the light went on upstairs, "I have it," I said, I will take the wiper off, open the passenger side window, sit on the door, and I can wipe the windscreen as we go along.

The idea worked and we arrived at Paradise 15 minutes before the kick-off, with one small problem, by now I was almost frozen to the car and had terrible frost bite, and wind burn on my face and hands. The match had just kicked off and Jim went and got somebody from the first-aid ambulance team, as he was worried about my condition.

I was taken down under the stand and was given a really hot cup of Bovril, and some ointment was put on my hands and face. I was then given a large blanket, and taken to a seat on the sideline, where I watched the game in comfort, and was also close to the tunnel. I managed to shake hands with some of the players as they left the field after a resounding victory. P.S. We went home in the train.

TOM J. CONNOR, Celbridge, Co. Kildare

Dixie's green party and the end of Joe's jinx

THIS just had to be the most exciting day of Joe's young life. He had hardly slept a wink the previous night and now awoke to a gloriously sunny Saturday morning in Glasgow. But this wasn't just any Saturday – 6 May 1972 was Scottish Cup Final day and Joe would be going to watch his beloved Celtic side take on the might of Eddie Turnbull's Hibernian at Hampden.

It wasn't Joe's first Cup Final but in an era of almost unprecedented success for Jock Stein's side, he seemed to be the kiss of death where big cup games were concerned. Joe was already beginning to believe he had been born ten years too late and it was difficult to dispute the facts. His first Cup Final had been back in 1970 against Aberdeen when, as a diminutive nine year-old, he perched on a railing in the North Enclosure to peer over the 108,000 crowd and watch his dreams disintegrate, as a combination of bizarre refereeing decisions from Bobby Davidson and a teenage strike sensation called Derek MacKay took the Cup north to the Granite City.

Within a matter of weeks, Joe was cutting short an after-school kick-about at Cowlairs Park to run home in time to catch the TV coverage of the European Cup Final from Milan. Celtic were overwhelming favourites to dispose of the comparatively-novice Dutch side Feyenoord and regain the trophy so historical-ly won in Lisbon three years earlier. After all, hadn't Celtic comfortably disposed of the pride of England, Don Revie's Leeds, both home and away in the semi-final, a fixture referred to as 'the final before the final'? Hadn't they also elimi-nated the champions of Portugal and Italy en route in the days when there was no margin for error and the title of Champions Cup was still valid?

Big Tommy Gemmell's early opener seemed to confirm the inevitable before it all went horribly wrong and a comedy capers winner from the Swede, Ove

Kindvall, took the European Cup to Rotterdam and commenced a period of Dutch domination of European football that would stretch for four long years.

The next two domestic Cup Finals were out of bounds for Joe as they were both against the 'other Glasgow side'. Joe's dad was a hero figure who followed Celtic all over and took Joe and his brother along wherever and whenever it was sensible to do so - and often when it wasn't! Joe loved the tale where his dad had been left literally holding the baby one Saturday and his two year-old brother ended up at Broomfield. However, the Rangers' games were different – going was not up for discussion. The League Cup Final that October saw a sixteen year-old Derek Johnstone score the only goal of the game to give Rangers their first trophy since 1966.

Joe heard the score through the tannoy at Petershill Park as he watched the junior game taking place there and felt that, judging by the crowd's reaction, there must have been as many Rangers fans at Petershill that day as had made the trip to Hampden! The Scottish Cup Final in May 1971 was an infinitely more enjoyable affair for those of the Celtic persuasion. Despite a late Rangers equaliser in the first game, Jimmy Johnstone was in one of his magical moods in the replay and Celtic won much more convincingly than the 2-1 scoreline might suggest. Joe's consolation treat for missing the Cup Final had been a weekend trip to Aberdeen at the end of April to watch the vital League Championship decider.

Harry Hood scored the early goal that gave Celtic the point required to pip their closest rivals and gain a measure of revenge for the shock Cup Final defeat the previous year. Whilst the fathers hit the pubs in Union Street to celebrate 'six in a row' on the Saturday evening, Joe and the other sons were being petrified by the Wicked Witch of the East at the Aberdeen Odeon. Memories like that you can't buy!

Joe's next visit to Hampden on Cup Final business came in October 1971 and would certainly prove to be unforgettable. The League Cup Final of 1971/72 saw Stein's Celtic paired with David McParland's newly-promoted young Partick Thistle side in a classic David v Goliath confrontation. The damp grey Glasgow weather was to prove ominous for Joe's hopes of seeing his first Cup Final victory. Nevertheless, his boyish confidence was sky-high as he left home advising his mum that the Celts would win 6-2, no problem! That prophecy was to come back to haunt him as the Jags roared out of the blocks to hit Celtic with a stunning first half display of attacking football.

The 62,000 crowd watched in disbelief as one attack after another finished with the ball in Evan Williams' net. Remember that, in those days, on the unusual occasions where the opposition dared to score first, Celtic simply ran up the park and scored twice. Should the unbelievable happen and the Celts fall two goals behind, the question was when, rather than if, they would come through to regain the lead. However, as Joe watched the horror unfold at the far end of Hampden, all his instincts told him that this game was something else entirely. By half-time, the Celts needed 'five goals to win'.

A solitary Dalglish second-half goal at that same Mount Florida end, by now swelled with hundreds of defectors from Ibrox, unable to believe the news from their own stadium tannoy, was the only moment of cheer in a dark day in Celtic's history.

The fallout from that match was severe. Whilst the Maryhill Magyars, not forgetting the good people of Bearsden and Milngavie, rejoiced in the aftermath of their amazing victory, Jock Stein's Celtic and their legions of followers licked their wounds, finding ever new ways to avoid work contact with their colleagues of the opposite persuasion. Glasgow reacted like only Glasgow can and the young Jags assumed legendary status.

However, as the song goes, 'night is darkest just before the dawn'. Stein, the master, looked to shuffle his pack and looked in the direction of Motherwell. In the days of petty cash rather than seven-figure cheques, Jock's ability to create superstars from journeymen was priceless. His target on this occasion was a stocky striker by the name of John 'Dixie' Deans. Noted for his aerial prowess and disciplinary record, Stein saw something special there. With change out of £30,000, Dixie became a Celt. From such ordinary beginnings are legends born.

Back on the field, there was still a double to be won, not to mention the European Cup. Media attention focused on a League fixture the following month, which now took on an additional dimension, Partick Thistle v Celtic at Firhill. The old Maryhill stadium was creaking at the seams as some 36,000 packed in, not quite sure what to expect. Within one minute they had their answer as Celtic scored direct from a corner kick. The next 89 minutes followed a similar pattern as the Champions put the Firhill upstarts in their place with a thrilling 5-1 victory. The healing process had begun.

This was to be no ordinary season for Joe as a number of events unfolded which would memorably impact his young life.

On the morning of his eleventh birthday, 22 March 1972, Joe ripped open his birthday card envelope and a couple of pieces of paper fell to the floor. Joe opened out the paper to reveal two main stand tickets for that night's European Cup Quarter-Final second-leg tie with Ujpest Dosza at Celtic Park. What a present! These were the pre-environmentally-aware days when the Parkhead stand tickets resembled the old 'Green Citizen' or mythical 'white fivers' for size. These were real big game tickets.

The first leg in Budapest had been memorable for two things. Firstly, the game itself where a Hungarian defender called Horvath succeeded in scoring one of the all-time great own goals from around 30 yards before equalising at the correct end in the second half. However, a late Lou Macari strike gave Celtic a precious advantage to take back to Glasgow. The Scottish press, however, had a bigger story the following morning with details of Liz Taylor's 40th birthday party hijack by Celtic fans staying at the same Budapest hotel. You just can't take them anywhere.

There are few views in football to rival that from the main stand at Celtic Park on a big European night. The hairs on Joe's neck stood on end as Celtic took the field that night in front of 75,000 baying fans. The match sizzled from end to end as Ferenc Bene gave the Hungarians the lead to tie the aggregate score at 2-2. However, that man Macari popped up again near the end to take the Celts through to the semi-final.

Shortly after this, Joe was walking into the main stand at Fir Park, Motherwell with his dad when a *Celtic View* photographer approached him. The View had a regular feature at the time, Celtic Boy, where a young fan would be interviewed and photographed, then invited to a future match at Celtic Park to meet his favourite player before taking a VIP seat in the stand. Kitted out in scarf and sacred hooped tammy, knitted by the Carmelite nuns for his dad to wear at Lisbon, Joe posed proudly for the View. The abuse from his brother for being the oldest Celtic Boy in history or the first ever bearded Celtic Boy would follow in due course. For today Joe was Celtic Boy. A couple of weeks later, Joe and Dixie Deans stood at the entrance to the Parkhead tunnel discussing that day's match with Hearts. Does life get any better?

The answer to that is 'yes - but not without some more pain first'. Celtic had been drawn against the might of Inter Milan in the European Cup semi-final – a repeat of the Lisbon final of 1967. Celtic had fought bravely in the first leg in Milan to earn a goalless draw and set up a mouth-watering return in Glasgow a fortnight later. Two weeks down the line, Joe was getting worried about the lack of discussion regarding his attendance at that match but was far too scared to ask the direct question for fear of the likely response. When the big day came and Joe had survived school with his nerves still slightly intact, it was obvious that he would be sitting in the Springburn TV Stand. Inconsolable, Joe locked himself in the bathroom sobbing at this injustice. There can be only one outcome when a doting dad is faced with this dilemma and a wet Joe was ushered out of the house and onto the supporters' bus to take his place at the biggest game of the season. Lifted over the turnstile and placed on the front barrier at the Celtic end, Joe settled down for the roller-coaster ride of the evening to follow.

The legend of Dixie's penalty miss is well chronicled in Celtic folklore. The Daily Record cartoon depicting two astronauts finding the ball was a cruel if humorous summary of the nation's main topic of conversation over the next couple of weeks. For Joe, it only served to reinforce his belief that Celtic's recent run of cup defeats and his attendance on the scene were not altogether unrelated. But today would be different.

On this day, Joe and the thousands of Celtic fans who would make the pilgrimage to Hampden – those for whom Saturday was the reason for living the other six days of the week – would watch the stuff of dreams.

Eddie Turnbull's Hibernian side came to Hampden with a reputation for exciting attacking football backed up by an iron defence. They had run Celtic very close in the title race and were unquestionably the best Hibs side in 20 years, when Turnbull himself formed part of a 'Famous Five' forward line that terrorised Scottish football for a decade. Their support travelled through from the east in huge numbers, ensuring that Hampden was 'covered in banners of green', just like the Coronation Cup Final of 1953, immortalised in song like so many famous Celtic victories.

Joe sat on a stanchion at the top of the East Terracing and marvelled at the sight before him. Over 106,000 supporters bathed in glorious sunshine awaiting the arrival of the teams. The game itself had a stunning start when Billy McNeill latched onto a deep cross to open the scoring with barely two minutes on the clock. Joe could hardly contain his joy at this turn of events. However, that joy was short-lived as within ten minutes, Alan Gordon had scrambled an equaliser for Hibs following a mix-up in the Celtic defence. Game on. The next twist in the tale came when Dixie Deans rose majestically to bullet home a header for Celtic and the exorcism of his Inter penalty demons commenced. Half-time arrived with the Celts leading 2-1 in an absorbing contest. No-one there could possibly have foreseen the events which would transpire in the second half.

The moment that will forever epitomise the 1972 Scottish Cup Final arrived early in the second half. Deans chased a long hopeful ball to the edge of the Hibs box where he managed to knock it past the goalkeeper towards the bye-line. Faced by a couple of Hibs defenders, he somehow managed to squeeze through on goal where he was again confronted by Jim Herriot blocking the Hibs goal. Dixie dragged the ball across the goalkeeper and, from a seemingly impossible angle, shot past two defenders on the line for one of the best Cup Final goals ever. He then careered towards the corner of the stadium where Joe and 30,000 Celtic fans were joyously punching the skies to produce a celebratory somersault that Olga Korbut herself would have been proud of.

That goal won the Cup for Celtic but there was still a game to complete. A hat-trick for Dixie followed soon after when he met a Tom Callaghan pass to power a shot past Herriot for 4-1. Lou Macari put the icing on the cake with a late two-goal finale, both following excellent runs from Jim Craig down Celtic's right, the Lisbon Lion's last contribution to Celtic before commencing a new life in South Africa. As Jock Stein sprinted from the tunnel to embrace Bobby Murdoch in a captured moment that would still tug heart strings some thirty years later, the Celtic fans celebrated a historic 6-1 triumph.

The biggest winning margin in a Scottish Cup Final since 1888 - the year of Celtic's inception - and the first Cup Final hat-trick since the Mighty Jimmy Quinn put Rangers to the sword some seventy years earlier were impressive records that would take their place in football folklore.

However, for Joe, the greatest day in his young life stood for something altogether more meaningful – a long-awaited first Cup Final victory and a monkey off his back.

MATT CORR, Bearsden, Glasgow

THE torrent of rain stung my cheeks as I sat down, amidst the Manchester United fans, in the Jungle for Tommy Boyd's testimonial. Larsson and Celtic were causing trouble for are leaky defence, just as they were to do against us at Ryan Giggs' testimonial. In the end, it finished 2-0 for United, but the atmosphere of that night was not to be outdone because the sea of emerald green and white that made up the support of the Bhoys roared to their lungs were raw, and despite me being a Red, that was a sight to be envious Green and White about!

JAMIE DOHERTY (age 15), Manchester

Celtic v Juventus

IT was Halloween, children everywhere were counting who had the most sweeties and nuts. But not me. No, I was watching my Bhoys.

I was sitting in my living room with my cousin, mum and auntie. As the game reached kick-off my nerves began to settle and the excitement took over. I felt happy as I felt we had picked the strongest team possible, with Lubo playing from the start. After Del Piero scored that wonderful free kick for the opener I felt a bit down. But five minutes later and we were back on track with a great header from Joos Valgaeren. We were all cheering and hugging, even the adults don't normally support Celtic. As the game reached half time I went to the toilet and when I came back I saw a Celtic header going in the net I just assumed that it was a replay, until I saw that the clock still running and Chris Sutton running away.

"Was that another goal?" shouted my cousin Rachel. "Yes" I screamed and started jumping up and down. When half time came I felt on top of the world. My cousin went home and my brother and dad came home from guising. My brother Michael is a huge Rangers fan so the conflicts in our house about football come on a daily basis.

The second half kicked off and we all settled down to watch it. When David Trezeguet came on I felt scared because I know what a prolific goalscorer he is, as we soon found out. On 50 minutes he came on and scored. It was such a blow seeing as we were in front. I feared that we would blow it. Celtic were playing brilliantly with Agathe running like an Olympic athlete down the right and the defence and rest of midfield being solid it was down to the front two to produce the goods.

It didn't take long for the Hoops to go back ahead when Birindelli pulled Chris Sutton's shirt. Henrik once again and slotted home the penalty. He has missed a few this season but I had every faith in him. Although I had to watch it on TV, I could practically feel the atmosphere at Parkhead.

Celtic were having chance after chance and all the possession so I felt we could get another goal. When Lubo Moravcik was substituted I felt so proud of him and then Stan Petrov came on. After a free-kick, the ball came to Sutton he hit it straight away and volleyed it into the net. Well I have never had such a rush of excitement. Straight away I checked Teletext to see if Rosenborg has possibly equalised but no still 1-0.

When Trezeguet scored I didn't really care because nothing could take our performance away from us. As the final whistle loomed I started singing every Celtic song I knew. I knew we were out of the Champions League but I was so happy that we had beaten one of the best teams in Italy, Europe maybe even the world.

I have been a Celtic fan since I was born and have never worn my Hoops with such pride. I was looking forward to the UEFA Cup and had fond memories of the Champions League with three home wins and a winning performance in Turin!

Later that night on Champions League highlights, Ron Atkinson said that Celtic were the "Pride of Britain" and I felt so happy that an Englishman would say that about a Scottish team, because that so rarely happens.

So that is my feelings about that special Halloween night and if Mr O'Neill gets his wish to strengthen the squad then may we look forward to more of those great European nights.

LAUREN CLARK (age 13), Inverness

The super team 01/02

A little of Petrov on the wing.
A little bit of Larsson and O'Neill, they're our kings.
A little bit of Bobo, the big man
He's gonna flush Rangers down the pan.
Here comes Agathe with the ball, he gonna skin them all.
That's it, that's the end,
but Moravcik crosses the ball which can bend.
Goal! ... That's it, Henrik has put Rangers in the pit.

DALE DOOGAN (age 8)

Thi boays wae the Hoops

Since ah wis a wee lassie
Ah always loved Celtic
So dae awe ma family tae.
The furst time ah wen' tae Parkheid
Ah felt thi excitement in thi middle oh ma stomach
Ah wis that scared they wid looze
In front oh mae, wis hunners o' fans
Awe dressed in green an' white
Whit a sight tae see
I hud a hot dog an' a coke at half-time
Celtic won tha' day.

This year When wae won thi league
Two weeks ago Ah wis watchin' on thi telly
Larsson scored an thi crowd went mad
Then Hartson got thi baw
Anuther goal shot intae thi net
An' before half-time Larsson scored again
Ah couldnae believe it, Celtic were brill
Ah wis jumpin' about all over thi place
Wi ma hons in thi air.

Livingston scored in thi second-half
But it made nae difference
Cause Larsson had a hat-trick an'
Hartson scored again tae make thi final result 5-1
Thi whole crowd wur celebratin'
Singing an' huggin' an aw that
"WE ur thi Champions" wis in this air
Martin O'Neill wis really happy
His hands were in thi air tae
He wis speechless, Just like me!

DIANNE DEY, St Joan of Arc School, Glasgow

A Belfast memory

By Bernard MacLaverty

OUR two rented houses faced each other across Atlantic Avenue - my father's house at 73 and Aunt Cissy's at 54. There was another brother, Father Barney, who used to call round most Sundays to Cissy's for his dinner. In the evening they all played poker and Father Barney would drink whisky and do mock shouting and clowning. The others would roll their eyes. If the children were good and provided Father Barney wasn't 'beyond his beyonds' they were allowed to watch. My father always left early saying he had his work to go to in the morning. My mother said he just couldn't stand Uncle Barney any longer.

I did not have a clear idea of what my father did at work. I knew it was something to do with drawing and lettering. I'd found things in the cupboards - small blocks of wood topped with gray zinc metal. If there was lettering on this metal it was always backwards, unable to read.

'Mum, what are these?'

'They're to do with your father's work.'

In cupboards there pages of pink paper, thick as slices of bread, with lettering pressed into them and bulldog clips full of newspaper adverts he had done. Also he was illustrating a Bible for schools. He'd shown me a drawing for the Cure at Capharnum and made me read aloud the caption. It was dead easy.

"They could not get in because the house was crowded out, even to the door. So they took the stretcher onto the roof, opened the tiles, and let the sick man down."

Occasionally, at weekends, he would work at home. I remember one day in particular when I was about eight or nine. It was a Sunday and felt like a Sunday. Family Favourites was on the wireless. He sat beneath the window for the best light.

'What you doing?'

He held up the drawing. It was good.

'Abraham and his son, Isaac,' he said. An old man with a white beards hurried along beside a boy carrying a tied-up bundle of sticks on his shoulders. 'Where is the victim for the sacrifice? That's what the boy is saying.' My father put on a scary, deep voice and said, 'Little does he know...' he drew quietly for a while. The pen scratched against the paper and chinked in the ink bottle. He had a pad on the table and sometimes he made scratches on it. 'just to get the nib going.' Sometimes the pen took up too much ink and he shook it a little. 'You're no good if you can't make something out of a blot.'

The hall door opened and the footsteps came in off the street. My father stopped and looked up. It was my cousin, Brendan who was q year and two months older than me. He was a good footballer.

'It's yourself, Brendy.' Brendan stopped in the middle of the floor and said.

'Charlie Tully's in our house having a cup of tea.'

'Go on, are you kidding?'

'No.'

My father gave a low whistle.

'This we will have to see.' He wiped he pen on a rag, then rinsed it in a jam jar of water. He blew on his drawing then folded the protective tissue over it.

'Come on.' All three of us went across the road. The only car parked on the street belonged to Father Barney.

'Did Barney bring him?' Brendan nodded.

'And Terry Lennon.' Terry Lennon was a blind church organist. He had a great Lambeg drum of a belly with a waist stretched tight over it. He would sit in the armchair by the fire - a lot of the time he would stare at the ceiling. Little crescent of white shone between his eyelids, which were always shut. He smoked constantly, never taking the cigarette from between his lips. Now and again he would run his fingers down the cigarette to dislodge the ash onto his waistcoat. Aunt Cissy called him Terry Lennon the human ash-tray.

When we went in Terry Lennon was in his usual chair. Father barney stood in front of the fire with his hands behind him getting warm. On the sofa a man, still wearing his raincoat, drinking tea. His hair was parted in the middle. He was introduced to my father as Charlie Tully.

'You're welcome ,' said my father. 'Is that sister of mine looking after you properly?' Charlie Tully nodded, the cup to his mouth.

'The best gingerbread in the northern hemispere,' said Father Barney. 'that's what lured him here.'

'Where's the old man?' said my father.

'The last I was of him was heading up to the lavatory with the Independent.'

'He'll be there for a week.' My father turned to the man in the pale raincoat. 'I bet he was delighted to see you Mr Tully - he's a bit of a fan.'

'So - how do you like Scotland?'

'It's a grand place.'

'Will Mr Tully have a cigarette?' Terry Lennon reached out in the general direction of the voice with his packet of Gallagher's Greens.

'Naw, he only smokes Gallagher's Blues,' said Aunt Cissy and everybody laughed.

'I don't smoke at all. Shorten the breath.'

'If you'll forgive me for saying so Mr Tully,' said Terry Lennon, 'the football is not an interest of mine. You understand?'

'I do. You were making some sound with that organ this morning.'

Terry Lennon laughed.

'Loud ones are great. Or Bach is great for emptying the place for the next mass.

The philistines flee.'

There was a ring at the door and Brendan went to answer it. When he came back he said it was Hugo looking for a drink of water.

'And run the tap for a while,' said Aunt Cissy laughing. 'Bring him in.'

'The more the merrier' said my father.

'Wait till you hear this, Mister Tully. Our Hugo.' Brendan went down the step into the kitchen and everybody heard him running the tap very fast into the sink.

Brendan carried a full cup up the step into the room. He called Hugo from the door. Hugo appeared with another boy called Jimmy McGlinchey. They edged into the room and Hugo accepted the cup of water. There was silence and everybody watched him drink. Hugo was a serious young man who was trying to grow a beard.

Father Barney joined his hands behind his back and rose to his toes. He said, 'So you like to run the tap for a while?'

'Yes, Father.'

'And why's that?'

'The pipes here are lead. And lead is poison. Not good for the brain.'

'The Romans used a lot lead piping,' said Father Barney, winking a Charlie.

'Smart boys, the Romans. They didn't do to badly.'

'No - you're right, Father. But maybe it's what destroyed their Empire,' said Hugo. 'Being reared to drink poison helps no one.'

Father Barney sucked in his cheeks and rolled his eyes. Everybody laughed and it was hard to tell if they were laughing at Hugo or at Father Barney's reaction to him.

'I need a whiskey after that slap down.' Aunt Cissy moved to the sideboard where the bottle was kept and poured Father Barney a whiskey. ' Cissy fill her up with water, lead or no lead. Will anybody join me? What - no takers, at all?' He held up his glass. 'To Mister Tully here. God guide your golden boots.' Everybody laughed politely at Father Barney's toast.

Granda came downstairs and had to push the door open against the people inside.   'What am I missing?' he said hearing the laughter.

'A drink,' said Father Barney. Granda looked around in mock amazement.

'He's getting no drink at this time of day,' said aunt Cissy. Granda found a seat at the table. He threw the newspaper onto the sideboard. He was still wearing his dark Sunday suit and waistcoat with his watch-chain looped across it. On his way to mass he wore his black bowler hat. He had a full head of white hair an a small white moustache.

'It's getting a bit crowded in here,' Granda said, looking around the room smiling.

'Reminds me of the day McCormack sang in our house in Antrim. There was that many in the room we had to open the windows so's the neighbours could hear him outside.'

'Count John McCormack?' said Charlie, open-mouthed.

'The very one.'

'How did the maestro end up in your house?'

'Oh, he was with Terry there, some organ recital.'

'And what did he sing?'

'He sang everything that day. Everything but the kitchen sink. Down by the Sally Gardens, I hear you calling me. She moved through the fair. Everything.

'It was some show,' said Terry Lennon, putting his head back as if listening to it again in his head.

'Would you credit that?' said Charlie. 'I met a mean who knows Count John McCormack.'

There was a strange two noted cry from the hallway 'Yo-ho.'

'Corinna,' said Cissy and pulled a face. The door was pushed open and Corinna and her sister, Dinkey, stood there.

'Full house the day,' said Corinna. She eased herself into the room. Dinkey remained just outside.

'The house is crowded out, even to the door,' said my father.

'Is there any chance of borrowing an egg, Cissy. I'd started the baking before I checked.' Cissy went down the step into the kitchen and came back with an egg which she handed to Corinna.

'Thanks a million. You're too good.' Corinna stood with the egg between her finger and thumb. 'What's the occasion?' She vaguely indicated the full room.

Cissy tightened her mouth.

'Charlie Tully,' she said. 'This is Corinna Coyle. And her sister Dinkey.' Cissy pointed over heads in the direction of the front hall. Dinkey went up on her toes and smiled.

'A good looking man,' said Corinna.

'Worth eight thousand pounds in transfer fees,' said Father Barney.

'He's above rubies, Cissy. Above rubies.' And away she went with her eff and sister.

'You can choose you family but not your neighbours,' said Cissy.

'Naw - naw. They were fine,' said Charlie.

'So ,' said Granda, 'will we ever see Charlie Tully playing again on this side of the water? I miss seeing you tying people up in knots.'

'Yeah, I'm sure.'

'Internationals,' said Hugo.

'Charity matches.'

'It's not the same thing,' said Granda,' as watching a man play week in week out. That's the way you get the whole story.'

'There's talk of a charity game with the Belfast boys later in the year,' said Charlie.

'Belfast Celtic and Glasgow Celtic?' Granda was now leaning forward with his elbows on the table. 'That'd be some sight. There wouldn't be a foul from start to finish.'

'Where'd be the fun in that?' said Father Barney. 'Cissy, I'll have another one of those.' Cissy went to the sideboard, refilled the glass and topped it top the brim with water from an ornamental jug. She handed it to father Barney, saying in a low voice,

'Remember you've to drive the car.' Barney ignored her and pointed to my father,

'Johnny there, would design you a program for that game. For nothing. He's a good artist.'

'Like yourself Charlie,' said Granda. ' A ball artist.'

' Is that the kinda thing you do?' Charlie said.

' Yeah sure,' said my father. Barney started mock shouting as if he was selling programs outside the ground. Some of his whiskey slopped over the brim of the glass as he waved his arms. 'Official program, get your Official program.!' My father smiled.

'Have you been somewhere - before here?'

'On a Sunday morning?' Barney leaned over to Charlie Tully, 'Johnny does work for every charity in town. The YP pools, the St Vincent de Paul, the parish, even the bloody bishop - no friend of mine - as you all well know - his bloody nibs. Your Grace' He gave a little mock inclination of the head. Cissy ordered Brendan out of his chair and told Barney to sit down. Granda grabbed the opportunity to speak again.

'So Charlie - the truth form the insider - is there no chance of them star-ing up again?'

'Not that I know of.'

Granda shook his head.

'We gave in far to easily. In my days when somebody gave youa hiding, you fought back.'

'Aye, it's all up when your own side makes you the scape-goat,' said Aunt Cissy.

'I mean to say,' Granda voice went up in a pitch. 'What were they think-ing of?'

'The game of shame.'

'The came screaming across that pitch like.. like.. bloody Indians.'

'Indians are good people,' said Hugo.

'...and they kicked that poor young fella half to death. Fractured his leg in five places. And him one of their own.'

Father Barney slapped the arm of his chair.

'Take it easy, Da, don't work yourself up. There's nothing you can do about it.'

'You were at the game?' said Charlie Tully.

'Aye and every other one they've ever played,' said Granda. 'I don't know what to do with myself on a Saturday afternoon now. I sometimes slip up to Cliftonville but it's not the same thing. Solitude. It's a good name for that ground.'

'A bunch of amateurs.'

'That's what they are.'

'I just do not understand it.' Granda was shaking his head for side to side.' What other bunch of people would do it? The board of directors,' he spat the words out. 'The side get chased off the pitch, it's players get kicked half to death and what do they do? Okay, we're going to close down the club. That'll teach you. In the name of Jesus...' Granda stopped talking because he was going to cry. He looked hard at the top of the window and kept swallowing. Again and again. Nobody else said anything. 'Why should we be the ones sacrificed? Is there no one on our side who has any guts at all?

'Take it easy,' said my father. 'They have the sectarian poison in them. And no way of getting it out.' He reached out and put his hand on Granda's shoul-der. Shook him a little. Granda recovered himself a bit and said,

'It would put you in remind of the man who got a return ticket for the bus - then he had a row with the conductor - so, to get his own back he walked home. That'll teach them.'

There were smiles at that. But then the room became silent.

'It was a great team,' said Charlie Tully at last. 'Kevin McAlinden, Johnny Campbell, Paddy Bonnar..'

'Aye.'

'And what a keeper Hugh Kelly was.'

'And Bud Ahern...'

'Billy McMillan and Robin Lawlor.'

'Of course.'

'Jimmy Jones and Eddie McMorran and who else?'
'You've left out John Denver.'
'And the captain, Jackie Vernon.'
'And yourself, Charlie,' said Granda. 'Let's not forget yourself, maestro.'

Sometime later that year - which became known as 'the year Charlie Tully called in Cissy's' - as opposed to the year Granda referred to as 'the year McCormack came to the house in Antrim and sang' - I noticed drawings and sketches my father was working on lying about the house. Black and white cartoon bodies of players in Celtic hoops in the act of kicking or heading a ball. Their bodies were tiny but their heads were made of oval photos of the real players.

It was many years later - half a century, in fact - before I would remember these drawings again. My father died when I was twelve and my mother was so distraught that she threw out all his belongings. If she was reminded of him she would break down and weep so every scrap of paper relating to him had to be sacrificed.
  Recently I was in Belfast to visit that same mother and I wondered if there might be a second -hand match programme lying around Smithfield market. I found a small shop entirely devoted to this hobby of football programs so I went in and t9old them what I was looking for - a Belfast Celtic v Glasgow Celtic Match programme from the early 50's.
  The man looked at me and tugged the waist of his jumper down. He said,
  'Put it this way. I am a collector and I've never seen one.'
I was disappointed. Then he said,
  'If you catch up with it, you'll pay for it.'
  'How much?' I was thinking in terms of twenty or thirty quid.
  'A thousand pounds. Minimum.'

I am not really impressed by that kind of rarity value - but in this case I thought,
  'Good on you Johnny.' After all the work for charity.

If that price is accurate I don't want to own the real thing - but I wouldn't mind seeing a photocopy. A photocopy would be good. Above rubies.

Bernard MacLaverty is the author of a number of best-selling novels, including Cal, Lamb and Grace Notes

Index